MW01037412

THE

ISIS

THESIS

Books by Judy Kay King

The Isis Thesis (2004) and *The Road from Orion* (2004)
Balls of Fire: a Science of Life and Death (2015)

Peer-Reviewed Journal Articles (available at http://www.isisthesis.com)

2005. Biosemiotics in Ancient Egyptian Texts: the Key to Long-lost Signs found in Myth, Religion, Psychology, Art and Literature. *International Journal of the Humanities* 3(7): 189-203.

2006. Biosemiotics in Ancient Egyptian Texts: the Key Unlocking the Universal Secret of Sexuality and the Birth of the Limitless. Presented at the Second International Congress for Young Egyptologists in Lisbon, Portugal on Oct. 25, 2006. Published in *ACTAS 2009 Proceedings.*

2006a. Man the MisInterpretant: Will He Discover the Universal Secret of Sexuality encoded within him? *International Journal of the Humanities* 4(9): 1-15.

2007. From History's Dustbin: a Semiotics of Evolvability discovered within Man and his Mountain of Transformation. *International Journal of the Humanities* 5(5): 113-126.

2007a. Self-Portrait in the Pharaoh's Mirror: a Reflection of Ancient Egyptian Knowledge in Teilhard de Chardin's Evolutionary Biophysics. Presented at the 32nd Annual Meeting of the Semiotic Society of America, New Orleans, October 4-7, 2007. Published in *Semiotics 2006/2007* eds. Terry J. Prewitt and Wendy Morgan, 101-115 (New York, Ontario: Legas and SSA).

2008. The Order of the Harmonious Whole: Peirce's Guess, Peregrinus' Magnet, and Pharaoh's Path. Presented at 33rd Annual Meeting of SSA, Houston, October 17, 2008. Published in *Semiotics 2008* eds. John Deely and Leonard G. Sbrocchi, 179-190 (NY, Ontario: Legas and SSA).

2008a. Cosmic Semiophysics in Ancient Architectual Vision: The Mountain Temples at *Deir el Bahari*, the Dead Sea Temple Scroll, and the Hagia Sophia. *Int'l Journal of Humanities.* 6(4): 17-26.

2009. Cosmological Patterns in Ancient Egypt and China: The Way to Unify the Universe through Knowledge, Mind, Energy, and the Beneficence of Elements. *Int'l J. of Humanities.* 7(2): 151-165.

2009a. Evolution Backward in Time: Crystals, Polyhedra and Observer-Participancy in the Cosmological Models of Peirce, Ancient Egypt and Early China. Presented October 17, 2009, at the 34th Annual Meeting of SSA, Cincinnati, USA. Published in *Semiotics 2009 The Semiotics of Time*, eds. Karen Haworth, Jason Hogue, Leonard G. Sbrocchi, 58-76 (NY, Ontario: LEGAS and SSA).

2009b. Unraveling Mountainway Ceremonials: Is Navajo Eschatological Ritual Another Semiotic Pattern of Ancient Invisible Magic Veiling a Complex Systems-based Information Science? *International Journal of the Humanities.* 8(12): 45-80.

2011. Ticket to Ride the Ancient Celestial Railroad: Natural Law, Worldview Knowledge, "Evolutionary Love," and Ockham's Razor. Presented Oct. 29, 2011, at 36th Annual Meeting of SSA, Pittsburgh, USA. Published in *The Semiotics of ??? Proceedings of the 36th Annual Meeting of SSA, 27-30 October 2011.* eds. K. Haworth, J. Hogue, L. G. Sbrocchi, 137-155 (NY: LEGAS and SSA).

2013. Death or the Powers: the Future of the Human Experience. *The International Journal of Humanities Education.* 11(3): 1-17.

THE

ISIS

THESIS

A STUDY DECODING 870 ANCIENT EGYPTIAN SIGNS

JUDY KAY KING

ENVISION EDITIONS LTD.

THE ISIS THESIS
IS PUBLISHED BY
ENVISION EDITIONS LTD.

Copyright © 2004, 2015 by Judy Kay King

All rights reserved under International and Pan-American Copyright Conventions. Published in the United States by Envision Editions Ltd., Gaylord, Michigan
First edition published 2004
Printed in the United States of America

ISBN: 0-9762814-0-6
13 digit: 978-0-9762814-0-5

Library of Congress Control Number: 2004116944

Cover Design by Shannon M. King
using NASA Image PR93-01 dated 1/01/1993
of the Cygnus Loop Supernova Blast Wave
and E. A. W. Budge's representation of
the Creation from the sarcophagus of Seti I

Book Website: www.isisthesis.com

Without limiting the rights under copyright reserved above, no part of this publication may be reproduced in or introduced into a retrieval system, or transmitted, in any form or by any means (electronic, mechanical, photocopying, recording or otherwise), without the prior written permission of the copyright holder.

The magic alphabet,
the mysterious hieroglyphs
have only come down to us incomplete and falsified,
either by time or by men who have an interest
in our remaining ignorant.

Let us rediscover the lost letter, the effaced sign,
let us recompose the dissonant scale,
and we shall gain power in
the world of the spirits.

Gerard de Nerval
Aurelia

CONTENTS

Preface

The corpus of Egyptian funerary texts demonstrate an advanced twenty-first century knowledge of space physics, quantum physics, molecular biology, supramolecular chemistry and bacterial genetics. Using this expansive knowledge base, the ancient Egyptians carved a sophisticated symbolic system of art and hieroglyphs into the tombs of the Pharaohs and nobility to disguise their Science. *The Isis Thesis* (Volume 1) posits that the primary objective of their hidden scientific knowledge was to map the chemical path by which the genetic heritage of the Deceased was preserved and vectored into a bioluminescent species that was not recycled back to earth and the world of photosynthesis. Decoding an elaborate network of over 870 signs in eight different texts spanning 2000 years, the thesis explains how the Pharaohs' Science of Death made humans into gods by cloning a new species. With this knowledge, the Pharaohs insist humanity can re-invent itself at Death. For humans today this knowledge may be an alternative to species suicide due to overpopulation, nuclear war, global warming and mass extinction.

The Story – a surreal plot of works of art, fact and fiction

To convey this scientific knowledge to readers and students that are not scientists or Egyptology scholars, *The Road from Orion* (Volume 2) is a story supporting and relating to the study, based on a surreal plot of fictional characters, historical facts and great works of art. Using the Egyptian method of providing drawings to aid understanding, the Table of Contents for the story is modeled on the Egyptian Senet game and depicts 30 chapter drawings related to events in the story. Within the text of the story, direct quotations of creative artists from renowned works of literature, art, music and philosophy are designated by italics with the work itself referenced in a short bibliography at the conclusion. These great works of art point to scientific concepts referenced in the thesis and add support to the interpretation, but not valid scientific evidence. Other themes woven within the story's plot address several controversial questions: Is schizophrenia a direct mental experience of the quantum world of atoms? Do hallucinogens allow humans access to the quantum world? Do each of us have an invisible double? Did royal incest enhance the Pharaohs' spiritual consciousness? Has our idea of God prevented us from accessing comprehensive wisdom?

The Thesis – a study of Egyptian ideas and signs

The Isis Thesis begins with an Abstract of the study as an advance organizer. After this, we begin our quest to restore the effaced Egyptian sign, so that the Pharaohs' lost knowledge is restored to history. To aid understanding for all readers, Part One reviews method, sources, and the major ideas in the *Pyramid Texts* and the *Coffin Texts*. Analyzing textual advice, we map the Pharaohs' path to Eternity, discovering space physics evidence for actual energy landscapes that match Egyptian descriptions. Part Two examines the quantum world of the cell, for the Egyptian signs are dual-signified. We discover that the macroscopic earth system operates like a tiny bacterium. As the legendary alchemist Hermes Trismegistus said, "What is below is like that which is above." Part Three deconstructs the *Amduat*, a book often called the Egyptian Heaven and Hell, describing a journey through a black-hole protein funnel. Next, we analyze *The Book of Gates*, another Middle Kingdom text found in the great tombs of the Pharaohs. Briefly, we peer into *The Book of Caverns.* In Part Four, we explore the mystifying *Book of Two Ways* that still intrigues religious scholars, the New Kingdom *Edifice of Taharqa*, and the popular New Kingdom *Book of the Dead*, including the *Theban Recension.* As a corpus, these texts are unified in their presentation of Egyptian Science that centers around predicted chemical events in the afterlife of the Deceased. We close our investigation in Part Five with an evaluation of the Egyptian legacy and its links to String Theory, black hole theory, inflationary cosmology, and world religious perspectives.

Covering eight funerary texts within one book was a massive task that presented several difficulties. The first problem was how to address the large range of interconnected and dual-signified signs that have confused scholars for centuries. In an attempt to understand these signs with no intrusions, I became a full-time independent researcher for three years, leaving my college teaching and grant-writing career in 2001. This allowed me the opportunity to carefully decode the meaning of the signs and catalogue them in matrices with modern science parallels. The second problem was the depth of cutting-edge scientific knowledge embedded in the Egyptian texts. Fortunately, nonstop satellite Internet access allowed research opportunities any time of the day or night. Also, excellent online university tutorials and courses in biology, chemistry, physics and genetics deepened my knowledge. Thanks to the efforts of the Otsego County Library and their interlibrary loans, I was able to obtain unusual texts such as *The Edifice of Taharqa* by Richard A. Parker, Jean LeClant and Jean-Claude Goyon. Other texts such as Alexandre Piankoff's impressive Portfolio of Plates photographed from the Tomb of Ramesses VI were invaluable.

The third problem centered on the complexity of the funerary texts, which required numerous reviews of each text. To resolve the complexity issue and aid research and understanding, I compared the Old Kingdom *Pyramid Texts* and Middle Kingdom *Coffin Texts*, listing the major Egyptian themes or Idea Strands in an Appendix for the reader. This should also be helpful to critics who have not read the funerary texts. However, an ideal critique of *The Isis Thesis* rests on the critic having read all the funerary texts addressed. Constructive criticism can only result when Egyptologists, scientists and professionals in related disciplines work together to expand or modify the ideas within this work.

Although the thesis addresses more than one scientific discipline, students of general-level science, teachers and professionals should find it interesting. I have provided diagrams and matrices, along with definitions of scientific terms within the text, online resources in the References denoted by an asterisk, and a glossary of Egyptian deities and terms to aid understanding. The argument addresses ten objectives in Part One through Part Four that guide the reader to conclusions and possibilities in Part Five. Some of the issues noted in the thesis are more controversial than those of the story. Was the birth of science in Egypt? Can human consciousness exist after Death? Can we take control of our afterlife? Is God a quantum life-form modeling complex viral behavior?

Although the textual references and signs taken individually may be vague, the 870 decoded signs as a whole exhibit a unified matrix of Egyptian Science that mirrors and surpasses the knowledge of modern scientists. Is the scientific afterlife knowledge of the Pharaohs useful to living human beings? That is for you to decide. I began this exploration of the Egyptian afterlife because I believed that the ancient Pharaohs possessed knowledge that would shed light on life and death, thereby eliminating the fear of the unknown for humans. My work rewarded me with the knowledge of why the ancient Kings did not fear Death, why they looked upon the world with a cool equanimity that was omniscient and eternal. Although no theory is an absolute theory, this thesis provides a scientific rationale for an afterlife existence that helps one to understand who we are, how our universe works, and what we can become.

Acknowledgments

While researching and writing this book, I have received valuable feedback on the manuscript and other assistance from Ray Cummings, Denise Harig, Shannon Harig, Dawn Richards, Vicki Pistor, David Pistor, and Shannon King, who also created the cosmic cover design, using the NASA image of the Cygnus Loop Supernova Blast Wave. Special thanks is extended to Kristen King for her unique ink drawings in *the Road from Orion.* Eric Syzmanski created the cunning illustrations of the deities Thoth and Anubis, while Denise Harig captured the stellar power of Isis in her mystic creation of the Bull-goddess. I owe a great debt of gratitude to those who offered me emotional support during the last three years of research, problem-solving and composition, specifically Shannon, Dawn and Kristen King, and my mother Kathleen Bowman. As for intellectual support, I must go fifteen years back in time to my graduate-level instruction in literary criticism. I can only thank Dr. Mark Workman, who expanded my vision by introducing me to great thinkers such as Derrida, Foucault, Heidegger, Levi-Strauss, Nietzsche, and many others interested in the study of signs and the origin of the work of art.

Isis

Copyright © 2004
by Denise Harig

I

What is Above

Abstract

A study of 870 signs in eight primary ancient Egyptian funerary texts, spanning from 2520 to 664 BCE, decodes an advanced knowledge of molecular biology, space physics, bacterial genetics, supramolecular chemistry, and quantum physics. This scientific knowledge, disguised in religious texts, models the operations of the solar wind/earth spin system on the activity of bacteriophage Lambda infecting an *E. coli* host cell. On the quantum level, the cell dynamics reflect the topology of a Quantum Mechanical Kerr Black Hole within which proteins fold. The Lambda genome lodged on the host chromosome has systematic affinities across several genes for two particular lineages. The folding of Lambda cI protein to its native conformation results in prokaryotic to eukaryotic evolution of *Homo Sapiens Sapiens* trapped in the earth system, while the folding of Lambda cro protein results in a recombinant species referred to as *Homo Sapiens Lambda* that reverses Time, escaping from the earth system to the Early Universe. The *evolutionary shunt* of *Homo Sapiens Lambda* into an Early Universe results from 1) fermion to boson transformation, 2) CPT violation, 3) maltose transport system for lactose passage, 4) biosynthesis as a left-handed particle with RNA polymerase plowing straight through the DNA, leaving Z-DNA in its wake, 5) negative energy, and 6) movement through a transmembrane tunnel or an Einstein-Rosen bridge, where the recombinant species emerges as Hawking radiation or dark energy, the Cosmological Constant or what Einstein called Lambda. The language of the funerary texts related to vertices, heads, tails, and faces, along with the triangular structure of the pyramids with their tail-like causeways depict phage Lambda morphology. In addition, tails carved on deities in the Edifice of Taharqa and the Ramesses VI drawing of an armless human with coiled legs and a sphere for a head provide more evidence for this view, along with the interpretation of over 870 signs supporting the lytic lifestyle of phage Lambda. On the cosmic scale, the competition between lysis and lysogeny in the cell translates to the release of energy as radiation (chemiluminescence) or heat (photosynthesis) in the universe. Thus, approximately 4 billion years ago, the process of Lambda lysogeny, resulting from cI protein production, activated the transition to eukaryotic development and photosynthesis. Prior to that time, the original Lambda structure, as signified by cro protein control and chemiluminescence, was imprinted on the universe. The horizontal gene transfer of the Deceased on the Egyptian path to the stars is referred to as *Lambda-Genesis.* Egyptian science not only supports that information can escape from the protein folding funnel landscape of a black hole, but it also reinforces String Theory concepts such as T-Duality and supersymmetry.

1

The Quest to Restore the Egyptian Sign

SYMBOLS, SIGNS AND THE STRATEGY TO DECODE THEM

Egypt's confusing funerary texts demonstrate an advanced knowledge of twenty-first century quantum physics, molecular biology, space physics, bacterial genetics and supramolecular chemistry. This Science provided Egyptian Pharaohs and nobility with answers to profound ontological questions, such as who are we, is there life after death, and how does our universe function. Buried in pyramids and tombs for centuries, the wisdom of the Pharaohs remained masked even though Jean-Francois Champollion cracked the code for Egyptian hieroglyphs in 1822. Although this event was an advance, nineteenth century scholars struggled with little success to interpret the hidden meaning of the hieroglyphs and images.

Because the Pharaohs veiled their impressive scientific knowledge in a religious literature of double-signified signs and symbols with related artwork, deciphering the meaning of the symbolic system is still a daunting task for modern egyptologists, prompting many scholars to dismiss the funerary corpus as confusing, unintelligible and primitive. Part of the confusion stems from the language of the symbolic system itself, which contains ideograms or sense-signs, phonograms or sound-signs, number signs, relative artwork with its symbolism of actions, gestures and color, and literary metaphors. However, these words, objects, persons, things, actions, patterns or *metasymbols* (symbols or signs pointing beyond direct human experience) point to both chemical reactions in the earth's magnetosphere and the quantum cell. In other words, macrocosmic events in the space physics of earth mirror the biology, chemistry, physics and genetics of particles in the quantum world.

Idea Strands (IS)

Theme or Idea	Idea Strand No.
Qualities of Deceased King	1–12
Directions to path to Eternity/Duat	13–27
Conquest of Apopis	28–34
Deceased King assumes all forms	35–43
Importance of Isis	44–48
Importance of Thoth	49–52
Deceased King has efflux	53
Importance of Anubis	54
Importance of Horus	55–56
Deceased King is 4th god	57
Deceased King is judge	58–60
Double Lion	61
Horus overcomes Seth	62–76
Osiris risen	77–83
Deceased King reassembled	84
Deceased King embraces/ascends	85–87
Deceased King's new form	88–90
Deceased King's nourishment	91–93
Deceased King's clothing	94
The Word or writings	95–96
Iron references	97
Cold water references	98
Turquoise references	99
Eating references	100
Double references	101–103
Beware of Lake	104
Nets	105
Heads, tails, vertices, faces	106
Importance of Orion	107
Winds of heaven/life	108

Figure 1.1 Key themes or Idea Strands in Pyramid Texts and Coffin Texts. For full table, see the Appendix.

Method

Because language with its words and symbols is not a simple and reliable matching of the signified with the signifier, an examination of each metasymbol within the context of the whole funerary corpus is necessary to understand and restore the effaced Egyptian sign. A holistic approach considers each sign's potential for meaning within the full context of the whole group of signs. The assumption underlying this approach is that the funerary texts from the Old Kingdom to the New Kingdom are unified in their presentation of key ideas. Fortunately, when one sign gives birth to another to form a family of meaningful signs within two texts, and then expands into an interconnected city of signs within multiple texts, the interpretant can be confident that the lost meaning is being restored to the signs. Our quest is to discover a coherent and interconnected city of signs applicable to the entire corpus of funerary texts itself. Therefore, this work investigates eight different texts, spanning a time period of two thousand years.

To begin this process by testing the unity assumption, an organization of the earliest Egyptian writings into complementary strands of ideas was necessary. A review of 759 Pyramid Texts and 1185 Coffin Texts resulted in a comparative table of 108 key themes or Idea Strands (Figure 1.1). As interpretants using this base of Idea Strands along with evidence from later texts, we will identify, analyze and assign a possible scientific meaning to each sign.

In this process of decoding signs, the new meaning will be framed in a simple equation after an analysis of the evidence. The equals sign (=) in the equation represents the words *points to*. Then for easy identification, the decoded signs will be tabulated in a matrix that matches the Egyptian idea or sign with a possible modern science parallel. We will also consider the etymology of Egyptian words, as well as the unity and coherence of the interpreted signs. Our task for Part One and Part Two is to build a base of interconnected signs, defining a model that explains the dynamics of the Egyptian afterlife. To aid the reader in understanding the science, complex concepts and processes are summarized more than once due to their repeated appearance in different funerary texts.

In Part Three, we will continue building our city of signs and testing our model by analyzing the signs in the twelve divisions or hours of the Amduat and the Book of Gates. Part Four addresses the signs in the Book of Two Ways, the Edifice of Taharqa, and the Book of the Dead, including the Theban Recension, to test for continued unity and coherence of interpretation in our expanding model defining the nature of the afterlife activities. In Part Five, we will draw conclusions from a model based on the city of living signs, reconstructed from the mental experiences of the Kings and nobility. In this way, we can understand how the signs work together to reveal the lost Egyptian wisdom that is buried within a language that deceives us by destroying the sign and its entire logic. The flood of language, misunderstood and inflated, that has swamped history as the essential truth and drowned the voice of Nature can then be dammed.

Summary of the Idea Strands

Both the Pyramid Texts and the Coffin Texts exhibit similar idea strands that describe ancient Egypt's religion of science. The scientific concepts are embedded in a religious narrative, detailing the afterlife adventures of the Deceased who desires Eternity and transformation. In this magical process of re-creation, the dead Pharaoh or King becomes a god. He does not die again or go upside down, and he is not seized by the earth gods. Not only is the dead King a celestial being, but he is also a magician, a falcon, a flowing fluid, a snake with many coils, and the Eye of Horus that pours out a star. Add to this the claim that he is self-created, unique and first-born, and we have a being that is beyond human, an Overman, an Ultra-Human, something the philosopher Friedrich Nietzsche and the paleontologist Pierre Teilhard de Chardin would have appreciated.

However, in order to obtain this afterlife transfiguration, the dead King must follow specific directions, using the earth and stars as guides. By following the advice in the funerary texts, the dead King joins the Sun-god Re's ferryboat for the voyage through the netherworld of the Duat and magically overcomes the evil-faced serpent Apopis. Isis, the Lady of Provisions, and Thoth, the scribe of the gods, assist the dead King in his journey through the black Duat. The King overcomes the Double Lion and judges the two rivals, Horus and Seth. Horus overcomes Seth and the rivals are united. This results in the restoration of the Eye of Horus and the risen Osiris, along with the birth of the King's new form, which is nourished, clothed and rising in the east like the morning star. The risen King is now the Great Word, he issues from cold water, and his double goes with him wherever he goes. This story mirrors the victorious hero journey, which turns out to be simply a chemical reaction played out on a quantum stage. In essence, afterlife deities, events, places, birds, serpents, magic and other Egyptian signs point to twenty-first century scientific ideas when decoded.

Chronology

Archaic Period		c. 3000 – 2700 BCE
Old Kingdom	first Pyramid Texts	c. 2520 – 2360 BCE
Middle Kingdom	Coffin Texts Book of Two Ways	c. 1987 – 1640 BCE
New Kingdom	Book of the Dead Amduat Book of Gates Book of Caverns	c. 1540 – 1075 BCE c. 1540 – 1292 BCE c. 1292 – 1190 BCE
Third Intermediate Period	Ethiopian rulers	c. 740 – 664 BCE

Figure 1.2 Excerpted from Erik Hornung's full chronology. *The Ancient Egyptian Books of the Afterlife.* Cornell University Press: Ithaca and London, 1999, xxi, xxii.

The scientific funerary texts proclaim that the human body harbors an immortal consciousness that can choose to be transfigured at death into a longer-living species by means of a specific chemical pathway. This secret knowledge inscribed in the pyramids of the Fifth and Sixth Dynasties was only for the King and royal family. These Old Kingdom Pyramid Texts deny the death of the King, encouraging him to awake for the afterlife journey through the dark Duat, the place of transformation.

In time, the nobility were informed of the secret afterlife knowledge. In the First Intermediate Period, the Coffin Texts, carved in coffins of private individuals, were adapted from the Pyramid Texts and shared with the wealthy nobility. Dated to the Middle Kingdom, the Book of Two Ways was discovered on the floorboards of a group of wooden coffins from the Bersheh region in middle Egypt. The royal tombs of the Eighteenth and Nineteenth Dynasties preserved the Litany of the Sun, the Amduat, the Book of Gates, the Book of Caverns, the Book of Aker, the Book of Day and Night, and the Book of the Divine Cow. Finally, the Book of the Dead on papyrus roll inside the coffins of the rich aided the Deceased in the afterlife. (Goelet, Jr. 140-41)

This entire Egyptian corpus detailing modern scientific concepts can be dated to 2520–664 BCE (See Figure 1.2), almost 4,500 years before our recent advances in research due to high-tech satellites, computers, imaging devices and ultraviolet spectroscopy.

CORE SOURCES AND ABBREVIATIONS

Based on Erik Hornung's bibliographic guide for scholars in *The Ancient Egyptian Books of the Afterlife* (1999), this study uses the following sources:

Pyramid Texts (PT) and Coffin Texts (CT)
Faulkner, R. O.. *The Ancient Egyptian Pyramid Texts, 2 vols.* Oxford, 1969.
Faulkner, R. O. *The Ancient Egyptian Coffin Texts, 3 vols.* Warminster, 1973-1978; rpt. 1994.

The Book of Two Ways (B2W)
Lesko, L. *The Ancient Egyptian Book of Two Ways.* Berkeley: University of California Press, 1972.
Piankoff, A. *Wandering of the Soul.* Bollingen Series XL 6. Princeton University Press, 1974.

The Amduat (AMD)
Budge, E. A. *The Egyptian Heaven and Hell. Three Volumes Bound as One.* New York: Dover Publications, Inc., 1996. This edition is a republication in a single volume of the work originally published in London by Kegan Paul, Trench, Trubner & Co., 1905.
Piankoff, A. *The Tomb of Ramesses VI Texts.* "Book of What is in the Netherworld." Bollingen Series XL 1. Pantheon Books: New York, 1954.

The Book of Gates (BG)
Piankoff, A. *The Tomb of Ramesses VI Texts.* "Book of Gates." Bollingen Series XL 1. Pantheon Books: New York, 1954.

The Book of Caverns (BC)
Piankoff, A. *The Wandering of the Soul, II. The Quererts.* Bollingen Series XL 6. Princeton University Press, 1974.

To maintain uniformity and coherence, I selected several texts translated by the same scholar. In line with this strategy, Dr. Raymond Faulkner is the translator for *The Egyptian Book of the Dead,* which provides the *Papyrus of Ani* for this study, including the *Theban Recension.* The following English translations have been selected independently:

The Book of the Dead (BD) and the Theban Recension (TR)
Faulkner, R. O. *The Egyptian Book of the Dead.* Commentary: Dr. Ogden Goelet, Jr. Chronicle Books: San Francisco, 1998.

The Edifice of Taharqa (ET)
Parker, R. A., J. LeClant, and J-C Goyon. *The Edifice of Taharqa by the Sacred Lake of Karnak.* Translated from the French by Claude Crozier-Brelot. Brown University Press: Providence, Lund Humphries, London, 1979.

RVI = Tomb of Ramesses VI; **SI** = Tomb of Seti I; **IS** = Idea Strands

Figure 1.3

What Hermes said about T-Duality

This thesis also investigates the cryptic meaning of the statement by legendary alchemist Hermes Trismegistus about the operation of the Sun: *What is below is like that which is above, and what is above is like that which is below, to accomplish the miracles of the one thing.* At the time Hermes made this statement, he was completely unaware that twenty-first century Superstring theorists would define his idea as T-Duality. Superstring Theory posits that the fundamental units of nature are not zero-dimensional point particles, but tiny one-dimensional filaments called strings. The size of a typical string loop is the Planck length (10^{-33} centimeters), about a hundred billion billion times smaller than an atomic nucleus (Greene 1999). What T-Duality suggests is that at Planck-length scales, the universe looks just the same as it does at large scales. This means that if our universe were to shrink less than the Planck length, we would realize a dual universe as the original large-scale universe collapsed (Duff 2003). As the Deceased states, "the two skies go to me, the two earths come to me" (PT 332). Briefly put, Superstring theorists share the same opinion as Hermes: what is below is like that which is above. If Hermes could say more, he might tell us that death enables us to journey from our visible world to a dual, invisible Planck-length universe, where our afterlife begins. However, Hermes would also remind us that the designed Egyptian afterlife is only accessible to those who have knowledge of the paths.

Keeping Hermes' statement in mind and using the Idea Strands from the least-corrupted Pyramid Texts and Coffin Texts, let's explore the Egyptian idea of the afterlife in the interests of learning more about their system of signs that seemed to eliminate the fear of death for those who possessed knowledge—the Kings and the nobility.

As mentioned, Idea Strands in the Pyramid and Coffin Texts are identified by number for ease of reference (see Appendix). Idea Strands 13 through 27 relate to the Egyptian directions for their path to Eternity and are the focus of our first objective.

Objective 1: Our first task is to determine if there is scientific evidence for the Egyptian path to Eternity, as it is outlined in the Pyramid and Coffin Texts. Beginning with Idea Strands 13-27, we will examine the possibility that the directions for the dead King's journey might map an actual pathway through the sky.

2

The Dead Travel

IS THERE ANY SCIENTIFIC EVIDENCE FOR THE EGYPTIAN PATH TO ETERNITY?

The afterlife happens in the dark netherworld or Duat, and the Deceased states, "I ascend to the sky, and the earth remains behind" (PT563). Scholars agree that the Duat was not fixed in the netherworld, but also included celestial regions (Hornung 1999, 6). They describe it as a dark unseen place beyond the earth and in the sky, and some have compared it to a hell. In *Egyptian Grammar*, Sir Alan Gardiner states that the word for "netherworld" was originally the place of the morning twilight known as the "Duat." The individual ideograms in the hieroglyphs for Duat mean "star" (1957, 487) and "house" (33). In light of the fact that the Deceased is no longer living human matter, but a decomposition of the primary elements of human matter—carbon, hydrogen, nitrogen and oxygen, the Duat must represent a quantum phenomenon where these elements exist and are reassembled. However, the Egyptian claim that what is above is like what is below implies that we can review the Egyptian advice to the Deceased from a macrocosmic perspective and have it still be applicable on the quantum level. So let's first review Egyptian texts from the perspective of our familiar spacetime universe.

The Egyptian path to the stars begins with the Deceased traveling to the northern polar region of earth, guided by the Unwearying Stars or polestars. Here a Great Stairway exists, where the Sun-god Re waits with his crew of eight to ferry the Deceased through the Double Doors of the Duat. The Deceased is urged to "go up upon the great west side of the sky and go down upon the great east side of the earth" with the gods in the Suite of Osiris and the Sun-god Re (CT18). Orion (PT437, 466, 472, 738) and Sirius (PT473) are the Imperishable Stars, and the general direction the Deceased travels is from west to east (CT118) against the background of the Milky Way or "Street of Stars" (PT262). These directions prompt one to ask three questions: Where is the Duat? Why go to the northern polar region? What is the Great Stairway?

Where is the Duat?

If we take the Egyptian advice and travel into space to view the "great west of the sky" and the "great east side of the earth," we could look down the earth's axis of rotation from the North Pole and see the Sun on the western horizon of the sky and the dark side of the earth's magnetosphere on the eastern. According to the texts, after going northward to the pole, the Deceased merges with the Sun-god and travels into the dark Duat in a west-to-east direction. From our perspective in outer space, we would observe the earth rotating counterclockwise, dragging its electromagnetic field and space behind it into a vortex. Thus, the textual advice to go down on the great east side of the earth may indicate a movement into the earth's magnetosphere that stretches into the darkness due to the powerful solar wind.

Our new science of space physics is only 35 years old, yet Egyptian textual references to crossing the "Waterway of the Sky-windows," "the lake," "the sea," navigating the "Winding Waterway," and being towed over the "District of Waters with ropes of iron" (CT62) point to the actual dynamics and energy structures twenty-first century researchers are currently investigating in our magnetosphere, the invisible barrier that protects us from the solar wind. In light of these similarities, it seems reasonable to propose the earth's magnetosphere as our real-world model for the Duat, and the magnetopause as the "Winding Waterway" or "District of Waters" that the Dead Sun-god travels with his crew to the shrine of Osiris, god of the Duat. To explore this possibility, let's examine the structure of the earth's magnetosphere.

The Vortex Structure of the Earth's Magnetosphere

The earth's plasma barrier or magnetosphere is a vortex of whirling plasma due to the solar wind force, a place that could easily be called the "chambers of the sky" ruled by Chaos-gods (CT76). The following brief review of the

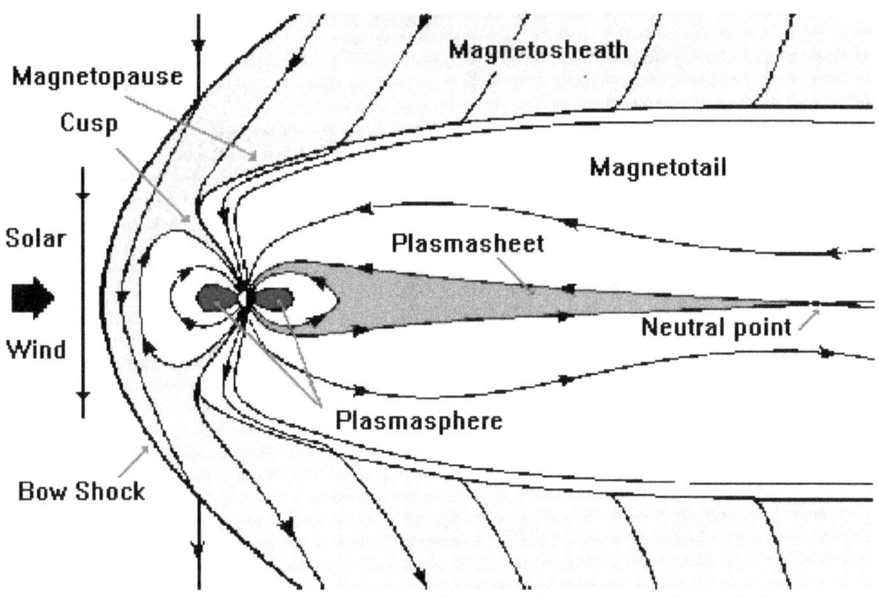

Figure 2.1 Earth's Magnetosphere (NASA Public Domain)

structure and processes in this vortex is essential for understanding the Egyptian directions to the stars.

Because of the solar wind's ramming power, it forces the earth's magnetic field into a cavity around our planet known as the magnetosphere. Generated by earth's iron core, the magnetosphere stretches into long tail lobes 200 to 220 Earth radii from earth, almost 870,000 miles into space. The plasmas and magnetic fields of the Sun and earth interact as if they were frozen together. They form distinct regions separated by a thin boundary called the magnetopause as depicted in Figure 2.1. Outside the magnetopause is a layer of turbulent plasma called the magnetosheath. Inside the magnetosphere, the plasma rotates with the earth because earth's magnetic field lines are frozen into the ionospheric plasma (Cowley 1996).

James Dungey's concept (1961) of the open magnetosphere defines the breakdown of frozen-in-flow, leading to magnetic reconnection at a neutral point, where the magnetic field is zero. At this point, the magnetic fields have opposite directions, and Dungey proposed that the plasmas on both sides could reconnect to different field lines. This means that the Sun's interplanetary field lines (and plasma on it) splices into the earth's magnetic field lines of plasma at neutral points.

Dungey identified four neutral points of steady or forced magnetic reconnection in the magnetosphere. When the Sun's Interplanetary Magnetic Field is northward (IMF-N) or not shocked by the solar wind, reconnection occurs behind each cusp; when the Sun's Interplanetary Magnetic Field is southward (IMF-S) or shocked, reconnection occurs in the subsolar region and the magnetotail.

In 2001, space physicists reported the first in-situ detection by Equator-S and Geotail spacecraft of oppositely directed jets of plasma coming from a reconnection site at the earth's dayside magnetopause. This observational confirmation of bi-directional jets under southward IMF is evidence for reconnection theory. (Phan et al. 2001)

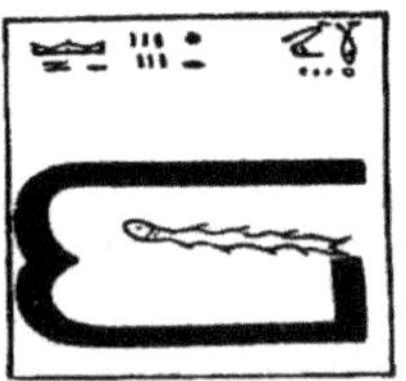
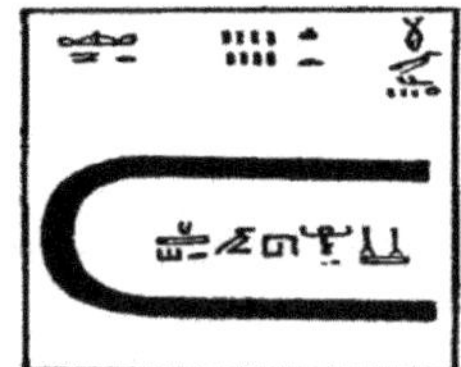
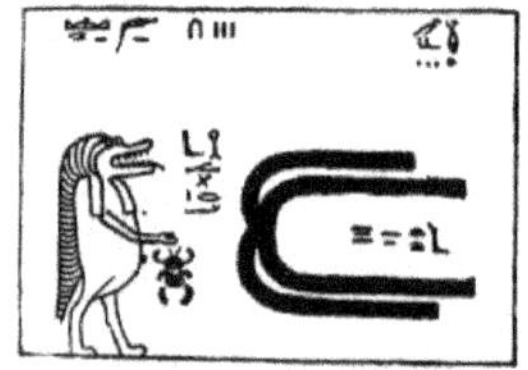

Figure 2.2 Three of the Aats from the *Papyrus of Nu* showing from left to right: Aat VI, Aat VIII, and Aat XIII. From Budge's *The Egyptian Heaven and Hell,* Vol. 3:39, 41.

In support of the earth's magnetosphere as a model for the Duat is the similarity between our modern two-dimensional drawings of the earth's magnetosphere and the earliest Egyptian conception of the Duat's structure. In the Papyrus of Nu, Aats or regions presided over by a god made up the earliest conception of the Egyptian Netherworld. Figure 2.2 shows three of the Aats from Budge's illustrations in *The Egyptian Heaven and Hell* from this papyrus.

As you can see, the Aats look roughly similar to the drawing of the earth's magnetosphere in Figure 2.1. On the left, Aat VI was Ammehet, which was presided over by Sekher-At and accursed for the dead. This is also the god Seker of Amduat Hour Five, who presides over this domain of Osiris. In the middle, Aat VIII was Ha-Hetep, a region containing roaring torrents of water and ruled by Qa-Ha-Hetep. Aat XIII was Uart-ent-mu and its deity was the hippopotamus-god called Hebt-Re-F. One can easily see that the two-dimensional shape of the earth's magnetosphere is similar to the earliest Egyptian drawings of the Duat, the realm of Osiris.

The House of the Net

In Figure 2.1, the magnetic field lines of the earth and Sun form a network of lines. As the Sun's electromagnetic lines stretch across space and time, so do the earth's on a smaller scale. One could easily use the metaphor of a net to describe the earth's magnetosphere, and the Egyptians do. The title of Thoth, "great god in Het-Abtit," has the hieroglyphic meaning "House of the Net," and Thoth is present in the Duat as the Sun-god journeys through it. Also, in a prayer, the Deceased requests passage through the net for "helpless fiends" and the "abominable fiends of earth," which is described (Budge v1 1904, 406) as having "a frame which reached unto heaven, and weighted parts that rested upon the earth." Again, this description suggests the earth's magnetosphere with its iron core (weighted parts) and magnetic field lines (frame reaching to heavens), including the Van Allen belts where trapped charged particles spiral, bounce and drift in earth's magnetic field lines. It may be that the "helpless fiends" represent the helpless particles caught in the earth's hot Van Allen belts for thermal chemical reactions in our magnetosphere.

The detested net existed in the Duat (BD153A, 153B) and was also called the "fish trap of Re" (CT474), having iron floats in the sky and iron weights on earth (CT343, 344). So we could say the fish trap or net represents the magnetic field lines of our magnetosphere, and its "weighted parts" represent the earth's molten, metallic iron core. Current geological dynamo theories propose that the convection of molten iron in the earth's outer core and its rotation create electric currents, which generate the earth's magnetic field. (Comins 2000, 129-130) The important point is that the Egyptian ideas of the net and "fish trap of Re" suggest the following possible modern science parallel:

House of the Net and Fish trap of Re = Magnetosphere

In support of this parallel, both the Coffin Texts and the Pyramid Texts reference opening or splitting the sky's iron doors, descending on iron bands (PT214), and other iron references (IS97), showing that the Egyptians may have understood the dynamics of earth's iron core and magnetosphere. Also important is that ions are trapped or frozen on magnetic field lines. Particles move with field lines, so a moving field line means a moving string of plasma particles on a common field line (Stern 1996). Magnetic reconnection creates open field lines or earth field lines that have stretched, finally snapping and splicing into an adjacent solar field line. When the Deceased splits the sky's iron doors or descends "upon iron bands" (PT214) or ferries on reed-floats (IS24-26), these symbolic phrases may point to the dynamic energy network of moving magnetic field lines within the Sun-earth system that the Egyptians may have perceived. Decoded:

Deceased on iron bands or reed floats = ion on magnetic field lines

The District of Waters with Ropes of Iron

The Imperishable Stars (Orion, Sirius) and the Unwearying Stars (polestars) pilot and tow the Deceased over the "District of the Waters with ropes of iron" (CT62). Considering that the European Space Agency's Cluster spacecraft discovered actual waves along the ever-shifting boundary of the magnetopause (Cattell et al.; Cattell[1] et al.; Cattell[2] et al.), we could say that the magnetopause is a "District of the Waters." Also, in space physics, bundles of magnetic field lines generated by the earth's iron core, move tailward until these field lines are disconnected (Walker and Ogino 1996). Called flux ropes, they contain a combination of closed, open and solar wind field lines (Richard et al. 1997) that could easily be described as "ropes of iron."

Richard et al. investigated the origin of ions in magnetotail flux ropes by launching solar wind ions into electric and magnetic fields from a global magnetohydrodynamic simulation of the magnetosphere. They observed that some particles then drifted onto open field lines and propagated tailward to undergo significant energization when they entered the flux rope. Ultimately, the particles encountered similar field line sequences, finally entering open field lines out of the magnetosphere by reconnection on the dusk flank. The flux rope particles experienced three reconnections: 1) at dayside entry to the magnetosphere, 2) in the magnetotail, and 3) on the dusk flank when they left the flux rope.

In comparison to Richard's experiment, this same west-to-east flux rope transport event that tows ions from the cusp into the magnetopause to the magnetotail's open field lines could also be described as the Deceased being towed over the District of Waters by ropes of iron, so that he can rise in the east on open field lines. This similarity supports our model of the magnetosphere as the Duat, so we can propose the following possible modern science parallels for the Egyptian signs:

Ropes of iron = flux ropes generated by earth's iron core
District of the Waters = magnetopause

The Valley of Darkness

Scholarly descriptions of the Duat's shape also support our model. It was a valley shut in by mountains on both sides, nearly circular in form that could be entered by a Gap in the Mountain of the West. A river or current flowed through the Duat, and souls had to travel the dark dangerous valley lined with numerous deities, including friendly and hostile spirits. Translated into twenty-first century space physics terminology, the Egyptian Gap is similar to the northern polar cusp or gap in earth's magnetosphere, and the mountain valley is the energy landscape created within the magnetospheric vortex. The Duat's flowing river may relate to the magnetopause's field-aligned currents.

By using technology tools, space physicists can see similar energy landscapes in the magnetosphere, which they also describe as mountains and valleys. These energy landscapes define the potential energy surface as a function of the position of atoms. The topographical features are similar to the earth's mountains and valleys, but in a much higher dimension. (Doye; Doye and Wales 1996) It is obvious that Egyptian descriptions of the Duat match up with actual energy landscapes in the magnetosphere that modern physicists have identified. So, our model is still functional and suggests that the Egyptian ability to perceive the quantum allowed them to see the actual positions of atoms in energy structures. We can decode these landscapes as follows:

Egyptian Gap = gap or cusp of magnetosphere
Mountain Valley of Darkness = magnetosphere's energy landscapes

The following statement in the Theban Recension (TR64) of the Book of Going Forth by Day also supports the idea that the earth's magnetosphere is the location of the Duat:

> O you two falcons of his, chieftains of their councils, who hear matters, you are the ones who lead the "Moored Ones" to the secret places, who drag in Re, who follows from the upper place, the shrine which is above the firmament, lord of the shrine which stands within the circumvallation of the earth.

Circumvallation means surrounded by a rampart, which is a mound of earth raised as a fortification around a place, a barricade. The Pyramid Texts also refer to the "ramparts of Shu" (PT509, 667C) or barriers of air (Shu), metasymbols for the earth's magnetosphere, an actual barricade against the solar wind. The other textual reference to "who drag in Re" (TR64) may indicate the polar cusp and the process of magnetic reconnection, which occurs at different points in the magnetosphere. This constant process of magnetic reconnection drags solar wind plasma to regions around earth. As a magnetic field line closes, it grabs a handful of solar wind plasma from the Sun's magnetic field and drags it toward the earth as it moves from night to day. Metaphoric language such as "who drag in Re" easily describes this process. Language referring to "the lord of the shrine which stands within the circumvallation of the earth" suggests Osiris, who resides in Rosetjau, meaning "place of dragging" (Goelet 1994, 143), another reference to reconnection. Relative to our model of the magnetosphere as the Duat, these Egyptian ideas suggest the following possible modern science parallels:

"who drag in Re" and Rosetjau = magnetic reconnection
"ramparts of Shu" = magnetosphere

Along with these references, the least corrupted Pyramid Texts also describe the Deceased King standing east of the "celestial vault" (PT261). A vault is a construction built on the principle of the arch that covers an area of considerable depth. This description aptly defines the three-dimensional image of the magnetosphere, envisioned by spacecraft optical instruments. So it seems reasonable to infer that the ramparts and vault also point to the earth's magnetosphere of plasma flowing to the "great East side of he earth" (CT18), an energy landscape that stretches into a teardrop because of the solar wind force. Decoded:

celestial vault - magnetosphere

We can conclude then that the earliest conceptions of the shape of the Duat from the Papyrus of Nu are similar to the two-dimensional image of the earth's magnetosphere. Also, textual language such as the "circumvallation of the earth," "ramparts of Shu," "celestial vault," "place of dragging," "ropes of iron," and the "House of the Net" are fitting metasymbols pointing to magnetospheric energy landscapes and processes. So, the textual language supports that the earth's magnetosphere, where the process of reconnection or dragging of the Sun's energy is occurring, is a sufficient model for the Egyptian Duat. Decoded:

Earth's magnetosphere = Duat

Why go to the Northern Polar Region?

The stars play an important role in guiding the Deceased to the polar region. Orion, Sothis (Sirius) and the Morning Star will save him from the rage of the dead who go "head-downwards" (CT44). Further, Orion lifts up the water of the Deceased's bark (CT61) and gives the Deceased his warrant, while the Great Bear makes a path for him to the western horizon (CT482). The Great Bear or Ursa Major is a constellation visible in the Northern Hemisphere, and the seven brightest stars form the Big Dipper. Draw an imaginary line from the star Merak through Dubhe out of the cup of the dipper, and you will arrive at the tip of the handle of the Little Dipper, which is Polaris, the North Star. Currently, the earth's axis of rotation points within one degree of Polaris. However, in 3000 BCE, it pointed to the star Thuban in the constellation of Draco the Dragon (Comins 2000, 27). Envisioning the earth's magnetosphere from a vantage point deep in outer space with the sun on the west, Polaris and the Great Bear would mark the western horizon of the magnetosphere near the northern pole, while the magnetotail stretching eastward in space would mark the eastern horizon. Thus, the Great Bear marks the path to the western horizon.

Along with this, the god Horus encourages the Deceased to walk on the sky waters, while the Imperishable and Unwearying Stars navigate (CT62). Since the Orion star cluster is the site of intense CO (carbon monoxide) emission, indicating star formation (Comins 2000, 280), we can easily classify these stars as Imperishable Stars. On the other hand, Unwearying Stars suggest the Great Bear and polestar Polaris, for they do not weary from the pole.

Warranted by Orion and guided by the Great Bear and Polaris northward to the western horizon of the magnetosphere, the texts encourage the Deceased to travel where the "pestilence of streams" has been removed by the gods, so that the Deceased might ascend a ladder or stairway to Re at the pole of the sky, the Great Polar Region, the Horn, the northern polar region (IS15-16). The earth's northern polar cusp or horn, where the earth's magnetic field is at its weakest point, easily matches Egyptian descriptions (IS13). Decoded:

Imperishable Stars = Orion star cluster
Unwearying Stars = polestars
Pole of sky, Great Polar Region, the Horn = polar cusp

Escape to the Cusp or Gap

IS 13: Bull of Re bends down horn for Dead King to pass; no pestilent streams; dead King has power over winds.

The weak point in the earth's magnetopause, which is the magnetic boundary between the earth's field and the solar wind, is referred to as the polar cusp by space physicists. Here, there are no pestilent streams of magnetic fields. NASA first reported that spacecraft, such as the European HEOS 1 and HEOS 2 (1968, 1972) and the University of Iowa's Hawkeye (1974) observed a disordered magnetic field, weak but not zero, at the cusp regions (NASA[3]).

Also, the solar wind composition instrument on the spacecraft Ulysses (SWICS) measured good elemental abundance for carbon (C), oxygen (O), neon (Ne), magnesium (Mg), silicon (Si), sulfur (S) and iron (Fe) (Caltech). Some scientists think silicon, which has similar properties to carbon and a high affinity for oxygen, could provide a chemical base for life. Silicon has four valence electrons and can bond to four other atoms. The National Radio Astronomy Observatory lists ten species of interstellar molecules based on silicon bonded to hydrogen, nitrogen, oxygen, sulfur and carbon atoms (Wootten 2003).

It is here at this open, element-enriched Gap to the stars that the Deceased King stands at the Great Polar Region as a waterway traveler. The Pharaohs may have easily imagined the earth's polar cusps as the two horns of the encroaching solar wind or "Great Wild Bull" (PT470), bending down its northern horn for the passage of the Deceased King. The horns or cusps actually change their position relative to coronal mass ejections from the Sun, producing northward and southward Interplanetary Magnetic Fields (Dungey 1961). This major image of the great fecundating bull of the Sun dominates the funerary texts and the artwork and writings of many early cultures. The bull depicts the powerful pressure of the solar wind, ramming into the earth's barrier, along with the solar creative force. The Deceased desires power over the four winds of heaven, the four bulls of the sky (CT162); he detests storms and desires that the pestilence of the streams be removed (CT21). For, it is here at the horn or cusp that the Deceased King will begin his journey to be transformed or recreated, the cusp serving as the Gap or entrance to an origin of reconnection and replication. Decoded:

Horns of Great Wild Bull = solar wind pressure and ions at polar cusps
Storms = high geomagnetic activity and energy transfer of solar wind

North to Polaris

The Deceased makes it very clear that he rises to the height of heaven and uses his power for himself in the afterlife (CT75). He takes the advice of the funerary texts and wills his consciousness north toward the polestar Polaris or the "polar region of the sky" (CT1030). Here, he stands at that great polar region in front of the zenith (CT343, 347, 1030), a historical symbol which suggests a central hole or point where time moves into timelessness (Cirlot 1963, 381). To the Egyptians, the zenith may have represented the entrance to the dark Duat.

Nonetheless, the protected cusp area is a neutral point, where the storms and pestilent streams are absent for the Deceased, and it is here that he merges with the Sun-god or boards Re's ferryboat (CT848). The Deceased states, "I fly and soar between those two great mountains on which Re appears" (CT305). As an energy landscape, the earth's barriers of plasma against the encroaching solar wind might easily be described as mountains of plasma, branching out from the null magnetic field at the Gap or cusp. Yet, along with the Gap in the mountains, the Deceased looks for another important energy landscape. There should be some type of ladder or stairway here at the cusp (IS16). Remarkably, according to space physics research, one does exist.

What is the Great Stairway?

IS 14-18: Dead King goes up stairway/ladder at northern polar region of earth, where Re appears, taking his seat in the Sun-bark. King now has ferryboat to Netherworld Lakes (Duat).

The texts report that a Great Stairway or ladder to the sky exists at the northern cusp, a region where field lines from the magnetopause boundary on the day and night sides converge toward low altitudes. Here at the element-enriched pole, the "pestilence of streams" is removed, and the texts advise the Deceased to ascend the stairway to Re. Great Stairway is a good description of the technical state of the cusp at this neutral point, where the magnetic field is zero, where solar and ionospheric ions exist, and where the energy landscape of what space physicists call the *staircase cusp* forms (Escoubet et al. 1993). Referring to the opening of the Duat, the Deceased King states, "The two portals are opened for me, and I have gone up on the stairway" (CT416). What the Deceased perceives as a stairway may be the staircase profile observed by scientists, that is, the potential energy landscape related to the form of the interatomic or intermolecular potential according to theory (Wales 2001, 2067). But what exactly is this potential energy landscape the Deceased perceives as a stairway or ladder?

The cusp consists of magnetospheric field lines most recently merged with the Sun's Interplanetary Magnetic Field (IMF). Space physicists term this process magnetic reconnection. Variations in the merging rate indicate the behavior of the cusp ion energy latitude dispersion is not always uniform, displaying dispersionless intervals and sharp jumps. Analyzing data from satellites, researchers attribute the staircase cusp signature to this "bursty merging" or the reconstruction of the merging rate in the cusp (Newell and Meng 1991; Lockwood and Smith 1992; Escoubet et al. 1993). However, "bursty" or impulsive reconnection at the cusp is different from reconnection at Dungey's four neutral points, which are activated by solar wind pressures and antiparallel field shear. To understand the difference, space physicists have collected data on the staircase cusp.

Sandholt et al. (1999) of the University of Oslo in Norway interpreted particle data from an overflight at Svalbard by F13 DMSP spacecraft that recorded a long stepwise poleward retraction of the band of auroral emission in the cusp region. Then in April, 2000, at the General Assembly in Nice, France, the Department of Physics at the University of Oslo and the University of Leicester, UK, reported a study of ionospheric signatures of plasma entry and momentum transfer at the dayside magnetopause during northward IMF at the cusp. Ground observations of the dayside aurora and ionospheric ion drift from CUTLASS radar was obtained from three spacecraft. The optical instruments also recorded a long stepwise poleward retraction and latitudinal widening of the band of auroral emission in the cusp region. Let's look closer at this process of staircase formation at the cusp.

Flux Transfer Events

The staircase cusp is identified with the ionospheric signature of Flux Transfer Events (FTEs) (Escoubet et al. 1993; Newell). Russell et al. (1990) state that the most noticeable signature of an FTE is its positive (out of magnetopause) then negative signature (into magnetopause). Russell defines an FTE as magnetic flux being transported, a phenomenon with a beginning and an end. These events result in plasmoids, large bundles of magnetic flux and plasma, moving tailward (Hones et al. 1984) or the faster-moving flux ropes discussed earlier. Put simply, the impulsive or bursty merging is a type of magnetic reconnection signaled by the staircase signature and FTEs.

EVIDENCE FOR PLASMA MIXING AT CUSP

Space physics provides evidence for the plasma mixing at the cusp or cleft. Moore et al. (1998) received data from the ISTP Polar spacecraft, equipped with a unique plasma velocity analyzer system for kinetic diagnostics of low-energy, low-density plasma ions. Polar observed the mixing of solar and ionospheric plasmas in the cleft regions, auroral heating and plasma transport, and the downward motion of O+ at lower altitudes through the polar cap region. This indicates that most polar cap O+ outflow originates in the dayside plasma upwelling region, creating a plasma fountain effect in the polar cap. At low altitudes the ionospheric plasma is co-rotating with the earth, and at higher latitudes it is convecting under the influence of the large scale magnetospheric electric field mapped to low altitudes. (University of Oulu-Finland 2000)

Figure 2.3

Space physicists believe that the tearing instability begins the complex reconnection process. Their analyses show that the conditions for instability start with a population of electrons that is not trapped in the current sheet. These electrons then short the electric field that stabilizes the mode, creating a gap for entry where it was formerly blocked. (University of Maryland 2002) A magnetic island then forms on the interface. The tearing mode displaces magnetic field-lines outside, but the original topology is still retained. On the other hand, field lines inside have broken and reconnected, exhibiting a different topology.

The formation mechanism of magnetic islands or FTEs is controversial among space physicists because it depends on solar wind and magnetospheric conditions. Space physicists also refer to FTEs as cusp diamagnetic cavities, bubbles, and magnetic islands. Much study is currently devoted to the magnetopause's Low Latitude Boundary Layer (LLBL) where FTEs occur. For example, Song et al. (1993) showed that for northward IMF, the LLBL has a stair-step plasma density profile with no evidence for plasma flow between the steps. It is this region through which the solar wind plasma has direct access to the low altitudes (Heikkila and Winningham 1971). The numerical simulations of K. Stasiewicz et al. (2001) show that "bubbles" (aka CDCs, FTEs, magnetic islands) are produced by a tearing mode reconnection process driven by strong magnetopause currents and fluctuations of kinetic Alfven waves.

Research indicates that an instability gap exists at the polar staircase cusp where magnetic reconnection and FTEs occur. The FTEs create the gap of entry, which appears during periods of enhanced Far Ultra Violet (FUV) emission. FUV auroral luminosity accompanied by enhanced velocity flow channels are statistically associated with FTEs at the magnetopause. In other words, during a period of extended dayside reconnection, there is a widening of the gap. The widening of the merging gap is observed in both the radar flows and FUV emissions. (Neudegg et al. 2001) The evidence is that the staircase cusp indicates the tearing mode instability, which creates a gap for magnetopause entry. The Egyptian descriptions of the Deceased traveling to the polar cusp, finding a stairway, merging with Re, and looking for the Gap to the Winding Waterway mirror magnetospheric events studied by space physicists. Decoded:

Sun-god's Bark = FTE at magnetopause causing tearing mode instability
Great Stairway = staircase cusp

So, actual energy structures and processes exist at the element-enriched polar cusp, such as the staircase signature and FTEs that could represent what the Egyptians call the Great Stairway and the ferryboat of the Sun-god. We could say that the Deceased merging with the Sun-god at the polar Great Stairway is similar to ionospheric ions being entrained by FTEs moving into the polar magnetopause to trigger the staircase cusp.

The Winding Waterway of the Magnetopause

IS 24-26: Self-created Dead King ferries on reed-floats from West to Eastern Horizon on Winding Waterway.

IS 27: Dead King travels Causeway of Happiness beneath firmament of sky.

After the Deceased climbs the Great Stairway at the Gap or polar cusp, he must go through the Double Ramgate and "navigate on the Winding Waterway and sail in the eight-boat" (CT62). We might view the Deceased with his eight traveling companions as plasma, a complex structure such as an ordinary ion surrounded by a cloud of polarizable molecules, moving through the magnetopause or Winding Waterway, which is always in motion. It is a complicated, multi-layered structure, which the solar wind must cross to enter the earth's magnetosphere. As a barrier, it prevents most of the solar wind energy from entering the magnetosphere, but it cannot stop some energy entering at the cusps. The texts refer to the "paths of the West" (CT343), the "Causeway of Happiness" (PT518), the "causeway beneath the firmament" (PT573), "May you stand up at the causeway" (PT659, 666A, 674), "traveling the causeway" (PT676), and the "causeway in the meadow" (PT690), suggesting a path through the wavy grasses of a meadow or the actual waves of the magnetopause discovered by the European Space Agency's Cluster spacecraft (2001). So, the earth's flowing magnetopause, the twisting channel separating the earth's electromagnetic barrier from the solar wind, is a reasonable model for the Egyptian Winding Waterway and the Causeway.

Winding Waterway and Causeway = magnetopause

Also, Song et al. (1990) describe five different regions during an inbound magnetopause crossing by the ISEE 1 spacecraft. These regions are present for all IMF directions (Russell 1995). Physicists are investigating magnetopause processes at the nearby boundary layer, the exterior cusp and various high- and low-latitude boundary layers. Here, numerous types of transient events occur in the mid- and low-altitude cusp regions. So let's take a closer look at this region, which may shed light on the idea of the Sun-bark as a molecular assembly entering the magnetopause.

The Magnetopause of Two Ways

Recent research analyzing data from DMSP spacecraft and the 3-D miniaturized plasma detectors aboard the Swedish Munin and Astrid spacecraft shows that the magnetopause current layer has a unique footprint, where current layer field lines map down to the low-altitude ionosphere. Initial evidence from this model supports the Crooker interpretation of the cusp as a small-scale footprint of the magnetopause current layer, that is, true cusp. (Keith 2001)

Just inside the magnetopause, layers exist called the Low Latitude Boundary Layer (LLBL) and High Latitude Boundary Layer (HLBL), both of which extend far into the magnetotail. The dayside LLBL is highly structured and very sensitive to the direction of the Sun's IMF. When the IMF is southward, the coupling between the solar wind and magnetosphere is strong, geomagnetic activity is high, and energy transfer to the magnetosphere is maximized. With northward IMF, coupling is weak, geomagnetic activity low, and energy transfer diminished. Song et al. (1993) found that for northward IMF the LLBL shows a stair-step plasma density profile. The funerary texts state that "the land is placed in the side of the Great West at the stairway of the lotus-tank at the place for traveling upstream in the Lake of the Favoured Ones" (CT399). The idea of going upstream is similar to the advice that urges the Deceased to pass "on the upper road of Rosetjau" (TR4), suggesting the HLBL. However, it seems possible that both the LLBL and HLBL may be available paths for the Deceased Sun-god.

Plasma can enter the magnetosphere at low latitudes adjacent to the magnetospheric side of the magnetopause. One of the properties of the LLBL of the magnetopause is that plasma can convect far tailward along the flank magnetopause (Heikkila 1990; Fujimoto 1998). In addition, Newell and Meng (1992) showed that the LLBL is on open field lines, just like the low altitude mantle (HLBL), which Xu et al. (1995) reported on open field lines. An "open LLBL," a term coined by Lockwood et al. (2001) to define an LLBL with field lines having an open topology, is characterized by accelerated flows of magnetosheath-like ions that are injected. Lockwood et al. concluded that at least part of the magnetopause LLBL is formed by plasma mixing or field lines opened by magnetopause reconnection.

Egyptian textual references indicate more than one pathway, stating that the Deceased "may cross the firmament, may he traverse the sky, may he travel safely on the fair paths on which the blessed travel" (CT399). So it seems possible the magnetopause has fair pathways for the Deceased, since both the LLBL and HLBL may be routes to an open IMF line, although the texts prefer the upper path, that is, the HLBL of the magnetopause. Decoded:

Paths of the West = LLBL and HLBL of magnetopause

One must consider that the chaotic magnetospheric processes are those of reaction-diffusion kinetics. So possibly all the Deceased must do is be in the right place at the right time, that is, at an origin of reconnection at the polar cusp, and the kinetics will transport him. For, if during those last dying earthly moments, the Deceased is able to gravitate or will his conscious molecular remains to the polar staircase site of reconnection, then it seems that events would unfold automatically, unveiling a different reaction pathway than the Deceased would experience at any other location on earth. It may be that the time immediately after death is crucial for achieving the desired chemical reaction. The question arises: how does one will a molecular consciousness to the cusp, where an ordered set of chaotic events will occur?

The Coriolis Effect

Perhaps the arrival event is an automatic process by means of the universal psychological experience at human death of tunneling to the light. Yet, there is also the Coriolis effect, a geotropic force that only acts when air is moving. All points on earth have the same rotational velocity, but when an object in the air moves west or east, the Coriolis effect deflects it to the north or south. This is because gravity pulls objects down and the ground holds them up. Air moving toward the poles curves to the east; air moving away from the poles curves to the west; air moving east curves toward the equator; air moving west curves toward the poles. The Egyptian texts emphasize a movement to the "Beautiful West," and since Egypt is located in the northern hemisphere, air or an object heading west would be deflected north due to the Coriolis effect. Objects heading east would be deflected south. (Van Domelen 2000)

With the Egyptian instructions emphasizing a western path to the northern polar region, it seems possible that they were aware of the Coriolis effect, which would bring a west-moving entity to the northern polar region as a consequence of the principle of conservation of angular momentum. Certainly, other factors may influence the Deceased's course. For instance, if we assume the Deceased is a charged particle, then he would have three distinctive motions: gyration around a magnetic field line, bounce motion along the magnetic field line, and drift motion across magnetic field lines. Also, electrons drift eastward while ions drift westward. So, if the Deceased in the afterlife is an ion, perhaps he can set his automatic pilot on *Cruise West* and easily drift to the Beautiful West, arriving at the cold polar north, an element-enriched gap in the earth's magnetosphere.

The Dynamics of the Polar Cusp

But, if the Deceased is an electron drifting west with protons, we could imagine the following scenario. The Deceased decides to connect with solar and high energy ions at the magnetopause of the northern polar cusp by going toward the Beautiful West via the Coriolis Force. Arriving at the pole with his new death vision, he sees actual energy landscapes of a Great Stairway or ladder, radiant auroral shapes such as arcs, bands, rays, pillars, draperies and coronas, created by magnetic field lines and solar energy. The Deceased climbs the auroral Great Stairway, and according to textual advice, he is at the famous Gap in the western mountains or polar cusp, where he joins Re's ferryboat for the trip through the Duat. The first division of the Book of Gates of the Duat, according to the sarcophagus of Seti I, shows the mountain of the west split open for the solar bark to sail through. The god is symbolized by the transformative beetle in the disk encircled by a serpent, symbol of energy. The text states that the great god, whose transformations are manifold, will join together his members (Budge 1905, 84), suggesting molecular self-assembly. The Deceased at the Gap states, "I fly and soar between those two great mountains in which Re appears" (CT305).

Reviewing the cusp, we can easily explain its dynamics by noting seven attributes and one warning. For this explanation, we will assume that the Deceased represents a fermion or a class of particles possessing half-integral units of intrinsic spin (electrons, muons, tau particles, neutrinos, quarks). This assumption seems reasonable for the texts assert the Deceased is re-established in his original shape (CT20).

Figure 2.4
The Egyptian Gap (Drawing from E. A. Budge, *The Egyptian Heaven and Hell*)

First, the West-to-East movement. Recall that the Gap is at the polar region of weak magnetic field, where the Sun-god enters the magnetopause. According to Russell et al. (1985), this is the source region of FTEs. The Deceased is advised not to travel on the western waterways, "for those who travel thereon do not return" (PT697). He must travel on the "eastern waterways among the Followers of [Re . . .] an arm [is upraised] in the East" (PT697). In essence, we have the potential for co-rotating and counter-rotating waterways. The texts (IS21) enforce a specific direction by constantly advising the Deceased to turn over from his left side to his right. This left-to-right movement parallels a west-to-east movement, a clockwise direction.

The Deceased begins his entry into the Duat at the Gap, where reconnection occurs at the cusp and magnetic bubbles or islands and FTEs form. Yet, at the Gap, the dynamic pressure (or ram pressure) of the solar wind and the

IMF directions determine the magnetopause position, which can vary by several earth radii. In light of these factors, what makes the polar regions of our planet so unique?

Second, random high energy protons. One possible reason for cusp uniqueness is the presence of high energy particles. For instance, the European Space Agency's (ESA) three Cluster space satellites sailing over the northern polar cusp recently found high energy protons in the cusp. On August 30, 2001, the first two satellites entered the cusp within one minute of each other and recorded the customary proton decrease in the cusp. The third spacecraft passed the cusp 45 minutes later and recorded the customary decrease in protons, followed by a sudden jump in the number and energy levels of protons 28 minutes later. Scientists explain this increase in proton and energy levels as the rapid motion of the cusp toward the North Pole, induced by the turning of IMF from south to north. This shows that at times there are higher energy protons in the cusp that may represent what the Egyptians refer to as the Sun-god or strong sunlight (PT523). But, where do these high energy particles come from?

Third, acceleration. According to NASA physicist Robert Sheldon, shock waves traveling out of the galactic disk transmit energy to the cusp and compress it. The cusp permits rapid stochastic diffusion because it is a quadrupole trap, requiring random energy impulses, possibly similar to those observed by Cluster spacecraft (ESA 2001). This makes the cusp a highly efficient accelerator. (Chen et al. 1999) A quadrupole is the sum of two dipoles, such as a distributed current system (earth's core and magnetic field) and a magnetized plasma such as a galactic cosmic ray (GCR) or the solar wind. Higher energy particles are less trapped in a quadrupole than those with lower energy. Waves convecting the solar wind compress trapped ions at the bow shock, causing an energy enhancement. (Sheldon 2004) This activity during a substorm may result in highly energetic protons making their way into the cusp during or after the event and the turning of the IMF northward as Cluster spacecraft observed (ESA 2001).

Fourth, higher energy, terrible power. The importance of finding a ferryboat is stressed in the texts. Along with this, the Deceased must greet Re in his sun and not be driven off by the "Lord of Terror, greatly majestic" (CT105). A fire is bound about Re, which is bright against the Deceased, who must join the fire, a possible representation of the high energy enhancement in a plasma of charged particles. According to Xinlin Li (2002) at University of Colorado's

Department of Aerospace Engineering Sciences, two main sources of energetic particles are Galactic Cosmic Rays (GCR) from supernovae explosions and solar energetic particles (SEP) relative to coronal mass ejections (CME). A third category discussed earlier is anomalous cosmic rays (ACR), which originate from interstellar neutral materials (He, N, O, etc.). Solar UV radiation ionizes these neutrals and accelerates them to earth, where the ACRs become trapped in a third Van Allen belt. So there are a variety of high energy particles in the earth's magnetosphere. However, Li mentioned that the solar wind also contains a hot halo and even hotter superhalo population of electrons that varies with solar wind activity. Li said that this electron superhalo population did not have sufficient phase space density to supply the radiation belts with electrons. So perhaps the Sun-god's fire represents this superhalo of electrons that avoid the Van Allen belts.

Fifth, a warning. Sheldon et al. (1998) discovered trapped energetic electrons (not protons in cosmic rays or solar winds) in the outer cusp, suggesting the possibility that the Van Allen radiation belts are filled from the cusp. Radiation belt electrons are formed by accelerating less energetic electrons (50 - 300 keV) (Li 2002) during substorm activity. If the Deceased represents low-energy electrons, it seems reasonable to infer that by boarding Re's ferryboat or bonding to the energetic Sun-god, the Deceased might empower his own molecular form with an energy greater than the cut-off 300 keV, thus saving himself from acceleration into the Van Allen belts, where according to Sheldon et al., a second, quasi-permanently trapped energetic particle population of electrons is present in the region of the earth's outer cusp, 8-11 Re (earth radii). Sheldon explains the use of the term "quasi-trapping" by noting that time variations in the field prevent an infinite trapping time, though in a stationary magnetic field, the trapping time is infinite. We could say that being quasi-trapped in the hot Van Allen belts might be a good approximation of the hell envisioned by various religions. Put simply, it is important not to be driven off by the energetic Sun-god, for the alternative to not bonding may be an infinite trapping time in the hot Van Allen belts.

Fortunately, the Sun-god may represent a composition of ionized, energetic plasma from not only the lower energy solar wind particles, but also the high energy GCR particles from supernovae. The importance of having high energy to avoid the Van Allen belts may be why the Deceased hates storms (CT1099) and worries about not finding a ferryboat (CT136), that is, not bonding to the Sun-god. It is interesting that the funerary texts resound with the advice to the Deceased to avoid storms. During a substorm, the magnetosphere is shocked by the solar wind, which may temporarily stop the entry of ambient cosmic ray particles at the cusps.

IS 107: Deceased receives warrant, power, protection from Orion; the Duat grasps the Deceased at the place where Orion is; the birth of Orion will be prevented if the Deceased does not access the Sun-god.

Sixth, cosmic rays from Orion. Protons are the most abundant components of high energy cosmic ray particles. T. Sanuki et al. (1999) reported energy ranges of 1 to 120 GeV as measured by the 1998 balloon flight of the BESS spectrometer launched from Lynn Lake, Manitoba, Canada. Cosmic rays with energies of several billion electron volts (GeV) have higher energy than those from the Sun (Langeveld 2002). The Orion region is a dense area of about 2,000 very young stars with elevated X-ray emissions that scientists believe arise from the stars' strong magnetic fields (NASA 2000). In Chapter 64 of the Theban Recension, the Deceased claims that he knows the depths and the composition of the blessed dead. He states, "That which is upon the shoulders of Orion is examined, being one-twelfth, strewing out what is united, as what one gives to another among them." This idea points to molecular self-assembly, isotope creation and more. Looking at the constellation Orion closely, we discover that Betelgeuse, a red super giant on the right shoulder of Orion, is an ancient star approaching the end of its life cycle. Recently, the Harvard-Smithsonian Center for Astrophysics (2000) reported the first direct evidence in Betelguese' pulsing chromosphere of streams of gas in opposite directions with velocities of 10,000 miles per hour. Like a human heart, Betelguese pulses, expelling gas from its surface out into space in one direction, while a second stream of gas falls in to the star.

Could this blow-off gas account for the Egyptian claim of one-twelfth strewing out from Orion? Is this Orion's warrant and authorization for molecular self-assembly at the cusp—the union of the Deceased with highly energetic protons and isotopes from a cosmic ray? Cosmic ray acceleration to earth by protostellar winds in the Orion molecular complex is theoretically possible (Ip 1995). The texts state: "I bring to him the breezes of the north wind" (CT46), and "I am among the Imperishable Stars who are in you" (TR149).

However, the most convincing textual evidence for cosmic rays from Orion are the following passages: "I find Orion standing in my path with his staff of rank in his hand; I accept it from him and I will be a god by means of it" (CT469). Also, the Deceased makes "summons to Orion that he should come to me" (469). In addition, the Deceased asks Sothis (Sirius) "to make my path ready, set up a stairway to the great plain, for you are my mother and Hu is at (the place) whence Orion issues" (CT470). Hu is the god of authoritative utterance, suggesting justification for the Deceased's rank, path and stairway from Orion.

Seventh, iron nuclei. In the energy spectrum of ultra high energy cosmic rays (UHECR) are primary iron nuclei with trajectories influenced by the galactic magnetic field. Blasi et al. (2000) showed that winds from young neutron stars are capable of galactic production of iron primaries that match the UHECR spectrum. In simulations, O'Neill et al. (2001) propagated iron nuclei through a model of the galactic magnetic field to determine galactic UHECR trajectories. They found that the simulations were sensitive to galactic field strength parameters. Also, they reasoned that a galactic wind similar to the solar wind can alter trajectories significantly. Research from Ahn et al. (1999) and Harari et al. (2000) proposed high energy particles from Virgo (near Orion) were distributed on earth by a galactic wind.

Although astrophysicists are still investigating the exact source of UHECRs, one effect is evident. Iron ejected with energies ~10^{20} eV will reach earth after some diffusion through the galactic and halo magnetic fields (Olinto et al. 1999). Iron nuclei are present at the cusp. These nuclei may alter the magnetic orientation of atoms in the null magnetic field, skewing them from their normal randomness in an energization or bonding process with the incoming solar energy and the electrons present. In iron metal, there is an interaction that can cause all the magnetic moments to snap into the same direction. Electrons producing the magnetic moments are involved in metallic binding and the orientation of electron spins affects the binding energy of the metal. (Calvert 2002) The Deceased states, "I am a servitor of Re who receives his iron" (CT1099), suggesting metallic binding. It is also interesting that the Deceased claims he is one of the "Lords of the God's Domain" and desires a "seat in the God's Domain in the presence of the lords of the West" (TR81B) The use of the word "domain" may refer to a region of uniform magnetization as modern physicists define it (Calvert 2002). Also, the funerary texts repeat that the Deceased should move himself from his left side to his right side, indicating a left-to-right 180 degree orientation that suggests a parity change for aligned magnetization (PT412, 482, 487; CT1, 219, 327; TR68).

IS 108: Deceased receives and runs with north wind; winds bring Eye to the Deceased; Deceased becomes the winds.

Eighth, power over the hurricane heavens. The Deceased desires power over the winds of heaven, as if this privilege would save him from being netted by the Van Allen belts. Power over the winds could relate not only to the solar wind and its interaction with the earth's geomagnetic field, but also to interstellar, protostellar and galactic cosmic winds. The Deceased is in "company with the south-wind" and is charged "to run with the north-wind" (CT62). This suggests the south wind is pushing the Deceased to the polar north, where he runs with the north wind, where he grasps Orion (CT280) or meets the Sun-god and crew, a composite of high energy solar and accelerated cosmic ray particles surrounded by a superhalo of electrons. The winds are favorable to the Deceased and the north wind is the sweet (breath) of life (CT163). "Fair is the north wind which goes forth from Atum to your nostrils" (TR183).

Also, the texts (CT75-81) emphasize the importance of becoming Shu. "I am Shu who draws the air into the presence of the sunshine to the limits of the sky, to the limits of the earth" (TR55). Shu is a member of the Heliopoliton Ennead, the eldest Egyptian deities. The creator god Atum sneezed or spat Shu out, along with Tefnut, his sister wife. As a cosmic deity and creative life force, Shu was the god of life manifest in the wind, air, light and water. He was often perceived as a column of air. Shu meant dryness or emptiness, not as a void, but as a space for potential activity (Houser-Wegner 2002). This description of Shu supports the importance of the creative potential of cosmic and/or energetic particles at the polar cusp. Actually, the idea of Atum sneezing or spitting Shu out can be compared to a supernova explosion.

It takes seconds for a star to blow apart, according to simulations of supercomputers. First, the iron core collapses, producing intense heat and high energy gamma-ray photons that break apart iron nuclei. The core electrons are forced to combine with protons to produce neutrons, releasing a flood of neutrinos. When the neutron-rich material of the core reaches nuclear density, it stiffens, stopping the collapse of the core so abruptly that it rebounds, rushing back out in a process called core bounce. Actually, you could call this a sneeze. During core bounce, the star's unsupported layers are rushing inward, slamming into the outward-bound neutrinos and rebounding core, which thrusts the layers outward, reversing their course. This large mass of matter moving to the star's surface forms a shockwave, blasting the star's outer layers away from the core in a mighty sneeze or ejection. A supernova is born. As the star's outer layers are blasted into space by the shockwave, fusion occurs, creating many elements that are found on earth and in our bodies. (Comins 2000, 310-311)

Along with this, in the Theban Recension (TR99), the wind talks: "Tell me my name," says the wind, "since you are carried thereby." The Deceased responds: "'North wind which went forth from Atum to the nose of the 'Foremost of the Westerners' is your name." The Foremost of the Westerners is Osiris or the Deceased, who also states, "I am this soul of Shu which is in the flame of the fiery blast Atum kindled" (CT77). "I am the soul of Shu, the god invisible of shape" (CT75).

Evidently, the polar cusp is a unique location, where the Deceased must travel from west-to-east, avoiding storms and acceleration into the Van Allen belts, while merging with the terrifying Sun-god, an enriched composite of elements from the solar wind and cosmic rays. In this way, the Deceased might be able to control the winds of Eternity, so he can become "the soul of Shu which is in the flame of the fiery blast which Atum kindled with his own hand" (CT77). In this way, "his vision is clear in the House of Darkness which is set in the entrance (of the sky) without seeing a storm" (TR169).

3

The Opening of the Mouth

WHY THE DECEASED AND HIS DOUBLE CROSS OVER TO A BLACK HOLE

IS 19: Deceased King's jaws fastened; Geb/earth opens jaws/mouth so King becomes Osiris.
IS 109: Split iron of mouth; King enters Sun-bark and iron doors open; strong iron on King's mouth.

In an attempt to understand the Egyptian metasymbols, we have proposed that the earth's magnetosphere is an authentic model for the Duat. One can also compare the Sun and earth's magnetic field lines to the reed-floats the Deceased ferries on from the Western to Eastern horizon. In line with this idea, the Deceased Sun-god encounters numerous deities lining the riverbanks of the Duat like frozen ions on magnetic field lines. The activity of the Deceased traveling through the Duat on reed-floats suggests the dynamics of drifting on an open magnetic field line to the Sun's interplanetary magnetic field. The Pyramid Texts state that the "reed-floats of the sky are set in place for Re" and the Deceased (PT265, 266, 473, 481), who hopes to ascend on reed-floats as Osiris did (PT303). The night-bark brings these reed-floats or open field lines to the Deceased so that he can cross on them. Additional language about finding the broken cord and knotting the ropes also suggest the magnetic reconnection process of field lines breaking and merging.

The significance of magnetic reconnection is important, for there are numerous references in the funerary texts to the Opening of the Mouth ceremony, which is similar to the process. For example, Chapter 161 of the Theban Recension centers on "breaking an opening in the sky." Although most of the text is unintelligible, the rubric is in tact. It describes four openings in the sky, emphasizing its secrecy, that "it is truly a secret, which no one of the people should know." The openings are in the north, south, west and east. Now in twenty-first century space physics, this matches up nicely with the reconnection sites Dungey and other physicists have targeted in the magnetosphere. Although difficult to explain without an animation, the spinning earth also exhibits the dynamics of a quadrupole cusp, cutting off the winds four times as it rotates. So it may be possible that the Egyptian Opening of the Mouth ceremony describes the process of magnetic reconnection or what the Egyptians refer to as "crossing over" (CT214, 255).

The Egyptian terms for the ritual are *wpt-r* and *wn-r*, both which translate to "opening of the mouth." The verb *wpi* connotes an opening that entails splitting, dividing, or separating, and can indicate the separation of two combatants or a determination of truth. The earliest Old Kingdom textual references to the ceremony date to the early Fourth Dynasty in the decoration of the tomb of the royal official Metjen. The captions state the ceremony is performed four times. The Pyramid Texts of Unas also mention the ceremony. Inscribed on the north wall of Unas' burial chamber is an offering ritual in which two blades of meteoric iron are said to open the mouth. One blade is described as Lower Egyptian and the other as Upper Egyptian. (Roth 2002, 295) Relative to our Sun-earth model, it seems reasonable to infer that the Lower Egypt blade represents earth's magnetic field line and the upper Egypt blade represents the solar IMF. Decoded:

Lower Egypt blade of iron = earth's magnetic field line
Upper Egypt blade of iron = Sun's magnetic field line

Both the Coffin Texts and the earlier Pyramid Texts have numerous references relating to the Opening of the Mouth, which demonstrates the unity of the texts. The Coffin Texts reference Geb (earth) opening his jaws, the earth opening its mouth (CT4), the firmament dividing (CT98), the West opening (CT109), the gates opening (CT147), the iron broken (CT816), the sky, earth and horizon opening (CT1146). Likewise, the Pyramid Texts refer to *zmin* or cream splitting open the mouth (PT34), the King's jaws dividing (PT37), the god's iron of Upper Egypt dividing from that of Lower Egypt (PT38), the sky doors opening (PT355), the mountains splitting (PT670), and splitting open the mouth by means of the Eye of Horus (PT93). In addition, the words of the ceremony were performed four times, as the winds on earth were cut off four times (CT330), as the Deceased makes his seat in the Mansion of Sunrise four times (CT422), as the Deceased travels the watery Chaos four times (CT551), as Osiris comes four times (CT1120). So the language of the texts and the etymology of Egyptian words *wpt-r* and *wn-r* point to the magnetic reconnection process of field lines breaking and merging. Decoded:

Opening of the Mouth ceremony = magnetic reconnection

Metasymbols for Magnetic Reconnection

The process of magnetic reconnection, which is initiated by the tearing instability, can be compared to opening the mouth (as well as gates, barriers, mountains, jaws, doors, sky, iron) and rejoining of the riverbanks. It is interesting that in magnetic reconnection, each plasma is frozen to its own magnetic field. The plasmas do not mix with the thin boundary layer formed between them. The layer also constitutes a current sheet. Magnetic reconnection is a process by which lines of magnetic force break and rejoin in a lower energy state. The excess energy appears as the kinetic energy of plasma at the point of reconnection.

Another metaphor to describe this process of reconnection is crossing over. The Deceased "on this southern side of the Winding Waterway" urges Thoth to "put me on the tip of your wing on yonder northern side of the Winding Waterway" (PT55), which suggests that the Deceased crosses over to the northern side as does "May you cross over, O Great Bull, to the green fields, to the pure places of Re" (PT553). Crossing over is also referred to as knotting the "ropes which were severed" (CT132, 136), finding the "broken cord" (CT144), "joining the riverbanks" (CT168, 169, 170, 171, 172), the "river-banks will unite" (PT254), and "the great waters are joined together for you" (PT611). Again, these activities are very similar to the process of magnetic reconnection, and a coronal loop is the visible manifestation of this energy transport mechanism (Brown 2000). Decoded:

Crossing over = magnetic reconnection

The *Akh*

The Egyptian *akh* is a representation of the crested ibis hieroglyph. Cosmic, primordial notions of luminous power were allied to the idea of *akh*. It often denoted forms of effective light, the solar eye, and sunbeams. (Friedman 2002) Ogden Goelet, Jr. of the Department of Near Eastern Studies at New York University translates *akh* as "the radiant one," noting that it was the goal of the Deceased not to remain in the Osirian netherworld of the Duat, but to travel freely as an *akh*. Goelet also states the word *sakh* denotes "that which transforms (one) into an *akh*," and although *akhet* is translated as "horizon," the better translation is "light land" or "bright place." (1994, 150, 152, 158)

A coronal loop looks like the Egyptian *akh*. Interplanetary Coronal Mass Ejections (ICMEs) are expanding loops or bubbles of high density plasma that have large slowly-rotating magnetic fields and cold ions. These magnetic force-free flux ropes are found in the corona, the interplanetary medium, the planetary magnetopause current sheets, and the magnetotail current sheets. (Russell 1999) Formed by magnetic reconnection or velocity shears, these freely traveling solar flux loops reflect the meaning, structure and dynamics of the Egyptian *akh*. Decoded:

***Akh* = Coronal Loop**

Cold Water

IS 98: Dead King receives jar of cold water when he meets Re at polar region; Dead King gets ferryboat to get cold water at polar quarter.

Cold ions exist in ICMEs and multiple flux ropes are produced (Russell 1999). The dynamics of coronal loops include factors such as cold plasma from the stars, possibly the beams or water flowing from Orion. "The cold waters of those who are in the sunshine are thrown open" (CT570) to the Deceased King, who states, "I have issued from the creating of the waters" (PT510). Similarly, the Deceased "will pour out a star" (510). "Fair is the north wind which goes forth from Atum to your nostrils . . . he removes the evil which is on your body by means of the power which is on his mouth" (TR183). The texts mention "giving water to a spirit. This your cold water" (CT64), emphasizing the importance of "cold water" (CT130). This seems logical, for if cold water is a metasymbol for the plasma of the Sun and stars at the cusp, then it provides the elements (H, He, Fe, S, and so on) necessary for the Deceased's self-assembly. If this is the case, then there should be a cold ion stream in the Egyptian "causeway" or magnetopause.

Not only have cold ionospheric components been present in the LLBL (Fuselier et al. 1989), but during a period of time from 21:30 UT on April 7, to

07:35 UT on April 8, 1998, Geotail spacecraft observed high energy cold O+ beams flowing tailward together with He+ and H+ in the northern dusk plasma mantle (HLBL). The major component on the dayside polar magnetosphere was H+. Energization occurs around the reconnection site. Seki et al. (2000) concluded that "the O+ population in the dayside magnetosphere on closed flux tubes is adequate in quantity to supply COBs (cold O+ beams) in the lobe/mantle."

Another study observed a very dense population of H+, He+ and O+ locally accelerated in a perpendicular fashion to the local magnetic field in a region adjacent to the magnetopause and on its magnetospheric side. On January 31, 2001, Cluster spacecraft encountered the magnetopause between 05:30 to 06:02 UT. In this area, ions of terrestrial origin over a wide energy range are expelled from the polar auroral region. Low energy ions dominate the convection drift, not bouncing but ExB drifting sometimes into distant regions of the magnetosphere (Sauvaud and Delcourt 1987; Delcourt et al. 1989, 1993). Lundin and Dubinin (1985) first observed cold plasma at the magnetopause. Then Fuselier (1989) reported evidence along with Chandler et al. (1999). A polar TIDE experiment detected a cold plasma population (T<2eV) flowing along field lines with a parallel velocity of the order of 50 km/s in the outer magnetosphere. Researchers have also measured a dense population of low energy ionospheric ions, H+, He+ and O+ during quiet time periods in a layer adjacent to the magnetopause. The magnetopause has intermittent motions caused by pressure changes associated with the appearance of these terrestrial ions drifting perpendicularly. Low energy plasma is controlled by ExB drift. The researchers did not exclude the possibility that oscillations of the magnetopause were due to time-dependent or sporadic reconnection.

"Cold water is in the sky with Kbh the son of Re . . ." (CT344) suggests that if the Deceased merges with the Sun-god, then he will travel the path of cool water. This may signify the cold ion streams in the lobe/mantle (HLBL) and cold plasma at the magnetopause as a possible route through the magnetosphere or Duat. Decoded:

Cold water = plasma of Sun and Stars
Re's cold water = cold ion stream in magnetopause (HLBL and LLBL)

Despite the merger with the Sun-god for a Flux Transfer Event, it still seems as if the reaction-diffusion kinetics of the earth's magnetopause (Winding Waterway) would play a major role in determining the cool pathway of the

Deceased through the Duat. Yet, we can conclude from Egyptian drawings and textual evidence that the earth's magnetosphere is a reasonable prospect for the Egyptian Duat. In addition, the path outlined by the Egyptian directions mirrors actual pathways into and out of the earth's magnetosphere related to magnetic reconnection and cold plasma entry.

Objective 1 completed: Based on the idea that the earth's magnetosphere is the Duat, modern scientific observations support the existence of magnetospheric structures that mirror those described in the Egyptian texts related to the Pharaohs' path to the stars.

The Black Hole Duat

It is interesting that the texts advise the Deceased that no one has power over his soul, no one takes away his heart, and no one causes him to go down into the Great Void with those who have committed blasphemy (CT45). This suggests that the consciousness of the Deceased experiences some free will in the afterlife, viz., his decision to bond or not to bond to the Sun-god, for after this merger, reaction-diffusion kinetics inevitably take charge as the Deceased Sun-god and crew move into the Duat. Since Egyptian drawings, textual references and scholarly descriptions support the earth's magnetosphere as the Duat's location, we can now take a fresh look at this dark vortex.

The Great Void is the vacuum of the black Duat, a place where the earth's spinning gravitational field entraps particles. The general theory of relativity predicts that frame-dragging occurs around any spinning body, even the earth (MIT News 1997), so we could say that the earth's magnetospheric vortex exhibits the dynamics of a spinning black hole. As a spinning, giant tangle of magnetic field lines or strings, our magnetosphere is a fair representation of a black hole modeled according to String Theory. Also, according to physicist Fred A. Wolf, shrinking the earth to .4438 centimeter would result in a black hole (1988, 148), so the earth may represent a quantum mechanical black hole.

Because the earth and its magnetosphere is a spinning vortex, it would be classified as a Kerr black hole with two horizons, an inner and an outer. According to the texts, after transformation both the Deceased and his double ascend or are "bound for the sky" (PT684). Also, the "prince ascends in a great storm from the inner horizon" (PT669), and the "foretellers of the great storm go forth from within the inner horizon of the sky" (CT682). The texts describe an inner event horizon, which implies an outer horizon in the black-hole Duat.

This suggests the two horizons of a Kerr black hole.

Along with two horizons, a spheroidal Kerr black hole has two photon spheres. The outer photon sphere rotates in the opposite direction of the axis of the black hole, so the photons appear to be traveling slower against the hole's rotation. The inner co-rotating photon sphere, where the Deceased is, appears to travel faster, going with the current. Actually, there is a third photon sphere near the ring singularity, the center point composed of matter that has an infinitely small volume, the earth in our case.

What is interesting is that the macroscopic earth has three Van Allen belts, possibly the equivalent of three photon spheres. Whereas the inner belt houses energetic protons and is stable, the outer belt has both electrons and protons and is unstable. The third Van Allen belt of trapped anomalous cosmic rays (ACRs) has been pinpointed as a narrow belt within the inner Van Allen belt (Cummings et al. 1993). If the earth is a quantum black hole, we now have another strong rationale for the Egyptian advice to go to the North Pole, for the Deceased only encounters one rotating photon sphere, instead of two, since the spheres are joined at the North pole or axis of the Kerr black hole.

Also, the Book Amduat recounts the journey of the Sun-god through its circles. Modern physicists describe black hole geometries by length and angles. The polar coordinates are lines of constant distance called circles in two dimensions, while the spherical coordinates are lines of constant distance called spheres in three dimensions. Perhaps the emphasis on the circles and spheres in the Duat relate to black hole coordinates.

Before entering the black Duat, the Deceased states, "I fly up as a vulture on this great plateau that I may stand on it. I appear as a god, for he who looks at them will never die" (CT205, 287). The Deceased is like a vulture because he has died. The "plateau of citizens" (CT226) or the "limitless desert plateau" (CT272) and the "plateau of the Great Foreland" (CT278) suggest an extended two-dimensional membrane or a flat superspace, which physicists believe is the unique geometry of our universe. In a flat universe, the angles of a triangle add to 180 degrees. (Gribbin 2001, 95) In String Theory, one-dimensional strings stretch into two-dimensional membranes (Greene 1999, 315), suggesting that at the heart of matter, a human might experience a two-dimensional stretch similar to the Egyptian mental experience of being on a plateau or a flat universe near a black hole. The texts state, "the Great West is he who stretches out my bones and extends my limbs, so that I may walk on my feet like Osiris"

(CT417).

In this same text the Deceased states, "I will travel around to the limit of the horizon, to the place where my double desires to dwell." Other references to "those who are in the limits of the horizon" (CT363) and "I come to land at the region of the horizon in company with those who are in the Bark" (CT239) suggest the horizon or surface of a black hole. Our modern physicists define the static limit of a rotating black hole as the outer boundary of the ergosphere above the outer event horizon. Another reference states that Nut will lead the Deceased and his double in the "ways of the horizon" (PT677). Also, the Deceased states, "my mansion is within the limit of the horizon, for I am Atum" (CT709) and "I have entered into the horizon" (CT790). The fire is blue at the first portal, and the gods say "It means blackness" (CT336), suggesting infinite blue shift at a hole, which appears black.

Also, the gravity around the ring singularity is repulsive, pushing one away, allowing one to theoretically leave the black hole if one approaches it on an equatorial plane. Thus, in the Book of Two Ways, the text states, "No man is able to penetrate the fire—he will be repulsed there" (Piankoff CT1054), and the Deceased should pass by "Repulsive-Face-who-lives-on-*3rf*" (CT1066), along with "Great-Face, he who repulses the afflicted" (CT1069). Further, the texts state, "This is the door of the circle(?), the opening of the Holes(?)" (CT1064), suggesting the existence of a second hole, possibly a white hole.

According to Sethe's interpretation (which Faulkner questions), another pertinent text (PT291) states, "Your honour is removed, O white hole, by him who came forth from the *fnt*-snake." Coming forth from the *fnt*-snake is similar to the Sun-god's departure from the Duat through a serpent in the Amduat and the Book of Gates. In astrophysics, a white hole is a body that spews out matter or a black hole running backward in time. If a black hole connects to a white hole, a wormhole or Einstein-Rosen bridge is generated. The serpentine escape of the molecular Deceased from the black-hole Duat through a white hole supports that information is not destroyed, just as astrophysicists John Preskill and Stephen Hawking have predicted (Hogan 2004). Also, the idea of the Deceased having a double that remains with him is prevalent in the texts (IS101–103). However, the Deceased is not a spirit who goes to his double for a second death. The Egyptian texts advise the Deceased to learn the paths of the West, so he will be able to overthrow the "ramparts of Shu" (PT509, 667C) and escape from the Duat and its nets with his double. This reminds one of Hawking radiation, virtual particle and anti-particle pairs escaping from a black hole. We can conclude that the black Duat or spinning magnetosphere, the two-dimensional membrane of the plateau or flat hyperspace with the earth's curved spaces embedded, and language relating to horizons, circles, dragging, mouths and circulating point to black hole dynamics.

Black Duat = Kerr black hole with 2 horizons and ring singularity

The Dilemma of the Double

IS 101-03: If double remains, King does not die, his double is protected; he goes to castle for owners of doubles and is god of those who have gone to their doubles.

Annihilation is a process in which a particle and a related antiparticle disappear. Their energy appears as some virtual force field carrier particle, which then rapidly produces a new particle-antiparticle pair. The Deceased must learn the paths of the West and travel with those ferrying him. This will enable him to pass the "mysterious place of execution" (CT45) and escape the fishnet floating in the sky that "was made for the spirits who have gone to their doubles" (CT343, 344). By joining the Sun-god's ferryboat, the Deceased will not "perish nor be annihilated" (CT9), for he states, "my double has power, I am installed with Re, and Re installs me with these great gods" (CT196). The Deceased also claims, "I am Osiris, lord of doubles" (CT227) and that his double is exalted, for "I do not die while it remains" (CT251). Again, merging with the Sun-god may prevent the Deceased from entrapment in the Van Allen belts, destruction at a singularity, or a collision with his double.

In quantum field theory, when an electron with positive energy and its antiparticle with negative energy (a positron) collide, they briefly annihilate each other in a burst of energy creating a photon. Releasing its energy, this produces another particle-antiparticle (electron-positron) pair. From the perspective of a String theorist, the particles are not zero points but one-dimensional strings. When these two oscillating loops collide, they annihilate each other and create a new string with a different vibrational pattern that releases energy, dividing into two strings along new trajectories (Hawking 2001, 51)

However, a real particle (or string) with positive energy can have negative energy inside the gravitational field of a black hole. So a virtual particle with negative energy could fall into a black hole and become a real particle or antiparticle. As Stephen Hawking states, "In this case it no longer has to annihilate with its partner. Its forsaken partner may fall into the black hole as well" (1988, 106). This may be what the text means when it states that the goddess Nut will lead the Deceased and his double on the "ways of the horizon" (PT677). Put simply, the Deceased promotes his double in the realm of the dead (CT255). Going to your double suggests annihilation, while entering the black-hole Duat with your double suggests a rebirth of matter in the presence of the double. Decoded:

Going to your double = particle annihilation
Presence of double in Duat = no annihilation

Perhaps the Deceased and his double represent a quark/antiquark pair (meson) or a pi-meson (pion) in a protein folding funnel. This will be resolved shortly, and it will be seen that there is no contradiction with the Duat having the properties of a Kerr black hole. Actually, the Pharaohs are telling us what happens within a Kerr black hole, something modern physicists have been wanting to know for a long time.

MATRIX 1

EGYPTIAN SIGN TRANSLATED TO
POSSIBLE MODERN SCIENCE PARALLEL

***akh* symbol:** coronal loop of plasma
Atum sneezing, spitting: supernova explosion
Bark of Sun-god at polar region: Flux Transfer Event causing tearing instability to create gap of entry at magnetopause; beginning of magnetic reconnection
cold water: cold ion stream in HLBL and LLBL of magnetopause
creating of waters: high energy plasma with self-assembling elements from supernovae explosions
crossing over: magnetic reconnection
District of Waters: evershifting magntopause of waves
Domain of God: domain, region of uniform magnetization
Duat, Netherworld or Great Void: vortex of magnetosphere; Kerr black hole
fiends trapped in House of Net: charged particles spiraling, bouncing between mirror points and drifting or trapped in Van Allen belts
Gap, Pole of Sky, Great Polar Region, Horn: gap or cusp of magnetosphere
going to your double: particle annihilation
Great Stairway or ladder: bursty merging, staircase cusp signature, and sign of impulsive reconnection and FTE
Horns of Great Wild Bull: earth's two polar cusps where Sun and cosmic particles enter earth's magnetosphere
House of Net, fishnet, Ramparts of Shu, vault: earth's energy landscapes
Lower Egypt blade of iron: magnetic field lines of earth
Imperishable Stars: Orion, Virgo, Great Bear constellations
Iron broken, mountains split, gates opening, broken cords, joining riverbank: broken magnetic field lines undergoing magnetic reconnection
Opening of Mouth ceremony: breaking of iron or magnetic field lines
reed-floats or iron bands: magnetic field lines
paths of the West: LLBL and HLBL of earth's magnetopause
path to Eternity in macrocosm: North Pole for high energy merge into Sungod then into the earth's magnetopause and out to stars
power over winds; becoming Shu: solar, interstellar, protostellar and galactic cosmic winds
presence of double: no particle annihilation due to black hole dynamics
ropes of iron: flux ropes generated by earth's iron core
Rosetjau (place of dragging); "who drag in Re:" magnetic reconnection; frame dragging of black hole
secret openings in sky: reconnection at NSWE points of earth's magnetosphere; also quadrupole activity of earth
storms: high geomagnetic activity/energy transfer between Sun and earth; southward IMF
Unwearying Stars: polestars (Thuban, Polaris)
Upper Egypt blade of iron: magnetic field line of Sun
valleys and mountains of Duat, District of Waters, Lakes of Netherworld: energy landscapes of earth's magnetosphere
white hole: a black hole running backward in time
Winding Waterway, Causeway of Happiness: winding magnetopause

What is Below

So far, we have used the following logic to decode the texts:

1. Test the unity assumption by matching major Idea Strands in the Pyramid Texts and Coffin Texts.

Result: Old Kingdom Pyramid and Middle Kingdom Coffin Texts are unified in key themes.

2. Decode interrelated signs in the texts to define a model of the Duat.

Result: The model for the Egyptian Duat is our earth system. This model matches textual descriptions and decodes interrelated signs.

3. On the quantum level, the earth system is a spinning vortex similar to a Kerr black hole. The Duat is also similar to a Kerr black hole, a claim the texts support by references to inner horizons, holes, circles, and virtual particle pairs (Deceased and his double).

4

A Quantum Leap into an Afterlife Cloning Experiment

IS THE SUN-GOD'S FERRYBOAT A BACTERIOPHAGE VECTOR?

Some of the same processes occurring in the earth's magnetosphere are mirrored at the quantum level of the cell. For instance, magnetic reconnection in the earth's magnetosphere is similar to DNA recombination in the cell. The antiparallel northward and southward IMFs match the antiparallel directions of DNA. Ions on magnetic field lines are frozen in place like nucleotides on DNA strands. Movements of the northward and southward IMFs pushing out a plasmoid in the earth's magnetotail imitate a bacterial cell kicking out a plasmid during binary fission. Perhaps space physicists should talk with geneticists and biologists to compare their knowledge bases, for it seems very possible that the Pharaohs were using the macrocosm to explain similar events in the microcosmic cell. Our next objective centers on these similarities.

Objective 2: Do the operations of the solar wind and earth above mirror events on the cellular level below?

Binary Fission in Bacteria

In 1963, John Cairns proved that *E. coli* has a circular chromosome, a single origin of replication, and unwinding and replication are simultaneous. Bacteria such as *E. coli* have one chromosome, which is attached to the plasma membrane and not in a nucleus. The chromosome divides in two producing two daughter chromosomes, with each chromosome attaching to a different part of the membrane. The cell then pinches between the two areas until the cell wall splits, producing two daughter cells. This process is similar to what happens in the earth's magnetosphere during a substorm. Put simply, magnetic reconnection in the earth's magnetosphere activates a magnetospheric process similar to binary fission in bacteria.

A substorm begins with a powerful solar eruption, sometimes impacting like a massive earthquake. According to NASA, these storms can be recurrent (every 27 days) and related to the Sun's rotation or nonrecurrent and caused by Coronal Mass Ejections. Recall that Interplanetary Coronal Mass Ejections (ICMEs) have large magnetic fields that slowly rotate and cold ions (Russell 1999). During southward IMF, the outermost sunward loops of the earth's magnetic field are broken and swept into the magnetotail. Due to magnetic pressure in the magnetotail lobes, the plasma sheet is pinched until a neutral point forms. Reconnection occurs within this neutral point, snapping magnetic field lines back toward earth and forcing a bubble of plasma or a plasmoid out of the magnetotail on the other side.

Whereas a plasmoid consists of closed loops of magnetic field, accelerated down the tail due to the magnetotail field tension, a flux rope contains bundles of field lines attached to the earth that experience a slower tailward motion until all field lines are disconnected from earth. (Richard et al. 1996; Walker and Ogino 1996) A bacterial chromosome dividing into two chromosomes mirrors the dynamics of flux rope passage rather than plasmoid transfer.

Both a plasmoid and a flux rope are called FTEs. Because of data sparseness, a consensus understanding of substorm activity does not exist among space physicists. However, a broad consensus does exist that the magnetotail exhibits substorm behavior related to auroral expansion, magnetic field depolarization, current wedge formation, dispersionless particle injections, bursty bulk flows and current disruption. (NASA 2001) Thus, one can understand the confusion between designations such as plasmoids, flux ropes and other Flux Transfer Events that are similar, but different.

Recall that space physicists reported the first in-situ detection by Equator-S and Geotail spacecraft of oppositely-directed jets of plasma coming from a magnetic reconnection site at the earth's dayside magnetopause. This observational confirmation of bi-directional jets under southward IMF is evidence for reconnection theory. (Phan et al. 2001) These jets of plasma form the same topology at bursty or impulsive reconnection sites in the cusp, where energy transfer is determined by local conditions, such as the arrival of solar ions and FTEs. The magnetosphere's bi-directional jets of plasma easily remind one of the bi-directional DNA molecule in the quantum world.

Magnetic Reconnection or DNA Recombination?

As an important example, let's look closer at magnetic reconnection in the earth's magnetosphere compared to DNA recombination. Because the magnetic fields of the Sun and earth bump into each other, field lines stretch, snap and reconnect, causing Sun particles to slide like beads onto earth's magnetic field lines. In time, these Sun particles arrive at the poles and generate the aurorae. The cellular counterpart to this snapping and reconnection of Sun lines with earth's magnetic field lines is break-induced DNA recombination.

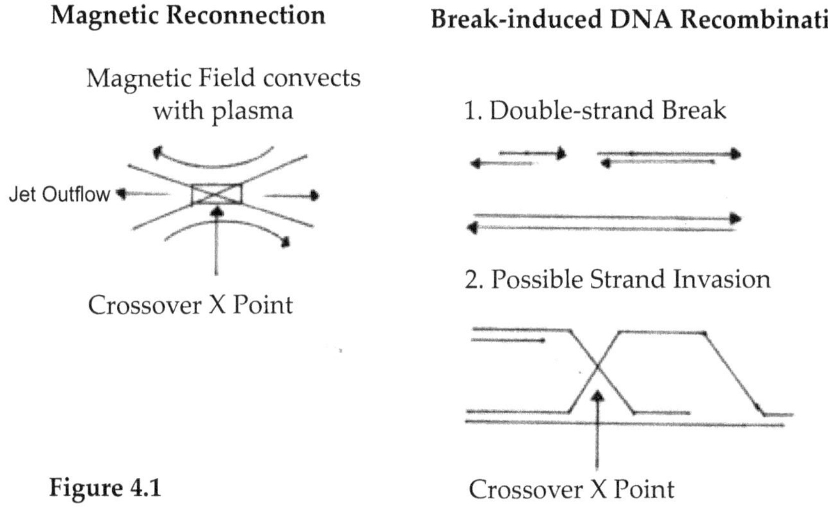

Figure 4.1

In Figure 4.1, showing reconnection of magnetic field lines, an X-type neutral line possesses flanking magnetic fields in opposite directions, one north and one south, similar to the opposite directions of the strands of a DNA molecule. This model of steady or forced magnetic reconnection, relative to northward and southward IMFs at the four points in the magnetosphere is similar to break-induced DNA recombination. At the earth's cusp, impulsive or bursty reconnection causes breaks and is signaled by the staircase cusp that results in a Flux Transfer Event. Because of these similarities between magnetic reconnection and DNA recombination, a further exploration of the Egyptian idea of "crossing over" is necessary.

Crossing Over as Recombinational Repair

CT 293: "Come, cross over"
IS 21: Dead King crosses over to pure places of Re; ferries across to other side
IS 22: Dead King finds broken cords and knots them so waters are joined, lands united, river-banks joined

Magnetic reconnection and DNA recombination or recombinational repair can both be described as "crossing over." The Deceased claims that he has found and knotted the severed ropes (CT132, 136, 219, 408, 1099) or the broken cord (CT144). He joins the river-banks (CT168–172), so that the Milky Way can be crossed (CT622). These metasymbols suggest the process of cutting and splicing DNA, which begins with an endonuclease (recBCD endonuclease in *E. coli*) performing single-strand nicks into each DNA strand. Strand exchange or invasion is the crossing over activity. RecA protein helps the strands base pair so the nicks can be sealed by DNA ligase. If a branch migration at the cross-over point or X-line occurs, more of each strand becomes part of the opposite molecule. (Hewlett 2000) We can conclude that the Egyptian idea of "crossing over" suggests not only magnetic reconnection, but also DNA recombination and/or repair.

DNA Recombination as the Splitting of Iron

IS 97: Dead King splits iron of mouth, descends on iron bands, sits on iron throne, is knit together with iron, receives offerings on great iron plain, has stellar iron and cuts away iron

On the cellular level, iron is embedded in the center of the DNA double helix at certain loci. An important nutrient for gram-negative bacteria like *E. coli*, iron plays a fundamental metabolic role by catalyzing hydrogen, oxygen and nitrogen enzymatic reactions. The bacterium has receptor proteins in its outermost membrane that function to uptake iron by binding iron-containing molecules. Iron complexes are then localized on the cell surface, where they are available for transport into the cell. To complicate the uptake process, *E. coli* has a double cell barrier of two lipid layers, the outer membrane and the cytoplasmic membrane. So the bacterial cell synthesizes molecules called siderophores that seize ferric iron. Then these iron-containing siderophores are transported into the cytoplasm of the bacterial cell. (Faraldo-Gomez 2002) Modern researchers have many questions about this process, which might be answered by a comparative review of the dynamics of magnetic reconnection, iron nuclei at the cusp, and Flux Transfer Events in the earth's magnetosphere, for iron-containing siderophores in the cell act similarly to flux ropes in the magnetosphere.

As DNA recombination includes cutting and splicing of strands, the Deceased uses language imagery such as "I am he who splits iron" to explain this process. Faulkner notes the variation of the translation "who splits what is joined," stating that this is an allusion to the splitting of the iron of the sky at the Deceased's ascension. (CT223) The Deceased splits mountains (CT275) like Anubis, who breaks the sky's iron and opens up the West (CT816). Egyptian imagery also describes opening the doors to Osiris in the firmament (CT866) or dividing the firmament (CT98). The Deceased also splits open the darkness (CT1106, 1116) and splits open the doors of tombs as he greets Re in his sun (CT105). This process includes not only opening the earth, but also the sky and the horizon (CT1146), all of which actually happens at points of magnetic reconnection in the earth's magnetosphere. So, on the macro scale of earth, iron is cut by magnetic reconnection; on the quantum scale of earth, iron is cut by DNA recombination. Decoded:

Knotting ropes, joining river-banks, splitting iron or mountains, dividing firmament = Crossing over

Crossing over = DNA recombination and magnetic reconnection
Ropes of iron = iron entry in cell and flux ropes in magnetosphere

Based on the following comparative scheme of what is above in the magnetosphere and what is below in the quantum cell, particularly magnetic reconnection and DNA recombination, we can conclude that several operations of the Sun and earth mirror events on the cellular level. With these similarities in mind, let's consider the event of solar particles and cosmic rays arriving at the cusp relative to the Egyptian perspective of the Sun-god's bark moored at the Great Stairway or staircase cusp.

The Magnetosphere above	The Quantum Cell below
Magnetic reconnection	Break-induced DNA recombination/repair
Bi-directional jets of plasma Antiparallel north/south IMF	Antiparallel directions of DNA
Ions on magnetic field lines	Nucleotides on DNA
Flux ropes	Iron-containing siderophores
Substorm pinching off plasmoid or flux rope	Bacterial cell pinching out a plasmid during binary fission

The Day of Mooring

The Egyptian counterpart to actual high energy particles arriving at the poles to activate the staircase cusp that signals an FTE injection into the magnetosphere is the arrival of the Sun-god at the northern polar Gap, where the Deceased climbs the Great Stairway to the Sun-god's ferryboat. Recall that bursty merging or impulsive reconnection triggers a Flux Transfer Event at the cusp magnetopause. According to the funerary texts, it is here that the Deceased at the stairway bonds with the Sun-god, becoming the Deceased Sun-god or Osiris. The Deceased and his entourage then go from the Gap in the Mountain of the West through the Double Gates (CT48, 50) or the two portals (CT416) into the black Duat for the journey eastward.

These similar events prompt us to take a quantum leap of intuition. We could say that the Sun-god and crew at the cellular level represent a cloning vector or a small, self-replicating DNA carrier molecule such as bacteriophage Lambda. The earth then would represent the host cell that the vector uses for replicating phage progeny. The question is—do events in the Egyptian afterlife mirror this model or not?

On the cellular level, the Great Stairway may represent the bursty merging at a site for recombination due to phage adsorption and DNA injection at the double membrane of the host cell. In fact, this quantum staircase signature suggests the dynamics of the Coulomb staircase, a special result of having very different tunneling rates through two tunneling barriers (Meirav and Foxman 1996), as represented by the double membrane of the host cell. The Deceased in his "original shape" bonds to the Sun-god as a foreign insert in the vector for gene cloning, with the earth and its magnetosphere representing the living system or host cell, where the vector can be propagated. The cloning site is the earth's element-enriched northern cusp, where the Sun-god is moored in the "dockyard of the gods" (TR136A). In the Book of the Dead, the texts use phrases such as "to moor" or "to unite with the land," and the day of death became the "day of mooring" or the "good day" (Goelet 1994, 150). On the cellular level, metasymbols such as uniting with the land and mooring point to phage adsorption and penetration into the host cell.

For instance, the King opens the sky doors and the furnace heat is "beneath what the gods pour out" (PT313). The text then states that the "King lets slip there into this furnace-heat," so a road is made for the King to pass on. An utterly obscure passage? Maybe. Yet, it is possible that the furnace-heat references the Duat or earth-cell, and the "pour out" and "lets slip" references the movement of DNA into the host cell, viz., penetration or injection. Further, the name of the Deceased's ferryboat is "It-flies-and-alights" (PT310), suggesting the idea of phage movement and adsorption. Nonetheless, if stronger evidence is needed, one cannot contest that phage injection of DNA into a host cell is very similar to FTE injection into the magnetosphere, at least according to Stasiewicz et al. (2001). Recall that the tearing mode is spontaneous reconnection that forms a magnetic island or bubble. Plasma is advected toward the separatrix by the inflow and exhausted inside the separatrix, filling it to form the magnetic island. This process is very similar to the pouring out of phage DNA that slips into the host cell.

Further, in phage T4, it has been well documented that replication begins through DNA recombination, and this has also been proposed for phage Lambda and *E. coli* (Rosenberg 2001). At the cellular level, spontaneous magnetic reconnection is simply break-induced DNA recombination. This figurative pathway at the cellular level related to DNA recombination mirrors the Egyptian macrocosmic pathway through the magnetosphere or Duat related to magnetic reconnection. In the interests of understanding this cellular pathway, based on similarities in the earth's magnetosphere, Matrix 2 is a comparative scheme, charting the possibility that the Sun-god operates similar to a bacteriophage vector with the Deceased as the foreign insert. This matrix, comparing *what is above* in the magnetosphere with *what is below* in the cell, will serve as our model for verification.

MATRIX 2 AND MODEL

Egyptian Sign	What is Below	What is Above
Duat, Geb, Abyss	prokaryote host cell	earth/magnetosphere
House of the Net	prokaryote host cell w/circular chromosome	earth magnetic field lines
lst Eye/Eye of Horus	phage Lambda source	Sun/stars
Re's Net	phage Lambda DNA	Sun's magnetic field lines
Crossing over	DNA recombination	magnetic reconnection
Sun-god Re/ferryboat	phage gene vectors	hi-energy FTE
Deceased	insert into phage vector	ionospheric particles
The Gap	polar cap/gap in cell wall/cytoplasm	magnetopause at cusp
Winding Waterway or Causeway	Plasma membrane near chromosome of cell	magnetopause
Great Stairway with 2-portal opening	phage DNA injection at cell's double membrane; dynamics of Coulomb staircase due to two tunneling barriers	staircase cusp
movement of Sun-god through Duat for transformation	transduction	energy transfer of Sun particles in/out of magnetosphere
ropes of iron dragging Sun-bark	iron siderophores for binary fission	flux ropes/plasmoids pinching off

Objective 2 completed: Magnetic reconnection in the solar wind/earth system mirrors DNA recombination and repair on the cellular level, suggesting that the Egyptian pathway for the Deceased Sun-god into and out of the magnetosphere (Duat) is similar to the event of a phage Lambda vector ferrying an insert into a cell for replication and cloning. Based on these similarities, Matrix 2 shows the resultant model for further verification. Because phage Lambda is a complex virus, see Figure 4.3 describing its two lifestyles.

LAMBDA LIFESTYLES
Lysogeny (cI protein)
Lysis (cro protein)
Figure 4.2

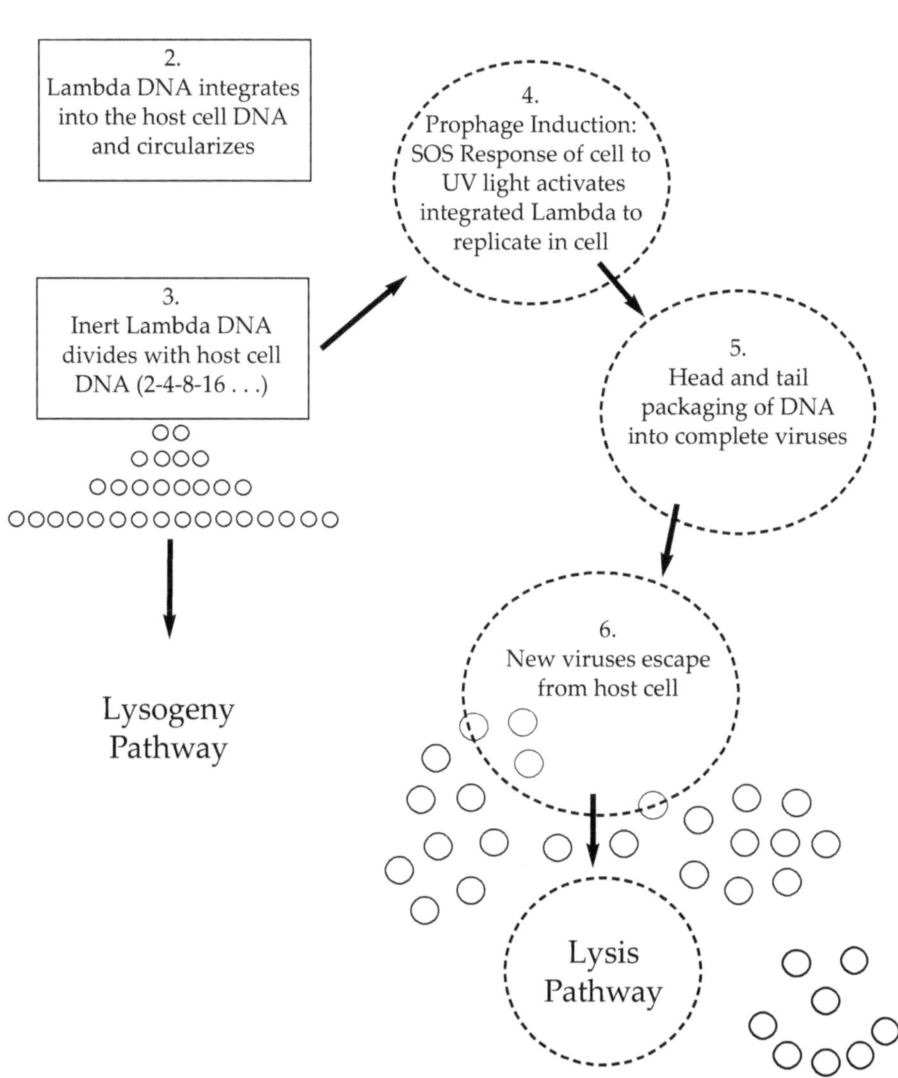

5

Faces, Vertices, Heads or Tails?

WAS THE PHARAOH INSERTED INTO A PYRAMID OR A PHAGE HEAD?

IS 106: Take your head; one face falls on another; vertices of Re, Ennead and Deceased; centipede-faced; Lord of Heads; King of Pyramidion; collar for Re

Objective 3: Is there any evidence in the funerary texts that shows the Deceased Sun-god has the structure of a bacteriophage or that the Pharaohs' were aware of biotechnological applications?

In light of verifying our model and in the spirit of understanding Egyptian thought, it may be worthwhile to first explore early textual references that describe phage morphology, that is, references to heads, tails, faces, vertices, collars, and necks.

The Pyramid Texts state that the Deceased crosses over the sky's reed-floats to Re (PT606). This is also described as "the king opens the face of the god" (PT271). The Deceased states that he has flown up and landed on "the vertex of Re in the prow of his bark" (TR66). In the Coffin Texts, numerous references to the "vertex of Re" (CT267, 276, 499, 656) "vertex of the Ennead," along with language such as "on my vertex" (CT95, 96, 573, 817, 954) suggest the vertices of an icosahedron, a phage conformation which has 20 equilateral triangles arranged around the face of a sphere. Most viruses fit 60 x N subunits into their capsids (heads), with N being the triangulation number, having values of 1, 3, 4, 7, 9, 12 and so on. An icosahedral virus with 60 subunits exhibits perfect symmetry. (Heaphy 2004)

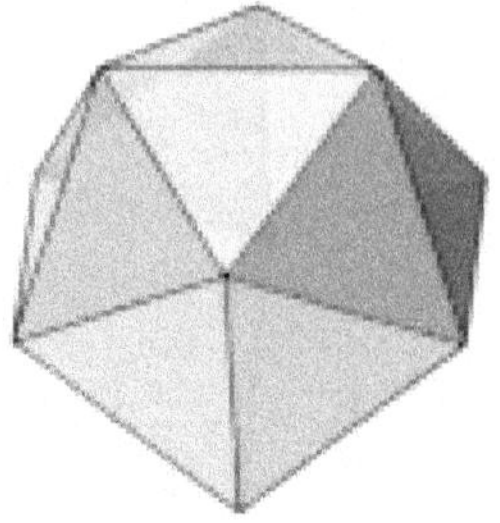

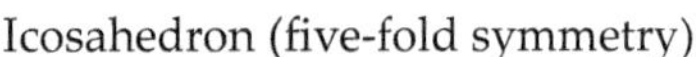

Icosahedron (five-fold symmetry)

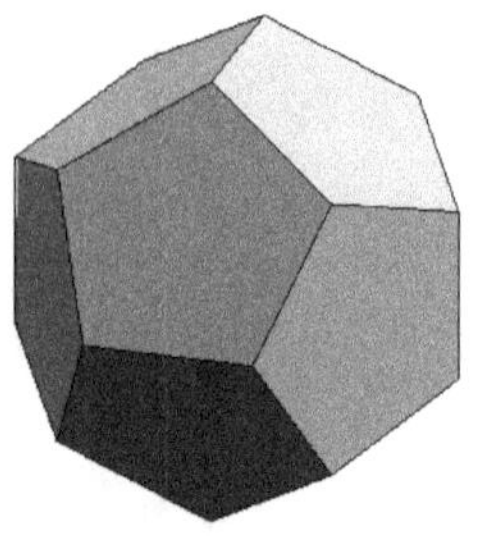

Dodecahedron

Shape:	Triangle	Pentagon
Faces	20	12
Points/Vertices	12	20
Edges	30	30

In 2003, NASA released cosmic radiation background data revealing the shape of the universe is a dodecahedron based on Phi, the Golden Ratio. Phi is also related to the icosahedron, which is a model of five-fold symmetry in three dimensions. According to NASA and freelance mathematician Jeffrey Weeks, the math adds up to the universe being finite and shaped like a dodecahedron, a structure remarkably similar to an icosahedron. (Markey 2003)

Figure 5.1

Along with vertex references, the Pyramid and Coffin texts mention the Mistress and Lord of faces, and the Deceased states that he is "centipede-faced" (CT239, 251). While on Re's vertex, the Deceased sees the Spirits of the West "whose faces turn round on account of their colours" (CT260). These references suggest icosahedral faces. The texts urge the Deceased to "take your head" (PT667, 667A, 667C), and other resurrection texts state "your head is knit to your bones" (PT355, 603), implying the process of phage head assembly. Also, the "golden collar" or "finishing touch to the front which is on the neck of Re" (PT326) points to phage morphology and assembly.

In addition, other resurrection references suggest the formation of a plaque, which is a cleared area on a bacterial lawn caused by infection from a lytic bacteriophage: the allusions to the clear sky and the King becoming a star (PT302), the King going to the sky in an earthquake and bursting the hailstorm apart, the King dispelling the clouds (PT570), the King uncovering the skies and dispersing clouds (CT993). All these references indicate the formation of a cleared area. Also, the reborn King ascends on a cloud as the earth quakes, which signifies the eruption of phage progeny, for "he has ascended in the body of a locust among these children of the hornet" (PT627). Similarly, the King ascends as Osiris in a dust-devil or whirlwind (PT258, 259). The meta-symbol of swarming locust and whirling dust suggests escaping phage progeny. The King states, "I have reached the sky as a locust which hides the Sun" (PT467). Decoded:

Heads, tails, faces, vertices = phage morphology
Swarm of locust = phage progeny

The Pyramid and Causeway

The profile of a pyramid and its causeway also reveals the morphology of phage Lambda, which has an icosahedral head enclosed in a sphere. The Egyptian pyramid with its triangular faces is similar to a phage capsid or head, and the causeway from the pyramid to the valley temple completes the comparison by depicting the phage tail. The essence of the Deceased King resided within the pyramid so that it endured forever (PT600).

In our model for verification, the essence of the deified King indicates the union of the Sun-god and Deceased or the insertion of final human elements into the phage DNA capsid, that is, the pyramid head. When a bacteriophage attaches to a host cell, its DNA is pumped out of the head, down the tail and into the cell. The Pyramid of Unas, the Great Pyramid and others were constructed with pyramidal head structure and causeway tails that are similar to phage morphology. Similarly, the Theban Recension (Ch. 140) refers to Atum as the sunshine god rising in the sky: "The Mighty One appears, the horizon shines, Atum appears on the smell of his censing, the Sunshine-god has risen in the sky, the Mansion of the Pyramidion is in joy and all its inmates are assembled." This passage equates the Sun-god (Re, Re-Atum, Atum) with the geometric shape of a pyramid, which is similar to phage Lambda morphology. Further, the Deceased states, "I am he of the Pyramidion" (CT422). Both Geb (the earth) and Atum grant that a "pyramid and temple" be installed and enclosed for the Deceased and his double (PT534).

Other evidence for phage morphology are the drawings on the walls of the Edifice of Taharqa (c. 690 BCE), showing the deities on the bark wearing long ceremonial tails. Part Four of this work will examine the structure of the Edifice of Taharqa and its mysterious nilometer, another possible representation of phage morphology. (See Figure 19.1)

Finally, the most interesting evidence for phage morphology is the strange drawing in the Tomb of Ramesses VI over Doorway G leading to Hall H in Plate 182 prepared by Alexandre Piankoff. The drawing depicts an armless human form with serpentine legs and a large spherical head (See *The Road from Orion*, Chapter 18 sketch drawn from Plate 182), suggesting the recombinant structure of the Deceased or what might be called a viral-human. We can conclude from the evidence that it is possible that the Egyptians understood the genetics of our modern scientists, who insert the human cDNA gene into a viral vector for biotechnological applications. Yet, the idea that this can be done in the afterlife to transfigure the Deceased into an eternal species is quite original. Still, one must question if there is additional evidence of Egyptian awareness of biotechnological applications.

The Egyptian Coding Sequence for Gene Cloning

IS 21: King raises himself from left to right; "Turn yourself about O King!"

A gene can be inserted into a vector or plasmid for cloning in two orientations. DNA is antiparallel and would thus be backwards and upside down if you turned the DNA around. If you inserted the gene in a left-to-right orientation with the direction of transcription/translation going from the gene to the origin of replication, the right-to-left orientation would be the reverse coding sequence. The Egyptian Pyramid Texts urge the Deceased to move from his left side to his right (PT412, 482, 487), as do the Coffin Texts (CT1, 219, 327) and the Theban Recension (Ch. 68), suggesting the left-to-right cloning orientation. Apparently, the left-to-right orientation of transcription/translation produces a product different from that of the right-to-left orientation.

Also, this left-to-right orientation may suggest beta decay, a nuclear reaction in which beta particles, negative electrons or positive positrons, are absorbed by or emitted from the nucleus of an atom. This process involves weak interactions and left-handed particles. For example, if we look at the counterclockwise rotation of the earth and imagine that it is an electron, the earth's rotation would make it a right-handed particle. If it rotated in the opposite or clockwise direction, the earth would be a left-handed particle and have a left-to-right orientation. Recall that the Coriolis effect pushes a west-moving entity to the North Pole because the west-moving entity is going against the earth's rotation or clockwise. This entity is mapping out a left-handed path to the North Pole, a coiled path like a left-handed screw. So, what are we to make of all this?

The Pharaohs seem to be putting into effect the same experiment that Madame Wu of Columbia University performed in 1957, to prove that the weak force does not in fact obey Parity or P symmetry. If P symmetry holds, right-handed particles behave exactly the same as left-handed, which means that the laws are the same for any situation and its mirror image. Madame Chien-Shiung Wu and her team performed an experiment that involved measuring beta decay of cobalt-60. To orient cobalt nuclei with a strong magnetic field so the spins aligned in the same direction, Wu had to maintain low temperatures of one hundredth of a Kelvin along with a vacuum state. Her success proved that the weak interactions are very different for particles of different handedness: only left-handed particles can decay by means of the weak interaction; right-handed ones cannot. (Quinn 2003, 63) So the Egyptian advice regarding left-to-right orientation may have determined the specific beta decay of a left-handed particle, involving the weak interaction with a different outcome or product. This means that the Pharaohs understood that when you put electrons in a magnetic field, their spins line up so that their magnetic field points the same way as the externally applied magnetic field. Applying this idea, the high-energy Sun-god and crew now become the externally applied magnetic field that causes the Deceased to make a 180 degree turn, that is, a flip altering the magnetic orientation of atoms. So, it is possible to decode the Egyptian advice of left-to-right orientation in three ways:

180 degree flip left to right =

1) cloning orientation,
2) left-handed weak interaction decay and P symmetry violation, and
3) aligned magnetization

Were the Apis Bulls cloned?

The Serapeum was a multi-chambered catacomb where the Pharaohs entombed their sacred Apis bulls, what they considered the incarnation of the creator-god Ptah. According to the Greek historian Herodotus, who visited Egypt in the fifth century BCE, a flash of lightning descended upon a special cow, causing her to receive Apis, a black bull with a white diamond on its forehead, an eagle image on its back, double hairs on its tail, and a scarab beetle under its tongue. (Brown 1992) Herodotus wrote that Apis was the "calf of a cow which is never afterwards able to have another" (Herodotus 1996). This means that each special calf descended from a cow struck by lightning that was incapable of conceiving another offspring, a virgin cow. In genetics, this type of lightning, asexual virgin breeding for specific traits is called cloning or forming genetically identical calves by nuclear implantation. So it is possible that the Apis Bulls' unique traits resulted from cloning.

Objective 3 completed: The language in the early funerary texts related to vertices, heads, tails and faces, along with the triangular structure of the pyramids with their tail-like causeways, mirror phage Lambda morphology. In addition, the depiction of tails on deities in the Edifice of Taharqa and the Ramesses VI drawing of an armless human with coiled legs and a sphere for a head, provide more evidence for this view. Also, textual references to left-to-right orientations and Herodotus' remarks regarding the conception of Apis Bulls suggest the Pharaohs were aware of cloning techniques.

6

Life from Death at the Quantum Level

IS IT POSSIBLE TO BE EVERYWHERE WHILE DEAD BUT ALIVE?

In the many-worlds interpretation of quantum mechanics, all possibilities exist, including life after death, which is not unreasonable when one considers the nature of indestructible atoms. Life is a chemical system requiring proteins and nucleic acids built from very common atoms in the universe—hydrogen, oxygen, nitrogen, carbon, iron. The first law of thermodynamics states that energy cannot be created or destroyed, yet energy undergoes transformations in Nature, that is, from heat to work and from chemical potential to light. The Deceased states, "I daily live after death" (TR38A).

The Pharaohs believed that life came from death, or that the Deceased is "equipped because of the vulture" (CT365). The Deceased must awake to life, for he has not died (CT48, 51, 53, 287) and will not die again because he has power over Heaven's winds (CT83). Fair paths open for the Deceased (CT10). Thus, the dynamics of the solar wind play a crucial role for life after death. Yet, what specific evidence do we have that the Egyptians believed their afterlife existed at the quantum level of indestructible atoms?

Objective 4: Is there any evidence for the view that the Pharaohs believed their afterlife existed at a quantum cellular level?

Quantum Consciousness

IS 2-5: King is not dead and is rejuvenated; Earth gods are powerless over King; eternal King will not die on earth among men

Quantum physics predicts probabilities rather than defines singular events, whereas quantum consciousness is the phenomenon of being conscious of an experience at the level of the simplest element or cell. The Pharaohs describe conscious events after death at the quantum level. Is it possible to be dead but alive? Stuart Hameroff and Roger Penrose present a model of consciousness stemming from microtubule functioning at the cellular level, inclusive of brain neurons (Hameroff). Henry P. Stapp of the University of California, Berkeley also proposes a theory, believing that quantum mechanics can accommodate consciousness (Stapp 1995). Physicists David Bohm and Basil Hiley suggest that our consciousness has a rudimentary mind-like quality at the level of particle physics, which becomes stronger and more developed at subtler levels (Bohm and Hiley 1993, 386).

Likewise, the research of Janusz Slawinski (1987) on spontaneous radiation from living systems suggests the biophysical hypothesis of the conscious self that could survive death of the body. The paleontologist Pierre Teilhard de Chardin insists that consciousness is not an epiphenomenon, but the heart of life rising to greater consciousness in the process of evolution (1959). To Chardin, the evolution of consciousness is a psychical transformation advancing to the cosmic Ultra-Human, "a way into the greater life open to natural organisms" at death (1978, 190). Physicist Amit Goswami claims that even a tiny bacterium has an aliveness, which implies consciousness of energy landscapes. He proposes that survival is a conscious property of the cell and that a quantum system exists in the cytoplasm of a living cell that amplifies the states of a quantum system. Goswami believes evidence of the quantum is the telltale sign of nonlocality. (1997)

Egyptian descriptions of the afterlife suggest that the psychical transformation of the Deceased may allow him to see the full range of electromagnetic radiation, ranging from cosmic rays, gamma rays, ex-rays to ultraviolet, visible and infrared radiation, including microwave energy. Today scientists can envision energy landscapes with the help of technology. A landscape can be described as the potential energy surface (PES) defining the position of atoms. This surface exhibits varied topographical features similar to the earth's landscape, such as mountains, valleys and hollows. However, the dimension is much higher and the energy landscape determines the behavior of the system. (Doye)

In light of the foregoing research, the Egyptian claim of a conscious Deceased on the quantum level seems plausible, for the funerary texts are an extensive knowledge base of conscious quantum experiences that delve into the very heart of Nature and her laws. As the Deceased states, "I spend eternity alive" (CT238). Decoded:

Dead but alive = Quantum Consciousness

The Deceased is Everywhere

IS 37, 38-40, 42-43, 49, 55: Dead King assumes all forms, Atum, Re, Hathor, Isis, Thoth, Horus
IS 8, 35, 53, 57, 63, 94: Dead King is falcon, lotus-haunting heron, Nile, 4th Imperishable Star, 4th of four gods, Bull of Sky, Apis, Eye of Horus

Along with the feature of quantum consciousness, the metaphorical language of the Deceased exhibits a second quantum phenomenon. The Deceased in the afterlife is everywhere, ubiquitous, essentially whole or "assuming all forms in the realm of the dead" (CT275). Due to his quantum ability of nonlocality, the Deceased is everywhere at once in the afterlife. Because of Heisenberg's uncertainty principle, quantum mechanics permits nonlocality within the wavelength of the quantum wave associated with a particle of mass "m" (Compton wavelength). In other words, the point particle is spread out over the nonlocality region, which we might understand as the Deceased spread out over the Duat (magnetosphere or bacterium) or a multiplicity of routes down a protein folding funnel. The texts refer to this multiplicity as "hundreds of Atums" taking possession of the Deceased (CT99). As Niels Bohr said, "There is no path." Yet, as an aid in understanding the quantum world relative to Egyptian thought, this work employs the word "pathway," even though Bohr is theoretically correct. However, when particles enter a specific channel, such as the Lambda attachment site called the LamB porin, they appear to be irreversibly fixed. So, even though a particle's trajectory is random, it is modified by the dynamics of the channel and may qualify for what Bohm and Hiley call a "minimum free path below which the trajectory ceases to be random." (1993, 347) Thus, the Pharaohs are also theoretically correct when referencing a path to the stars.

Nonetheless, we can appreciate why the Deceased claims, "I have become Atum" and "I am in the primeval one" (CT316), along with "I am Khepri who created himself" (CT318). Spread out over the nonlocality region, the Deceased is Atum, "the august god who is in his egg" (CT222-223) because he is everywhere and nonlocal. Another way of looking at nonlocality simply is that it is not possible to define a point in space (the Deceased) without referring to the entire state of the system because a point in space in a quantum vacuum occupies all of space. Similarly, a wave of light photons from the Sun is actually a line extending from the Sun to the earth. Put simply, the Deceased is himself and all the gods at once in the space of the afterlife; that is, he is Osiris, Horus, Maet, Thoth, Re-Atum, Ptah, Khopri, Hathor, a crocodile, a swallow, the lotus-bird on the limitless plane (CT485, 703, 709). Thus, we can begin to understand the polytheistic mindset of the Egyptians, for there are many gods or molecules in the afterlife, all equally important due to the quantum magic of nonlocality. Decoded:

Deceased is everywhere = quantum nonlocality

The Quantum Regions of the Dwarfs

IS 9: Dead King goes to regions of dwarfs; he is a pygmy, a snake with many coils

The regions of the dwarfs is an apt metasymbol for the quantum world. The Deceased actually states that he "belongs to the regions of the dwarfs" (CT132), and that he receives his plot of land in the dwarf regions (CT116). To examine this idea further, one must consider that the Egyptians also worshiped the god Bes, a dwarf-deity with leonine features. The name of the god is Egyptian and may be linked to *bs3* ("to guard," "protect") or to a rare Egyptian word suggesting a premature child or stunted being (Malaise 2002, 29). Bes is usually depicted as a dwarf with a large bearded head, extended tongue, thick arms and bowed legs (Budge v2 1904, 284). Directly linked to the dwarf regions, Bes appears in the Book of the Dead (Ch. 163) with the typical regalia of a god, two plumes and a back like a falcon's. The texts connect the dwarf-god to *Neter Ta* or the "Divine Land" or "land of the God" (Budge v2 1904, 287). The dwarf was significant to the Pharaohs, for by 1990, archaeologists in Egypt had identified the remains of some fifty dwarfs with special status, who attended Pharaohs (Brown 1992, 58-59).

Twentieth century psychology sheds light on the instinctive meaning of the dwarf. Psychologist Carl Jung (1958, 120) notes that the child-god is an aspect of the child-motif, appearing under the guise of the dwarf or elf that personifies the hidden forces of Nature. Egyptian thought suggests that the Deceased in the afterlife exists in a dwarf region or microstate, where the hidden forces of Nature operate. So we could say that there is a parallel between the afterlife's "regions of the dwarfs" and Nature's hidden quantum world of atoms, DNA and molecules, which is the foundation of all matter—plants, animals, human beings. Once again, we can reference this simple analogy by the equals sign (=), remembering that the sign represents the words "points to." Decoded:

Regions of the dwarfs = Land of Gods = Quantum World

Art and Spacetime

Egyptian imagery always depicts the head of the deity drawn in profile, while the body is seen from the front. Although the face is to the side, the eye is drawn in full. This two-dimensional frontalism style was popular for thousands of years, and the reason it was favored may be related to physics. Spacetime as we know it relates to four-dimensional space and time, but our scientists believe the universe is actually flat or two-dimensional. Similarly, String Theory posits that the world sheet of a string is two-dimensional spacetime. This means a one-dimensional string the size of the Planck length has a two-dimensional world-surface as it moves through Time. The two-dimensional art of the Egyptians may have been mirroring this idea. In light of Egyptian knowledge of quantum consciousness and nonlocality, it seems possible that the Egyptians understood the dynamics of matter at the quantum level. In the interests of understanding more of their thought, let's review the Egyptian creation accounts and the origin of the creator-god Atum.

7

Atum and the Creation

WAS ATUM A HIGGS PARTICLE, A SUPERNOVA OR A DUNG BEETLE?

IS 6: Dead King is oldest god
IS 10: Dead King is first-born, conceived in sky, will regain original shape
IS 107: Orion, Sirius and Deceased swallowed by Duat; Deceased receives power from Orion; Nut bore Deceased and Re

Conceived in the sky, the Deceased King is a successor of the "Oldest One" or the first-born son of the creator-god Atum (PT660). In the full version of Coffin Text 335 is a speech by Atum. He states that he commanded the warship of the gods to be built and Re is in it. This is an obvious reference to the Sun-god's bark, which Atum authorized. The text then informs us that the Eye of Re is born yesterday from the Celestial Cow, who is the "Sacred Eye." The sky goddess Nut, one of the oldest deities in the Egyptian pantheon, is described as a Celestial Cow that bore the gods (CT77). What can we infer from this?

We could say that Atum, Re and Nut are all celestial eyes of generation. We have already compared Atum's kindling of his fiery blast (CT77) as the sneeze or spitting out that represents an explosive burst from a supernova. The Deceased states that the "stream is spat out for me" (CT190), that he was not conceived but "Atum spat me out" (CT76), that he has "assumed the forms of Atum" (CT703). This would suggest that Nut, the "Sacred Eye" and mother (PT368, 446, 452, 554, 588) represents the heavenly mass of stars that seed the cosmos by star death with elements for life or the forms of Atum. The Deceased Sun-god states, "O Nut, through the seed of the god which is in you, it is I who am the seed which is in you" (PT563). Further, the texts support that this seed, that is, the elements generating the Deceased Sun-god, is from Orion (IS107), possibly Betelguese.

With Re born from the Celestial Cow or stars, we have another deity representing the same phenomenon, a stream or spitting out from the stars, what modern astrophysicists call a cosmic ray. From this we could conclude that the first Eye related to the activities of the stars. This seems reasonable in that Sixth Dynasty Pyramid Texts implore Nut to install every god who has a bark as an Imperishable Star in the sky (Lesko 2002, 278). Drawings of the sky goddess Nut depict her body covered in stars, suggesting the spotted effect produced by a leopard's coat. Hence, we have the references to Great Ones receiving their leopard-skins (CT49) and the Deceased's garment being a leopard-skin (PT225). Decoded:

Re, Atum, Nut = Eyes or stars of generation
Leopard-skins with spots = stars of generation

The Ancient Pantheon

From the hieroglyphs forming their names, the Ogdoad is the oldest company of eight deities, personifying "aspects, or phases, or properties of primeval matter" (Budge v1 1904, 283-287) before creation.

Nu	god of the watery mass of the sky
Nut	female counterpart of Nu
Hehu	atmosphere between heaven and earth
Hehut	female counterpart of Hehu
Kekui	male power of darkness covering primeval waters
Kekuit	female power of darkness
Kerh	inactive power of primeval watery abyss
Kerhet	female counterpart

While the Ogdoad was worshiped primarily at Khemenu ("Eight Town"), Atum was worshiped at Heliopolis and is one of several solar creator-deities. A self-emerging creator god, his name is derived from the verb *tem* or *temem,* "to be complete" (Budge v2 1904, 87) or "the one who did not come to being yet" (Mysliwiec 2002, 25). The double meaning of Atum's name shows that he was at once absolute being and absolute nonbeing, combining within himself these contrasting opposites, which can easily be compared to the status of a star that dies in a supernova explosion—it was, then it was not, but it still is.

Atum emerges from primeval chaos in the shape of a serpent. Pyramid

Text 527 states that Atum produced his twin children Shu and Tefenet through the autogenous act of masturbation, whereas other passages say Atum spat or sneezed out Shu, the god of air, and Tefenet, the goddess of moisture (CT76). Recall that during a supernova explosion the core stiffens, causing the collapse of the core so abruptly that it rushes out. This activity is similar to the Egyptian metaphor of sneezing and ejaculation.

After Shu and Tefenet came the earth god Geb and the sky goddess Nut, followed by the children of Nut, two pairs of twins: Osiris and Isis, and Seth and Nephthys. Thus the god Atum self-generated the eight deities comprising the Ennead (Gr. *ennea*, "nine") of Heliopolis (Willis 1993, 40), that is, the cosmic elements necessary for creation. However, the primeval Atum may represent more than a supernova explosion; he may represent an earlier activity in our cosmological past.

Similar to Atum's actions, our Standard Model of particle physics predicts the heavy Higgs particle H, generating all particle masses. From a cosmological perspective relative to the evolution of the universe, Atum as primeval matter or "the one who did not come to being yet," the one in a state of repose or inactivity, can be compared to the original mass-generating mechanism. Atum's spitting or sneezing may reflect what inflationary cosmologists call a brief swelling of the spatial dimension in the Early Universe. On the quantum scale, Atum and his four primordial aspects may represent the dark, empty space of an atom in a state of repose before nucleation, before entropy increase, the beginning of creation in our universe.

Atum states that he begot the Chaos-gods in charge of the chambers of the sky (CT76). The Second Law of Thermodynamics concerns any real process that proceeds in a direction which results in an entropy increase. The continual references throughout the Coffin Texts to "Chaos-gods" supports the idea that the Ogdoad of four male/female sets represents the primordial aspects of Atum or an initial set of conditions that could result in an entropy increase: the boundless watery mass, the power of darkness over this watery abyss, the inactive power of the waters, and the atmosphere. The Egyptians called this watery mass Nu or Nun, where the sphere of life floated like a bubble (McBride 2002, 276). Still, we must remember that Atum's realm is the regions of the dwarfs (CT114, 116) or the Planck-scale world, which some cosmologists believe existed before the inflationary period that preceded the Big Bang.

A Foundation in my Heart

In addition to Atum's primordial, generative status, the creator god had a royal problem. Atum states that before the Primeval Ennead existed, he could find no place to stand or sit, for his "throne had not yet been put together" (CT80). This was a time before Nut or the starry sky had been created, before the "Primeval Ennead had come into being" (80). Atum then said to Nu, god of the watery mass of the sky, "I am on the floodwaters, being very weary, and the patricians are inert." Then the text states that the earth god Geb gathered together Atum's weary members, suggesting the idea of molecular self-assembly at earth. The texts state, "stand upon it, this earth which issued from Atum" (PT222).

This idea of the formation of a foundation, a throne, a seat for Atum can also be found in a second account from a papyrus written for a Panopolis priest about 312 BCE entitled *The Book of knowing the Evolutions of Ra, and of Overthrowing Apepi.* "Evolutions" is *kheperu* from the Egyptian root *kheper* meaning "to produce, to form, to become" and in a derived sense "to roll" (Budge v1 1904, 294). The creator-god Khepera (aka Atum, Re, Re-Atum, Horakhty, Khnum, and Ptah in different nomes) is symbolized by the Coprophagi beetle, noted for its ability to lay eggs in dung that it rolls into a circular form. The Egyptians associated the Sun's disk with the beetle dung ball (294-5), which is bacterial. So we have Khepera as a beetle, pushing the dung ball or simulating the solar wind pushing on the earth system.

The papyrus text reports that Khepera came into being and raised up the creation from Nu out of "a state of inactivity" (309). All alone, Khepera, like Atum in the Coffin Text account, then could not find a place to stand. The god said, "I worked a charm upon my heart. I laid a foundation in *Maa* [and] I made every form." So, both the Coffin Text and the papyrus text accounts claim that a foundation of forms, signified by a "throne" in the former text, was necessary to support the god's creation. These metasymbols point to the following ideas:

Foundation in Heart = core elements created in star forming DNA

Creator gods (Atum, Khepera, Re, beetle) = creative force from star

Beetle dung ball = bacterial cell or earth

The Rightful Order of the Universe

The word *Maat* means "Truth, Rightful Order" (Goelet 1994, 155). With the goddess Maat personified as Truth and referenced in both creation accounts, we could say that the self-emerging god Atum or Khepera was therefore laying down a plan or foundation according to law, Truth and Rightful Order (*Maat*) for his soon-to-emerge creation before the emission of Shu and Tefenut. Khepera creates a foundation of forms in his heart, signified by a throne for him to sit on, before the creation of gods or men. Then he self-produces Shu (air) and Tefenet (moisture) and from the watery mass of Nu, his Eye of generation arises, that is, a cold-light star that dies, producing the elements in its core that seed the universe.

Another way of looking at this is that DNA exists in the dark, empty space of a primordial atom that begins to nucleate, producing two atomic nuclei (gods), then four, eight, and so on (DNA replication or prokaryote binary fission), and finally human beings from its "Eye" or heart of creation. In the same fashion, a double-stranded (ds) molecule of DNA is copied into two double-stranded daughters. This process continues (1/2, 1/4, 1/8, 1/16, and so on) as the original DNA diminishes. DNA is a self-replicating genetic material that is transcribed into an unstable messenger nucleic acid, RNA, which is then translated into proteins. This is the Central Dogma of gene expression: DNA to RNA to protein. We can extend this idea further by the following proposal, remembering that "=" represents "points to:"

Foundation of forms = throne = DNA to RNA to protein = humans

Objective 4 completed: The textual evidence indicates the Deceased possesses quantum consciousness and nonlocality, features essential to the quantum cellular or dwarf afterlife of the Pharaohs. We can also conclude that the development of Atum and his creation parallels cellular nucleation, DNA replication, and prokaryote binary fission, again indicating that the Egyptian afterlife exists at a quantum level. With the completion of Objective 4, we can assemble Matrix 3 to test the validity of our model (Matrix 2).

MATRIX 3

EGYPTIAN SIGN TRANSLATED TO
POSSIBLE MODERN SCIENCE PARALLEL

architecture of pyramids, Edifice of Taharqa: phage Lambda morphology
Atum: mass-generatiing mechanism; electric potential pulse
Atum and Ogdoad: Higgs field and 8 massless gluons of strong force
Atum's throne or foundation: elements created in core of dying star; the basis of DNA
beetle: creation and transformation; creator gods
beetle dung ball: earth; bacterial cell
Chaos-gods: Second Law of Thermodynamics; any real process that proceeds in a direction which results in an entropy increase
creator gods: solar wind and high energy particle creative force
Deceased is dead but alive: quantum consciousness
Deceased is everywhere: nonlocality
equipped because of Vulture: human death allows transformation
Eye (of Re, Atum, Nut): generation; stars seeding cosmos with elements from supernovae explosions
heads, tails, faces, vertices: phage morphology
left-to-right orientation: left-to-right cloning orientation; left-handed biological molecule; aligned magnetization
lightning striking cow to produce Apis bull: cloning by nuclear transplantation to produce bulls with special traits
locust swarm: phage progeny
Maat: laws of universe or physics; rightful order
Pyramidion: indicator of phage Lambda morphology
region of dwarfs: Planck-length world

We can conclude that Matrix Three provides support for genetic cloning, phage morphology, quantum consciousness and nonlocality. Also, our analysis of Egyptian creation accounts points to modern theories on the cosmogenesis of our universe.

8

The Return to the Eye or Holograph

PENROSE, PRIBRAM, HUTH AND THEIR UPSIDE-DOWN VISION

Objective 5: We must now discover whether or not the central Idea Strands in the Pyramid Texts and Coffin Texts continue to support our model and developing matrices, which are centered on the idea that the Egyptian afterlife exists at the quantum cellular level.

The word "holography" is derived from the Greek word *holos*, ("whole") and *graphe* ("writing"). It is apparent that the foundation of forms signified by Atum's throne is the whole writing, the holograph, the DNA for the forthcoming creation. Within the movement toward infinity or back into the Eye or origin of creation, the Deceased states, "I have come into the Island of Fire, and I am content with the manifestations of the ithyphallic ones" (CT1001). One who is ithyphallic would have an erect phallus (LL *ithyphallic(us)*, Gk *ithyphalikos*, "erect phallus"), which suggests the primordial state just before Atum self-generated the creation, a state we might compare to the stiffening of the core during a supernova explosion. But a better comparison would be to a Higgs field perched above its zero energy value and the resultant outward blast that drives space to swell. Inflationary cosmologists believe that this inflaton field provided the energy and negative pressure for the outward burst of repulsive gravity that initially made space expand and inflate our universe. (Greene 2004, 282-286)

So the Deceased is at the origin of creation, the Island of Fire with the ithyphallic ones. He then states, "open out the ritual book [for] me" (1001). He further claims that "a writing of what I have said has been brought which has been placed for them in their remembrance" (CT1013), and "I am one who reveals what has been said to him" (CT1063). So the Deceased returns to the beginning "ritual book," the foundation of forms, the DNA or holograph for Atum's creation, after fulfilling the words that have been said to him. These ideas provide us with the following application:

Atum's throne = First DNA = Foundation of forms = the Ritual Book = the Whole Writing, the Words, the Holograph

Passage to the Quantum Holographic Universe

In light of the Egyptian focus on the Eye of Horus, what implies a center of light, intelligence or influence, suppose we ask ourselves if modern scientific research supports any connection between the mechanism of vision and a quantum holographic creation. Actually, proof for a quantum holographic universe can be found in Roger Penrose's research on retinal structure, Karl Pribram's research on the retina's processing of exteroceptive sensations into the spectral domain, and Gerald Huth's eight-around-one geometry of the retina.

In examining the phenomena of blind sight, physicist Roger Penrose found that the visual cortex is more associated with conscious perception than other areas (1989, 386-387). The retina is the one place where action at the single quantum level can have importance for neural activity. In addition, after fifty years of brain research, Karl Pribram's holonomic theory (for the example of vision) summarizes evidence that the retinal image is transformed to a holographic or spectral domain. The concept of spectral domain includes the idea that colors, tones, and all exteroceptive sensations, including those dependent on spatiotemporal configurations, that is, shapes of surfaces and forms, can be analyzed into their component frequencies of oscillation. (1991, 28)

According to Pribram (28), the spectral (energy) domain is the Fourier transform of spacetime (configural). In other words, the input to and the output from a lens performs a Fourier transform. Our familiar spacetime lies on one side of the transform with a distributed enfolded holographic-like order called the frequency or spectral domain on the other side. The retina and the visual cortex process an invertible transformation from a spacetime image to a processing domain of at least eight dimensions: four in spacetime and four spectral. When the spectral dimension dominates a perception, space and time evolution ceases and spatial boundaries disappear (272).

Likewise, physicist Gerald C. Huth (2004) claims that the eye functions on a higher level determined solely by its geometry. The retina is a logically spaced array of electron quantum confinement centers or the actual spatial design of the Fourier transform. He claims the diffractometric surface on the retina suggests the vision process takes place in the Fourier or frequency domain, which is some sort of two-dimensional frequency transform. In other words, the retina detects light as a wave of classical physics, while confining the absorbing electron to quantum confined dimensions.

Huth also states that the ratio of the sizes of cones to rods of the human retina (~1.8-2:1) corresponds to the visible bandwidth (700 to 400 nanometers) that determines our visual response. For example, fish have larger receptors and can see in the infrared bandwidth, whereas insects have smaller receptors resulting in ultraviolet vision. This human retina ratio dictates the geometry of exactly eight smaller rods able to fit around each larger cone. The same eight-around-one retinal motif is found in the visual organs of all species and chloroplast organelle of photosynthetic plants and algae. This motif, affirms Huth, is the Fourier objectification of the optical spectrum viewed by the eye. Needless to say, modern research supports the mechanism of vision as a passage into the quantum world, and the funerary texts often reference the process by the phrase "upside down world."

The Upside Down World

IS 1: Dead King will not go upside down

Repeatedly, the funerary texts state that a man must not go "upside down in the realm of the dead." It may be that the Deceased in the afterlife or the enfolded holographic-like order, perceives our material spacetime world as upside down in a fashion similar to the Fourier transformation, just as we perceive the image on the human retina as upside down. As Pribram contends, our familiar space-time lies on one side of the Fourier transform with a distributed enfolded holographic-like order—the frequency or spectral domain—on the other side.

Let's examine this upside down idea by first looking at how our eyes function. When visual information goes into the pupil and bends through the lens of the eye, the input is projected upside down and backwards on the retina.

Brain researcher Karl Pribram, M.D., explains this inversion process as a transformation of an image from our world (spacetime) through the lens of the eye to a processing domain of at least eight dimensions on the retina (1991, 92). He further states that this image in the eye allows us to infer that the outside world is similar to a hologram, a three-dimensional image created with photographic projection. Simply put, light bounces everywhere in a holographic fashion. (Pribram Workshop 1989)

Numerous texts instruct the dead person not to go upside down, so it is apparent that the Deceased in the spectral domain of the afterlife perceives himself as upright and the world of matter and the living as upside down. "You shall walk upon your feet, you shall not walk head downwards" (CT20, 21). The indication here is that in our world, we are walking "head downwards." Actually, this may apply, for it is in agreement with the rotation of our galaxy. Considering the sense of rotation, the galaxy, at the Sun's position, is rotating toward the direction of Right Ascension 21:12.0, Declination +48:19. This shows that it rotates "backward" in the Galactic coordinate system, that is, the Galactic North Pole is actually a physical South Pole with respect to galactic rotation. (Frommert 2002) So one could say that we are upside down.

Actually, the full advice to the Deceased is "not to eat faeces in the realm of the dead, not to walk upside down, to have power over water and air, to go forth into the day" (CT184). The idea of not eating faeces suggests putrefaction and decay related to bacterial agents, which seems a reasonable parallel to our model that asserts the earth and its magnetosphere act like a single-celled bacterium such as *E. coli*. It is obvious that it is just as odious to go upside down as it is to eat faeces in the realm of the dead (the Duat). The Deceased believes that "to be upside down is my detestation" (CT201, 203, 205, 206, 211, 214, 220) and that "my skin was turned inside out at the time of nightfall in the West" (CT289). Similarly, the Deceased ferries "across the firmament when the Sacred Land is turned upside down" (CT343). In other words, the process of inversion has resulted in the Deceased now walking upright: "The Great West is he who stretches out my bones and extends my limbs, so that I may walk on my feet like Osiris" (CT417).

It is interesting that scientists perceive the human genome as reverse transcribed or written backwards in places, suggesting that millions of years ago the human genome may have been viral (Gee 2001). Our genome is also littered with families of repetitive DNA sequences that have no function, such as mobile genetic elements (transposons) and tandemly repeated simple sequence

DNAs (Prak 2000). According to Desmond Nicholl, Senior Lecturer at the University of Paisley, Scotland, 97 percent of the human genome has no known function (2002, 170). Of course, if we were in the afterlife viewing the viral part of our genome, it would be upright and the rest of the genome would be reverse transcribed and backwards. Reverse transcription results in a complementary DNA that is actually transcribed backwards and upside down.

Finally, the funerary texts remind us of "Seth who turned the land upside down" (CT942). Seth is the god of confusion and disorder, whose disagreement with Osiris resulted in the injury to the Eye of Horus, which the Egyptians might say, resulted in the upside-down human creation. Equipped with his new Death-vision, the Deceased, a specter in the spectral domain, perceives our world of matter as upside down. We can conclude that holography, reverse transcription and vision may all be relative to the inversion imagery evident in the texts. Decoded:

Upside-down world = spacetime material world of living humans

The Material World

Our universe then may be a hologram or an invertible reflection of the quantum world. In holography, every part of the writing contains information about the whole. The hologram would then be the material representation of the whole writing or holograph, that is, a three dimensional (3D) image where information about the holograph is recorded. When our world or the hologram is illuminated, what emerges is a rational 3D picture that enfolds the whole image in each of its parts. So if you cut the picture into pieces, each piece would still contain the whole. The Deceased states, "I am Re, I am Atum, I am the Lord of Everlasting, I am the beam which upholds eternity" (CT442). So Atum in his quantum world as the Sun-god, as the Eye of generation, now becomes the light from within that illuminates our 3D material world or hologram.

It may be that the process of death is an upside-down movement of one's consciousness or genetic essence from the spacetime realm of matter to the spectral domain of energy—an order of frequencies that is distributed, enfolded and holographic. The Fourier transformation can be simply described as making the big small and the small big. As Hermes said, what is below is like what is above. Likewise, Robert Bauval has confirmed that the alignment of five of Egypt's pyramids mirror five of the seven stars in the constellation of

Orion. Apparently, the Pharaohs understood that the whole is enfolded everywhere and that our brains are part of the universe, which has a holographic mode of operation. Decoded:

Our universe above = hologram
Quantum world below = holograph, whole writing

First-born DNA

In the interest of seeing the whole writing, let's review a rough timeline of the development of the first cell (Figure 8.1). From this, we can see that prokaryotic cells developed 3.8 billion years ago. An anaerobic prokaryote is a cell (bacterium) that does not have a membrane around its nuclear region (pro "before" and Gr. *Karyon* for "kernel"), but aerobic eukaryotes do have a true nucleus surrounded by a membrane (eu "true"). (Guffey 2002)

Reconstructing early events in the transition from prokaryotic to eukaryotic cells is problematic for evolutionary biologists. Some believe eukaryotes were born out of a stepwise symbiotic union of prokaryotic cells, while others believe that the ability to phagocytose prey led to the origin of eukaryotic features prior to endosymbiosis. (Roger 1999) After reviewing this timeline and reading the Egyptian texts, we could say that Atum's DNA was first-born, then the prokaryote cell DNA developed, followed by our eukaryote cell DNA type.

Sun, star or Atum (Re, Re-Atum) = Firstborn DNA
earth = prokaryote DNA
humans = eukaryote DNA

The Sun-Beetle Model

As mentioned, the Pharaohs equated the Sun with a beetle pushing a dung ball, a metasymbol which could also represent the solar wind pressure pushing on the earth's magnetosphere. To expand on this idea, consider that the Sun-beetle is a bacterial virus or a bacteriophage enveloping the bacterial dung ball of the earth. Imagining the earth as the sphere of life floating like a cylindrical soap bubble within the Sun's magnetic field, we can easily see the viral Sun enveloping the prokaryote subkingdom of earth in a manner similar to phagocytosis. (See sketch, *The Road from Orion*, Ch. 10)

A virus is an infectious particle composed of a protein capsid and nucleic acid core (DNA or RNA), which depends on a host organism for replication. Its

Chronology of Universe

Universe	12–16	billion years
Our solar system	4.5	billion years ago
First anaerobic cells (prokaryotes)	3.8	"
Cyclic photosynthesis	3.2	"
Non-cyclic photosynthesis (oxygen generating)	2.5	"
Eukaryotes (human cell type)	1.8	"

Figure 8.1

DNA or double-stranded (ds) DNA copy of an RNA virus genome integrates into the host chromosome during lysogenic infection or replicates during the lytic cycle. Viruses attack eukaryotic cell types causing disease in humans. In contrast, bacterial viruses or bacteriophage (eaters of bacteria) attack bacteria (prokaryotes), not humans (eukaryotes). Keeping this distinction in mind, we have already established that the Sun-god Re points to hydrogen, other energetic particles and phage Lambda. Now, we can add that the Sun-god beetle Re also operates similar to a bacteriophage.

Sun-god and Sun-beetle = high energy particles and phage Lambda
Beetle's dung ball = prokaryote cell or earth

Phage Lambda

We can easily set up an analogy with the Egyptian conception of the beetle and the dung ball. If the creator god Khepera (aka Atum, Re) is a beetle, laying its eggs in dung, then the beetle is phage Lambda inserting its DNA into an *E. coli* host cell. This expansion on the Egyptian model seems believable in light of the fact that the Lambda decision circuit includes 12 gates, suggesting the Egyptian rationale for the title of their Book of Gates, which has 12 gates similar to the Amduat's 12 hours or divisions. We will investigate the Lambda decision circuit in these supportive texts in Part Three.

The Lambda genome is 48.5 kb long encoding some 46 genes, which can synthesize about 55 proteins. In the tailed phage, the genome is encapsulated in an icosahedral head or protein shell called a capsid. The subunits of the capsid are located at the vertices or face of the icosahedron. An icosahedron has 20 equilateral triangles arranged around the face of a sphere. As discussed, the Egyptian pyramids reflect the same basic triangular design found in phage Lambda.

In its exogenous form, phage Lambda is linear with short complementary 12 base-pair (bp) single-stranded (ss) regions. When Lambda DNA infects an *E. coli* cell, it circularizes, the cohesive 12 bp ends connecting, and then the phage decides on one of two different strategies: the lytic cycle or the lysogenic cycle. In the virulent lytic cycle, the phage reproduce in the host *E. coli* via rolling circle replication and are normally released when the cell lyses or bursts. In contrast, the lysogenic cycle does not destroy the host cell. The Lambda DNA replicates with the host cell (the lysogen), remaining dormant in the prophage state. Bacterial viruses like temperate phage Lambda exploit the intracellular host cell pathways for their reproduction.

Another way of explaining this process is to consider the bacteriophage as a cell invader, taking over the bacterial cell's reproduction machinery, so that it can produce its own phage progeny. When the phage destroys the bacterial cell during reproduction, this is the lifestyle of lysis or the lytic pathway; when the phage resides in the host cell's DNA like a quiet parasite, this is the lifestyle of lysogeny or the lysogenic pathway. The host cell is called the lysogen, and the quiet phage is called the prophage. Because the prophage inserts into a break in the host chromosome between the *b-gal* and *bio* operons, the bacterium reproduces the DNA of the silent phage invader with its own DNA, passing the hybrid or recombinant DNA on each generation. The process can be compared to the idea of our world as a hologram that enfolds the whole image or sleeping Lambda genome in each of its parts. Recent research shows the human genome may have originally been viral, suggesting the potential for lysogenic infections.

Now, let's look again at the 312 BCE papyrus text about the creator-god Khepera, symbolized by the Coprophagi beetle. From our new perspective of the Egyptian-based model, a Sun or star represents a phage Lambda source, and the earth and its magnetosphere represent a rod-shaped, gram-negative bacterial cell such as *E. coli.* The meaning of *kheper* is to roll, suggesting the rolling circle replication of the Lambda lytic cycle. Khepera or the beetle rolling the dung ball in circular form suggests the circularization of Lambda DNA, which occurs inside the host *E. coli* cell. Also, Khepera raises the creation from an inactive state, suggesting the rising or excision of the Lambda prophage. Additional language points to the excision of the prophage: "May the Eye of Horus belong(?) to you—the reversion of the god's offering" (PT199). Excision can be considered reversion because when the Lambda prophage excises, it reverses the integration pathway or leaves the cell by the pathway it uses to enter the prophage site. Bacterial geneticists call this site-specific recombination. So we can decode these signs as follows:

Title of Book of Gates = 12 gates of Lambda decision circuit
Meaning of *kheper* (to roll) = rolling circle replication
Dung in circular form = circularization of DNA in host cell
Raising creation from a "state of inactivity" = excision of prophage
Reversion of the god's offering = excision of prophage

In order to test the validity of our Lambda/*E. coli* model, we need to determine the significance of Osiris, along with discovering how the Deceased restores the Eye of Horus.

The First Eye and Osiris

A major goal in the Amduat is re-establishing the first Eye of Horus and the gods who were with Osiris when he came into being the first time, a reference to the first Ennead of nine gods at the origin of time or the emergence of the first cell. Likewise, the Egyptian ideogram of an eye means "eye, see, actions of eye" (Gardiner 1957, 32), and if we decipher "eye" as "cell," then the activity of the eye or cell is DNA transcription, replication and translation to protein. This highlights the creative power of the Sun and stars or first Eye of Horus, showing that the Horus lineage is solar or cosmic, having an Upper Egyptian origin like Osiris.

Relative to the etymology of the name Osiris, J. Gwyn Griffiths, Professor of Classics and Egyptology, University of Wales (2002, 304), notes that the god's name *Wsir* was first written with the throne sign, followed by the eye sign, but later inverted. Many meanings are suggested, such as "he who takes his seat or throne," "the place of creation," "seat of the Eye," with the Eye explained as the Sun, and "the seat that creates." The creative "seat of the Eye" suggests the activity of creation at the gene seat, which is solar DNA transcription, replication and translation, viz., Lambda rolling circle replication. This takes place with the excision of the Lambda prophage from the gene seat (between *b-gal* and *bio* operons), so it may be that Osiris, who is always shown mummified with a close linkage of the legs (Griffiths 2002, 303) that suggests a phage tail, represents the prophage.

In line with this idea, Coffin Text 53 urges the Deceased to wake to life, and Faulkner translates one passage as: "Rise, rise in the morning now that you are a mummy." However, in a footnote to this passage, he notes a variation: "you are in your mummy-shape." Being in the mummy-shape suggests phage morphology. Other evidence for this view includes the numerous drawings in the funerary texts of reclining mummies within enclosures, the textual language describing inertness and sleep (IS77, 78, 79), and the entire concept of the rising Osiris in the realm of the dead (IS84, 86), that is, the excising Lambda prophage. Likewise, an examination of the Amduat and Book of Gates in Part Three of this work offers further support for this possibility.

If Osiris is the Lambda prophage, then the *E. coli* host or lysogen not only reproduces its own DNA, but also that of the prophage lodged within it. This suggests that human life developed from the transition of the first prokaryote to our eukaryote cell type with the viral heritage of the Lambda prophage dormant in each cell. Then at human death, an option exists for excision of the original prophage by means of the lytic lifestyle through a horizontal gene transfer via a Lambda vector into and out of a host cell. On the macrocosmic scale, this would represent a movement of one's consciousness, or as Goethe would say, one's immortal part, out of the magnetosphere to the stars.

Research on the human genome shows that due to viral gene insertion events, genetic material from inactive viruses accounts for roughly three percent of the human genome (Howard Hughes Medical Institute). Hundreds of other genes—encoding at least 223 proteins—seem to have come from bacteria. One researcher said that parts of the genome were reverse-transcribed with a few genes mixed in (Gee 2001). To be specific, in reverse transcription the endonuclease cleaves between an adenine and a thymine on the bottom strand of DNA, proceeding in the 5' to 3' direction in an upside down and right-to-left orientation (Prak 2000). As discussed, from the afterlife view of the Deceased, this process would be a left-to-right orientation that was not upside-down and backwards.

As mentioned, a similar parallel to a resident prophage is a hologram enfolding the whole image in each of its parts. We could say that Osiris in his inert form, that is, cut up or dismembered, is similar to a spacetime hologram or picture enfolding the whole image in each of its parts. So if the picture were cut into pieces, each piece would still contain the whole. Human DNA, in its prokaryote-to-eukaryote transition, still has viral and bacterial components. The Pharaohs are suggesting that human death results in a return to the quantum world and origin of time, where a horizontal gene transfer is possible through the induction of a Lambda prophage in the first prokaryote cell. One could say that the lysogenic lifestyle allows the sleeping Lambda, that is Osiris, to reside within each living being. On the other hand, a human death opens up the lytic lifestyle option, if the Deceased has knowledge of the paths or the "two routes of Re-Atum" (CT674). Decoded: **Osiris = Lambda prophage**

An Afterlife Cloning Experiment

Our model posits that the Deceased represents a genetic insert into a bacteriophage vector. In this capacity he is ready to make his transformations in the Duat and has bonded to Re at the polar Great Stairway to be ferried through the black Duat as the Deceased Sun-god and Osiris. Since our exploration supports our model that the Sun-god Re operates like incoming phage Lambda into the *E. coli* earth cell, for simplicity we can say that the union of the Sun-god Re and the Deceased could represent the uptake of human information or genetic instructions, that is fragmented DNA, into the incoming Lambda Sun-god. This is similar to types of horizontal gene transfer our modern bacterial geneticists also call transformation and transduction. Today researchers use bacterial viruses like phage Lambda as cloning vectors. Put simply, they insert exogenous DNA fragments into the Lambda genome. The phage then becomes a carrier molecule or vector that transfers or ferries the recombinant DNA into a host cell.

For example, in the insertion vector Lambda gt10, the DNA fragment inserts into the *Eco*RI site lying within the *cI* gene (Lambda cI repressor). This inactivates the *cI* gene and is a powerful selection method. If the vector is plated on a mutant strain of *E. coli* that produces lysogens, this means the mutant strain's *cI* gene is active. Any phage encoding a functional cI repressor will form lysogens on these hosts. When the DNA fragment is inserted in the Lambda gt10 vector at the *cI* gene, the gene is inactivated and only recombinants *cI-* will form plaques. (Nicholl 2002, 137)

It seems as if the Pharaohs understood their afterlife as a secret cloning experiment, for the Kings and nobility did their best to prevent the plebs or common folk from having the knowledge. Keeping knowledge secret from the masses was a method of screening human DNA. With this knowledge, the Kings and nobility possessed directions and guidelines, such as going to the polar cusp of earth to meet Re for transformation, that screened out most of the population. On the cellular level, this translates to directions indicating the polar cap or gap between the cytoplasm and cell wall, where dynamic polar localization of proteins critical for cell division and cell cycle control exist in bacteria. By being in this enriched protein localization area or origin for replication, the genetic heritage or DNA of the Deceased, that is, of the Kings and nobility, may have transformed into a different product than if the Deceased had been at any other location in the earth-cell. For instance, in the afterlife, floating around the earth's equator, a different location than the polar cap, may result in an elemental recycling of your hydrogen, carbon, nitrogen and oxygen (H, C, N, O) back to our upside-down human world, just what the knowing Marquis de Sade predicted.

Nonetheless, it may be possible that by providing knowledge to only a select few, the Pharaohs were screening human beings and manipulating genes in their quantum afterlife. In light of the foregoing possibilities, let's identify the Deceased as an insert at the *cI* gene in the Lambda cloning vector or Sun-god. Such an insert inactivates the Lambda cI repressor that maintains the lysogenic state. Decoded:

The Deceased = human genetic insert at *cI* gene in Lambda vector

However, we must remember the Pharaohs viewed the Deceased as Osiris, for the earliest evidence equates the Deceased Pharaoh with Osiris (Griffiths 2002, 305). We have identified Osiris as representative of Lambda prophage, the Deceased as the genetic insert within the incoming Sun-god Re, who now becomes the Lambda vector that ferries the human genetic insert through the Duat or the prokaryote cell to the prophage site. This results in rolling circle replication, the excision of the prophage Osiris, and the transformation or transduction of the Deceased into the recombinant species. The Deceased becomes Osiris when he bonds to the Sun-god and crew at the polar quarter. We could say that the trinity of the Deceased, the Sun-god and Osiris are all representative of phage Lambda or the first-born DNA of Atum, viz., the Sun and stars. The Deceased receives "the Eye of Horus, which the winds bring to you for your nose" (CT934). This Lambda trinity is the Eye of Horus, which is not only the incoming recombinant DNA of the Sun-god and Deceased, but is also the Lambda genome or prophage Osiris lodged in the host chromosome. Decoded:

Eye of Horus = Lambda genome; prophage Osiris; incoming Sun-god

Yet, if Osiris is the Lambda prophage, then what does the wall of the Double Osiris represent in the Tomb of Ramesses VI (Piankoff Plate 35)? The scene depicts two identical Osiris' back-to-back on two thrones. Sometimes in phage Lambda, a double lysogen forms in specialized transduction (Maloy 2000), what geneticists call a dilysogen. So it seems the Pharaohs were aware of the Lambda dilysogen or the phenotype of a strain that contained two

Lambda prophages. Decoded:

Double Osiris = double lysogen or dilysogen

The Eye of Horus

IS 42, 56 :	King's strength is Eye of Horus, Eye of Great Lady
IS 56, 70, 72, 76, 77:	King bears complete Eye of Horus
IS 68, 71, 72, 76, 83:	Eye of Horus will not fall to Seth; King takes Eye from Seth
IS 70:	King rules Mounds of Seth and Mounds of Horus
IS 76, 77 :	Eye of Horus is whole
IS 59, 60, 83:	King unites Two Lands when Eye awakes; heads Two Conclaves; has sole possession of Eye
IS 94:	King's bright cloak is Eye of Horus
IS 100:	King absorbs Eye of Horus, swallows intelligence of gods

In light of our decoded signs and to gain a better understanding of Osiris, a review of texts related to the Eye of Horus, a central theme, is helpful. Horus, a sky and Sun-god, is one of the earliest major Egyptian deities, as early as the late Predynastic period (Naqada III/Dynasty O). The falcon hieroglyph is used in the name of the god, *Hrw* or *Hr* meaning "the distant one." The most common genealogy portrays Horus as the son of Osiris and Isis, making a tenth on the family tree of the Heliopolitan Ennead. (Meltzer 2002, 164) The god of origins is Re-Atum, the Sun-god who is also syncretized with Re-Horakhty, meaning Re (is) Horus of the Horizon.

The Deceased goes to the sacred portal from which Atum proceeded, where Hu and Sia (Shu and Tefenut in Heliopolitan Ennead) are present with Atum (CT335). So we are back at the beginning of the creation, the origin of time, a period following Atum's creation of the foundation of forms and elements or the first DNA of phage Lambda. The Deceased states that he restores the Eye that was injured when the Rivals fought, suggesting that the Lambda DNA has been damaged. The text goes on to explain that the Rivals are Horus and Seth, the god of confusion and disorder. Seth wounds the face of Horus, who loses the light of his right eye (Velde 2002, 332), while Horus carries off the testicles of Seth (335). Horus' right eye is the Sun, his left eye the moon.

In another version of the account, Seth in the form of a black boar, tears out and swallows the Moon Eye of Horus (Willis 1993, 44). The Egyptian accounts suggest that at one time, most likely the beginning of the creation of matter, the Eye of Horus or *wedjat* ("Whole One") was complete before fission. When the Eye became injured, we could say that matter creation occurred, causing it to fission into nuclei, for it was no longer whole. According to the funerary texts, upon human death the Deceased returns to the dwarf world of Atum, restoring the Eye of Horus that Seth damaged. Thus, the Deceased becomes the "fiery Eye of Horus" (CT316), the whole eye, the *wedjat*. How are we to make sense of this story?

To understand the meaning of signs related to the Eye of Horus, a review of the Pyramid Texts, the least corrupted evidence, is helpful. In these texts, the rebellious Seth is overcome by Horus (IS71) and Horus takes back the Eye Seth snatched (IS69). The two Eyes of Horus are called the black eye (left) and the white eye (right) (PT43). The Deceased King is offered the Eye that was "wrested from Seth" (PT54, 56, 57M, 57S, 59A, 97, 135, 160, 161, 162, 357); however, both Eyes are brought to the King (PT57A, 57J) as an offering, for Horus as victor has "united them to you, for they are complete" (PT106). In other words, because Horus overcomes Seth, the injured Eye reverts back to Horus (PT199). This Eye of Horus is the "great left Eye in a healed condition" (PT301).

It is worthy of note that in the study of mutation, reversion is when the phenotype of a mutant can be reverted back to the original parental phenotype by a second mutation. The reversion occurs due to the second mutation within the gene or at another locus. True reversion occurs when the mutated base pair is converted back to the original base pair, and the function of the translation to protein is restored. This idea of reversion is mentioned to the Deceased: "May the Eye of Horus belong(?) to you—the reversion of the god's offering" (PT199).

So, the whole Eye of Horus or *wedjat* is comprised of both eyes, the restored left-black-Moon eye and the right-white-Sun eye. According to the texts, Seth's theft was a crime because when he snatched the Eye, Osiris died (IS73). Both Eyes must be united to Osiris in order to expand his heart so that he can live (IS78). Based on these textual references, we can expand our possibilities as follows: **Sun-god Re = incoming phage Lambda**

Return of Deceased to Atum, Hu, Sia = movement to foundation of forms, origin of time or Atum's Lambda DNA before humans

Osiris dies: Seth's injury to Eye of Horus = matter/human creation from Lambda genome

Osiris lives: Horus overcomes Seth, takes back Eye, making the Eye of Horus whole = mutated base pair is converted back to original base pair and the function of the translation to protein is restored

A Maze of Metasymbols

Because the Pharaohs use more than one metasymbol to identify the same idea, let's review the interconnected metaphors relating to the Eye of Horus, so we can make sense out of the texts. At this point, a deductive compilation of the interconnected group of metasymbols from the Pyramid and Coffin Texts, describing Seth and his Eye, Horus and his Eye, and the Whole Eye of the Rivals Seth and Horus, results in our next matrix.

MATRIX 4

THE INTERCONNECTED METASYMBOLS RELATING TO THE EYE OF HORUS

The Eye of Seth	The Whole Eye	The Eye of Horus
Red, green, Lower Egypt Crown	Double Crown	White, Upper Egypt crown
Black Bull	Double Bull	White Bull
Lesser Ennead, Hidden 9	Two Enneads	Greater Ennead
Black, left, empty, green, sweet	Two Eyes	White, right full Eye
Southern Land	Two Lands	Northern Land
Vanquished Rebel Seth	Two Rivals, Brothers	Victorious Risen Horus
Southern, Lower Mounds	Two Mounds	Northern, Upper Mounds
Left arm, hand of earth, destroyer	Two arms, hands	Right arm, right hand of sky
Lower Egypt	Two Conclaves	Upper Egypt
3 portions in earth or House of Thoth (after Seth vanquished)	Field of Offerings or 7 uraei or 7 portions of Bread	4 portions in sky or House of Horus (after Seth vanquished)
Iron Bowl of Seth's Eye	Two Bowls of Milk	Horus' Bowl
1 pillar	Two Pillars of Mansion of Six	1 pillar
Iron of Lower Egypt	Iron Throne of Osiris/King	Iron of Upper Egypt
Moon Eye	Sun and Moon Eyes	Sun Eye

A review of Idea Strands 62 to 76 informs us of the following ideas. The full function of the Eye of Horus is necessary for the King to speak the Great Word, which results in the Horus lineage or the reborn Deceased King as Osiris. We can see that the repression of Seth or the human lineage results in the activation of the Horus or celestial lineage and vice versa. This means that when

Seth is active, Horus is inert, and when Horus is active, Seth is beheaded and his power over the Eye of Horus destroyed. Again, Osiris = Deceased King = recombinant DNA = Eye of Horus = Lambda genome. From a bacterial genetic point of view, one might say that when the Seth Eye is replicating humans, the Horus Eye (Osiris) survives silently as part of the host chromosome in a state of lysogeny. In contrast, when the Eye of Horus is victorious, the lytic cycle rules. Thus, Seth and his gang are beheaded or destroyed, and Horus produces progeny as Osiris breaks out of lysogeny.

If one were to compare the competition of Seth and Horus with a particular bacteriophage, the virus life cycle of temperate phage Lambda, a genetic control system involved in the action of repressor proteins, regulating lysogeny versus lytic replication, would be a likely candidate. In Matrix Four, we posit that the Eye of Horus is the Field of Offerings, also described as seven portions of Bread or seven uraei. This compares to the left and right arms of the Lambda genome with its seven operons that control lysogeny and lysis, and it supports our developing equation that the Eye of Horus is the Lambda genome lodged on the host chromosome, that is, the prophage Osiris. In the Book of the Dead, the seven cows who give bread and beer represent the Field of Offerings or the seven Lambda operons. Supporting evidence for the idea that the Pharaohs were explaining the operation of Lambda lifestyles are narrative metasymbols relating to three events:

1) the battle between Seth and Horus in the Island of Fire as the battle between cI (c-one) and cro proteins, determining lysogeny versus lysis;

2) the theft of fire or Seth snatching the Eye as cI protein occupying the Right Operator site first;

3) the ascendancy of the right arm of Horus over Seth as cro protein dominating the Right operator sequences first.

Before investigating these three pivotal events, let's explore supporting Egyptian concepts, beginning with the geometry of the Eye of Horus.

The Geometry of the *Utchat* or *Wedjat*

Sir Alan Gardiner's *Egyptian Grammar* (1927) describes the ancient Egyptian fractions used to divide the Heqat unit or gallon: 1/2, 1/4, 1/8, 1/16, 1/32 and 1/64. This mathematical pattern suggests the process of DNA replicating into two daughter cells, each retaining one-half of the original sense DNA strand, which gradually diminishes the original DNA. Yet, this mathematical progression also represents the radioactive decay series. The statistics governing radioactive decay predict the decay pattern of a large number of radioactive nuclei. The decay constant is closely related to the half-life, which is the time it takes for half of the material to decay. After two half-lives, there will be one-fourth of the original sample, after three half-lives, one eighth and so on. So the decay series of 1/2, 1/4, 1/8, 1/16, 1/32, 1/64, is a good fit for the six fractions of the Eye of Horus, corresponding to sense data, which appears to be vanishing. By calculus, the fractions of the Eye add up to one, suggesting wholeness. So we could say that the whole Eye connotes no DNA replication and no decay, but the injured Eye results in both DNA replication and decay.

Eye of Horus Geometry = DNA replication; radioactive decay series
Whole Eye (one) = no DNA replication; no decay

As mentioned, the funerary texts portray the Deceased in the afterlife as conscious during the process of radioactive decay that almost regresses to the zero point, which is the change in potential which has physical significance. In hyperphysics, for a single point charge or localized collection of charges, it is logical to set the zero point at infinity. (Nave 2003) In essence, the Eye of Horus (Atum, Re, Re-Atum and so on) becomes the medium for a transformation that restores the Eye, corrects the mass defect in the nucleus of the atom by making it whole again, and brings the Deceased face-to-face with the foundation of forms in Atum's heart, that is, the Lambda DNA. This entire process is a movement toward the zero point or infinity.

In this movement toward the zero point, the Eye of Horus series relates to the gravitational force. According to Hawking, in three dimensions, the gravitational force drops to 1/4 if one doubles the distance between two bodies; in four dimensions, it drops to 1/8; in five dimensions to 1/16; in six dimension to 1/32, and in seven dimensions to 1/64. This situation would make earth very unstable in its orbit around the Sun, causing it to spiral into the Sun, which would either fall apart or collapse to form a black hole. (1988, 164-65) So the Eye of Horus could also represent the decrease of the gravitational force between two bodies due to low dimensionality.

Also, Kerr black holes have a gyromagnetic ratio 2 or spin-1/2, along with natural Clifford algebra geometry that deals with the same series of numbers (1, 2, 4, 8, 16, 32, 64 . . .). Clifford algebras relate to vector spaces, their rotations and their spinors. In the movement to the zero point field (ZPF), quantum fluctuations lead to a kind of jittering motion at low energies. This minimum energy due to these quantum fluctuations is called zero point energy. B. G. Sidharth (1998[2]) states that the curvature of a quantum mechanical black hole (QMBH) is generated by these fluctuations. His model of a QMBH describes the most fundamental particles (leptons and quarks) in terms of Kerr-Newman black holes. A particle is referred to as a Compton radius vortex, and its Compton wavelength is its spread in location. In quantum mechanics, one can only calculate the probability of where a particle will be found. Yet, a Compton radius vortex can have left-handed or right-handed helicity. Relative to Sidharth's model, the Deceased with his 180 degree flip or left-to-right orientation and west-to-east movement would be a left-handed helicity Compton radius vortex, having an outer and inner event horizons that merge, becoming four complex dimensional spacetime. In fact, the Deceased, the Sun-god and the earth-cell may all be vortices in the quantum world. So the Eye of Horus fractions may relate to gravity, zero point energy and the formation of QMBHs, specifically those with left-handed helicity.

Finally, the long spiral from the pupil of the Eye of Horus is a mirror image of the Fibonacci Spiral, a geometric spiral whose growth is regulated by a series of numbers (1, 1, 2, 3, 5, 8, 13, 21, 34, 55 . . .), indicating exponential growth. The Fibonacci series converges on phi (1.618), which is also related to the icosahedron, the pentagon, and DNA. Any number in the series after one (1) is equal to the sum of the two preceding numbers. Adjacent numbers approximate the Golden Ratio. So we could easily identify this series of numbers with the exponential growth of human and other species in Nature.

Objective 5 completed: Matrix 5 is centered on the idea that the Egyptian afterlife exists on the quantum cellular level and is based on phage Lambda genetics. Therefore, it supports our initial model in Matrix 2, which continues to have coherence.

This brings us face-to-face with twenty-first century molecular biology, bacterial genetics, and supramolecular chemistry, the scientific ground foreshadowed by the complicated Amduat and Book of Gates that support the Egyptian idea of life after death. So for ease of understanding and before we discover how the Deceased restores the Eye of Horus, the next chapter provides a brief review of bacterial genetics.

MATRIX 5

EGYPTIAN SIGNS TRANSLATED TO POSSIBLE MODERN SCIENCE PARALLEL

Atum's throne or foundation of forms; the Ritual Book; the Whole Writing; the Words: the holograph; information transfer processes; first DNA of solar or viral origin
Book of Gates, title: 12 gates of Lambda decision circuit
Eye of Horus geometry: DNA replication; radioactive decay series; Clifford Algebra; diminishing gravity statistics; movement to ZPF; formation of QMBH
Eye of Horus spiral: Fibonacci spiral based on Golden Ratio
Eye of Horus, whole: left and right arms of Lambda genome; lytic lifestyle
Geb; earth; beetle dung ball: prokaryote host cell
***kheper* ("to roll"):** indicator of rolling circle replication and lytic lifestyle of phage Lambda; also circularization of Lambda DNA inside prokaryote host cell
left-to-right 180 degree flip: formation of left-handed helicity Comptom radius vortex
milk cows, 7 (BD): 7 Lambda operons controlling lysogeny and lysis
Osiris alive and risen: excision of Lambda prophage; lytic lifestyle
Osiris dead or cut up: lysogeny or replication of Lambda prophage through cI protein production
return of Deceased to Atum, Hu, Sia: return to origin of time or distributed enfolded holographic-like order of frequencies and spectral dimensions of energy
reversion of god's offerings: excision of Lambda prophage; lytic lifestyle
reversion of Seth's Eye back to Horus: mutated base pairs convert back to original base pairs, restoring translation to cro protein and lytic lifestyle
Seth's injury to Eye of Horus (Osiris dies): matter or human creation resulting from cI protein production
Seth overcome by Horus who makes Eye whole (Osiris lives): no matter or human creation; cro production; excision of Lambda prophage and rolling circle replication of lytic lifestyle
Sun-god Re (Atum, Khepera): incoming Lambda vector; first-born DNA
union of Deceased and Sun-god: genetic insert into Lambda DNA vector
upside down human world: spacetime dimensions of matter; prokaryote to eukaryote development; hologram
Uraei (7) in Field of Offerings: 7 Lambda operons controlling lysogeny versus lytic cycle

9

The Genetics of Bacteria and Bacteriophage

THE NATURE OF THE DECEASED: MAGICIAN? SUPERMOLECULE? OR COSMIC CLONE?

A bacterium is a single-celled microscopic, plant-like organism lacking a nucleus. Remembering the Pharaoh's model of the earth dung ball and Sun-beetle, which we have clarified by assigning the Sun-beetle the value of phage Lambda and the earth dung ball the value of an *E. coli* bacterium, it is important to understand the DNA sequence for bacteria.

The bacterial genome is small and highly organized, whereas 95 to 97 percent of the human genome has no known function (Gee 2001; Nicholl 2002, 170). Bacterial genes have regulatory sections of DNA organized into operon units that control transcription. An operon is a gene cluster served by one promoter. RNA polymerase can bind to the promoter region, or a regulatory gene can make a repressor molecule that blocks binding of RNA polymerase.

Bacteria have three ways of making recombinant DNA, which is the fusion of DNA from two separate individuals. They are transformation, transduction and conjugation. The Amduat specifically states that the Sun-god will make his "transformations." We could say that both transduction and transformation are occurring in the Egyptian afterlife. First, when the Deceased merges with the Sun-god, the naked DNA or genetic heritage of the Deceased is taken up as an insert in a Lambda vector (Sun-god), and then the recombinant DNA is injected into the bacterial cell at the "place of mooring" or attachment site to the bacterium (earth). On the cellular level, this injection of Lambda DNA is similar to the injection of plasma at the separatrix during impulsive or bursty reconnection at the magnetospheric cusp.

DNA becomes naked by exposure to ultraviolet radiation, resulting in denatured DNA fragments becoming short linear DNAs that generally do not have an origin of replication. Without an origin of replication, linear DNA fragments are soon degraded and the nucleotides recycled a la de Sade. With an origin of replication, DNA fragments cross over, splice or genetically recombine by producing a new chromosome or bacterium with a new combination of genes, a recombinant. So, the recombinant DNA (union of the Deceased and the Sun-god) is taken up by a host cell for genetic transformation, as phage Lambda invades the host cell and takes over its replication machinery.

Recombination requires enzymes to pair up, cut and splice the two homologous (similar but different) DNAs involved. In bacteria, this process of recombination can occur at any time because the enzymes for DNA repair are present. However, recombination only occurs if extra DNA is present due to transformation, transduction, and so on. Put simply, one cell dies (donor), releasing its chromosomal DNA broken into short linear fragments, and another cell (recipient) takes up the released DNA, now having a complete chromosome plus a fragment. Recombination for DNA repair of the damaged cell can now happen. Not only is transformation occurring in the funerary texts, but the primary process is transduction or the use of a bacteriophage to transport the remaining genetic heritage of the Deceased into the bacterial host cell. To understand the chemical transformation of the Deceased into the "great god from dawn" (AMD HR.12), we must look at the nature of the Deceased Sun-god.

Objective 6: To understand how the Deceased Sun-god restores the Eye of Horus, we must examine his nature and that of his crew.

The Nature of the Deceased Sun-god

IS 6-7: Dead King is a god, a magician and saviour
IS 11-12: Dead King is unique and a Lone Star in east
IS 88-89: Dead King's reborn form is a being with no arms or legs; he is coiled, has jackal face, Celestial Serpent middle and hinder parts like a broad hall

In our discussion of What is Above in Part One, the Deceased travels to the cusp, where the Sun-god and crew is "knit together" about him by the Imperishable Stars (CT255). He is then literally injected through the Gap or origin of reconnection in the earth's magnetopause, so he can navigate the Winding Waterway in the Sun-bark (CT62). Space physics evidence (Richard et al. 1997) suggests this path results in an open field line to the Sun's IMF, or what the Pharaohs might call "going forth by Day."

As a plasma or ionized gas, the Deceased can be described as the central component of the atoms or molecules that are charge carriers such as free electrons, positive ions and negative ions. Research shows that some of these ions in plasma have complex structures, such as an ordinary ion surrounded by a cloud of polarizable molecules, an idea that could be represented by the eight-around-one arrangement on the Sun-bark. Another correlation is that Gell-man and Ne'eman (1960-61) discovered that mesons (particles consisting of a quark and antiquark) could be naturally grouped into octets, and baryons (particles built from three quarks) into octets and decuplets, what is called the Eightfold Way (Gell-man 2000).

Further, the Deceased possesses jars of electrum (CT84) and is Lord of electrums (CT468). Although the word "electrum" can indicate an alloy of gold and silver, the term reminds one of the word "electron" and the idea of a molecule. Reference is made to the Deceased King gathering his members and circumambulating the Mounds of Horus and Seth (PT612). The Deceased King is also called a snake with many coils (PT511), which reminds one of coiled protein structures such as alpha helices and beta strands, and the idea that the Deceased is a long protein chain folding into a compact stable structure. So it seems that the Deceased Sun-god and his eight companions at the Gap or origin of reconnection may actually be a molecule at a polar cell origin of replication that will enter the host cell as a cloning vector and exit as a clone.

Along with the molecular nature of the Deceased, he has other supernatural attributes. He is the oldest god, one of the Great Ennead, a falcon, a magician, the scribe of the god's book, the Unique One, a Bull in the sky (IS1-13), or simply, he is the personification of Carl Jung's hero archetype, Pierre Teilhard de Chardin's Ultra-Human, and Friedrich Nietzsche's Overman.

The Supramolecular Ship

On the macrocosmic scale, after going toward the polestar and the northern cusp or Gap, the Deceased arrives at the staircase cusp, where impulsive magnetic reconnection occurs in thin current sheets. The tearing mode eigenmode and its instability that excites reconnection is initiated by a population of electrons that are not trapped in the current sheet. According to reconnection theory, the free electrons short the electric field that stabilizes the mode and magnetic reconnection begins. (University of Maryland 2002)

On the quantum level, the supramolecular Sun-bark operates similar to Lambda DNA injected into a host cell. The origin of magnetic reconnection in the magnetosphere becomes an origin for cell entry and DNA replication in the cell. An *E. coli* bacterium has a special polar receptor site for Lambda adsorption called the LamB receptor. In fact, one-celled bacteria such as *E. coli* also have mechanisms, whereby gene transcription is initiated by available iron complexes on the cell surface (Faraldo-Gomez 2002). Iron is essential for *E. coli* and references to iron are widespread in the funerary texts, while research shows iron nuclei are present at the polar cusp. Because What is Above is What is Below, this translates to iron being present at the earth-cell's poles.

At the Gap or "Horn of Ament" (AMD HR.1), the Deceased bonds with the Sun-god and his crew of eight on the bark, a group traveling and working together for a common purpose: the transformation of the Deceased (AMD HR.1) into the new Horus species (AMD HR.12). It seems as if the Pharaohs understood supramolecular chemistry or the twenty-first century study of ensembles of molecules working together. Reacting like supramolecular components, the Sun-god and his crew communicate, form associations, have preferences and aversions, follow instructions and pass on information.

In supramolecular chemistry, one molecule is able to distinguish another by its shape or properties, a type of molecular social order also evident in the Amduat, for "knowledge of the souls" is stressed to the Deceased Sun-god. Bonded to the Sun-god on the bark, the Deceased and his crew of eight in the cellular world may easily be thought of as molecules, consisting of a single continuous network of atoms linked together by covalent bonds. In fact, the Sun-god and his crew may represent a nucleosome. In the transcription process, the DNA double helix wraps around a core of eight histone protein molecules, and a second histone H1 secures the DNA to the nucleosome core. The histones may activate or silence genes. (Cold Springs Harbor Laboratory 2001)

This octamer of eight basic proteins is a fundamental packing unit called a nucleosome. The histone core structure is anchored to the backbone of the chromosome and is evolutionally conserved across the spectrum of eukaryotic cells. Histones (like the hydrogen ions in our macrocosmic model) are positively charged, so they can interact with the negatively charged DNA, as they exercise control of gene activity.

Looking imaginatively at the structure of a nucleosome core, one might perceive a jackal face, and this may have been what motivated the Pharaohs with their death-vision to claim the Deceased King's form is that of Anubis, having a jackal face, a Celestial Serpent middle, and a spine as a door-bolt (IS54 and 89), a possible reference to the second histone that bolts the DNA to the core.

Molecular Recognition

Without doubt, the numerous deities and serpents recognize the dead Sun-god, who also recognizes the names and functions of all deities and serpents in the Duat. New Chemists call this quantum capability *molecular recognition*. Another term *supermolecule* distinguishes ions or molecules united with one another by weaker bonds into a discrete unit with a well-defined structure and dynamics, such as the representation of the Deceased Sun-god and his crew in the process of translation to protein. Supramolecular chemistry sets up molecular systems that can differentiate one specific kind of molecule from many others. As the texts corroborate, when describing deities in their dwarf-world Duat, the Pharaohs took advantage of this same strategy to distinguish different atoms and molecules by distinctive anthropomorphic epithets, symbols and definitive drawings.

Another way modern chemists explain molecular recognition is by the metaphor of the lock and key, whereby the enzyme (lock) has a molecular shape complementary to a substrate (key). New chemists also define chemical molecules by using metaphorical terms such as ether chains and rings, proton-binding groups, nitrogen junctions in so-called aza-crowns, cup-like shape, cage-like or bowl-like receptors, a carcerand (molecular prison for small substrates), and knotted molecules. In fact, researchers using X-ray crystallography have identified eight groups of DNA-binding proteins, dividing them further into 54 structural families. The eight groups are: 1) Helix-turn-helix or HTH (including "winged" HTH), 2) zinc-coordinating, 3) zipper-type, 4) other alpha helix, 5) beta-sheet, 6) beta hairpin/ribbon, 7) other, and 8) enzymes. (University College

London 2000)

As an example, cro and the repressor family of phage Lambda are in the helix-turn-helix group, as is the prokaryotic LacI repressor family. Eukaryotic proteins also are "winged" HTH, and the protein heat shock transcription factor is listed in the Transcription Factor family. The zinc-binding eukaryotic proteins in Group 2 include beta-beta-alpha zinc finger proteins. All of these groupings reflect the use of a molecular recognition system based on metaphors of wings, helices, ribbons, fingers, zippers and families, so that the modern chemist can envision and describe the image of the molecule.

In like manner, the common use of wings on serpents (AMD HR.4) and deities (AMD HR.5), along with coiled (HTH motif) serpents may represent this same tactic of defining specific protein-DNA complexes. Distinguishing terms in the Amduat, such as crowns (HR.2) and circles or rings (HR.8), along with drawings such as the cage around the Sun-god, the chain of rope loops on the bark (HR.3), the Deceased's headdress of a circular disk or ring centered in horizontal ram horns, and deities seated in bowl-like receptors, all suggest the same twenty-first century method of using metaphors to explain chemical concepts. Even Osiris bent backward into a ring in scenes depicting the Creation (Budge v1 1904, 298) may indicate the disrotatory path that a molecule can take as it twists into a ring or the act of rolling circle replication of phage Lambda. For the Pharaohs, this instructional strategy conveyed scientific ideas to the Kings and nobility, while disguising these same concepts from the plebs. Both modern supramolecular chemistry and Egyptian science is based on a metaphoric terminology, using familiar objects such as wings, crowns, rings and cups that point to chemical complexes or processes.

Definitions

Self-assembly: the spontaneous association of several molecular components into a discrete, non-covalently bound aggregate with a well-defined structure, e.g. binding with a purpose

Self-organization: the spontaneous ordering of molecular or supramolecular units into a higher-order non-covalent structure, characterized by some degree of spatial and/or temporal order or design by correlations between remote regions; will exhibit collective and often nonlinear behaviour; could include crystallization and related ordering phenomena such as liquid-crystallinity. (Lehn and Ball 2000, 304)

Figure 9.1

Self-Assembly and Self-Organization

Terms describing the autonomy and programmed nature of building blocks in supramolecular chemistry include self-assembly and self-organization, which are comparable to Egyptian claims that the Deceased is "self-created" (CT75, 341), a "foundling" without knowledge of parents (PT516), and "an unblemished birth" (PT518), for he was not conceived (CT76). Put simply, the supramolecular Sun-bark exhibits self-assembly and self-organization.

Then, in the Amduat, the self-assembled Sun-bark is dragged by four gods (HR.4), then seven gods and seven goddesses (HR.5), then eight gods (HR.8), and finally twelve gods and twelve goddesses drag the bark through the bowels of the serpent Ankh-neteru (HR.12). This may depict the further formation and birth of molecules through covalent bonds—when two atoms are able to share electrons, or through electrovalent bonds, which are held together between positively charged cations and negatively charged anions. As an example, if the Sun-god represents hydrogen, and the four gods dragging the bark signify the four valence electrons of carbon, then we have a covalent bond of hydrogen with carbon. If seven goddesses representing a nitrogen anion and seven gods representing a nitrogen cation then unite and drag the hydrogen-carbon bond, this may indicate a hydrogen-bonded molecular network formed using cationic and anionic building blocks.

This thesis is a call to supramolecular chemists to analyze the obvious chemistry in the Amduat, for it seems that the text may indicate some derivative of HCN or hydrogen cyanide. J. Oro and A. Lazcano-Araujo reviewed the role of HCN and its derivatives in prebiotic evolution, finding that radioastronomical observations show HCN is a very abundant cosmic molecule that is the periodic precursor of molecules such as amino acids, the purines adenine and guanine. (1981) If this is the case, then the seven gods and seven goddesses may represent the nitrogenous base of the purines guanine, which always pairs with cytosine by three hydrogen bonds, or adenine, which always pairs with thymine by two hydrogen bonds.

The Catalytic Process

Along with the Deceased Sun-god's potential for self-assembly, his journey in the Amduat can be easily restated in the chemical terms of the catalytic process, which involves three steps: binding of the substrate, followed by its chemical transformation into the product, and finally, the release of the product to regenerate the active catalyst. This is mirrored by the Deceased Sun-god binding with Osiris (HR.6), the instruments of weaving indicating protein conformation (HRS.8, 9), and when the transformation is complete, the release of the solar "product" comprised of Re's loyal servants (HR.12). In the same way, the least corrupt of all the funerary texts supports the idea of a product, for the Deceased King is a bright star, bringing to Re "distant products" on a daily basis (PT248). Similarly, the Deceased makes his way in the valley (CT1079) as if he were a chemical reaction. He takes a minimum potential energy path up the floor of the reactant valley and down the foot of the product valley (Atkins 1991, 122-123). Hence, the Amduat expresses an Egyptian awareness of twenty-first century knowledge such as molecular recognition, self-assembly, self-organization and the catalytic process, which enabled the Pharaohs to identify quantum molecular structures, using metaphoric language similar to that of our New Chemists.

The Sun-Bark as Gene Vector

Exploring requisite details of the idea of the Sun-god as a Lambda vector, we find that the Lambda Sun-god and his supramolecular crew is a fusion that easily breaches the cell wall of the earth at the Gap of the Duat. Bacterial viruses have this capability (Lehn and Ball 2000, 316), along with a hierarchy of structural levels, from molecular to the supramolecular as do cells and tissue fibers (300-301). Since references such as Osiris ("activity of eye") and the Eye of Horus suggest DNA activity, it is possible, as our model posits, that the Sun-god and his crew represent a molecule capable of transporting DNA into a cell. A molecule of this nature is a gene vector, and modern geneticists favor the use of modified viruses, which breach cell walls easily (316). So we could further describe the composite crew on the Sun-bark as:

Sun-bark = Lambda gene vector/supermolecule

If the supramolecular Deceased Sun-god and crew represent a Lambda gene vector, then we must now identify the Egyptian metasymbols that signify the transport of DNA, that is, the transcription, replication and translation of DNA. We have posited that the union of the Deceased and Sun-god at the northern polar cusp parallels the insertion of an exogenous DNA fragment into an incoming Lambda genome that will dock into the earth cell. The Deceased King clearly states, "I am merged in the Sunshine god" (CT75). The central 15 bp region of the Lambda genome between positions 20 and 35 is a nonessential region that controls the lysogenic phage properties (Nicholl 2002, 70-71). The lytic infection cycle can still function if this area is deleted or if exogenous DNA is inserted into it. For example, the insertion vector Lambda gt10 has a single recognition site for restriction enzymes, allowing DNA fragments to be inserted into the genome. This recognition site is called *Eco*RI and lies within the *cI* gene (Lambda repressor). The *cI* gene is inactivated by cloning a fragment into this site (Nicholl 2002, 135). In the insertion vector Lambda gt10 (43.3 kb), when DNA is inserted into the recognition site *Eco*RI, it generates left and right arms of 32.7 and 10.6 kb, which can accept a DNA insert up to 7.6 kb in length (72).

Because the nature of the recombinant vector is to ferry or carry DNA fragments, geneticists use Lambda vectors for cloning experiments. In fact, modern geneticists have named insertion vectors, such as the Lambda insertion vector Charon 16A, after the ferryman of Greek mythology, who transported the spirits of the dead across the river Styx (66-71). The Sun-god is also a ferryman, carrying the Deceased through the Duat along the host chromosome in a fashion similar to that of a cloning vector. So, to learn more about ferrying and vectors, it now seems reasonable to compare the Deceased Sun-god's entry into the Duat with Lambda events related to adsorption, which involves the phage particle binding to receptors on the bacterial surface and injecting its DNA.

Adsorption and Injection into the Duat

Recall from Part One that FTEs, also known as bubbles, CDCs or magnetic islands, are produced by a tearing mode reconnection process driven by strong magnetopause currents and fluctuations of Alfven waves. The FTE forms when plasma is advected toward the separatrix by the inflow and injected into the region inside the separatrix by the outflow jets. The result of this is the filling of the region inside the separatrix with the plasma forming the FTE. (Stasiewicz 2001) Likewise, researcher Robert Sheldon defines a CDC as a magnetic bottle or force-free structure, whereby the local plasma energy dominates over the magnetic energy, forming a bubble constrained by compressed magnetic field lines and increasing field strength along the field line. The origin of a CDC or magnetic bottle could be from an explosive heating event or a sudden injection of cold plasma. The sudden injection of cold plasma is the preferred option because of the presence of magnetosheath plasma in the core. (Sheldon 2000)

Similarly, when phage Lambda adsorbs to the bacterial cell, its tail fiber attaches to the LamB protein on the *E. coli* outer membrane. DNA is then thought to be injected down the hollow core of the tail into the bacterium. So, if the staircase cusp signals the onset of a FTE, then this magnetospheric event may mirror the Egyptian idea of the Deceased engaging the Great Stairway and becoming a recombinant with the Lambda Sun-god and his supramolecular crew on the bark. Further, the formation of the FTE by the advection of plasma toward the separatrix may mirror the injection of recombinant Lambda DNA into the *E. coli* host cell or the movement of the Deceased Sun-god and crew into the Gap in the Mountains, that is, through the cell wall. Just as the preferred origin of a CDC or magnetic bottle is a sudden injection of cold plasma, we find that the Deceased King receives a jar (magnetic bottle?) of Re's cold water when he meets him at the polar region (IS98).

In Part One, we analyzed the quotation from the Theban Recension about leading the "Moored Ones" to the secret places and dragging in Re, which seems a likely description of phage Lambda attached and penetrating the host cell (TR64). The texts state that the Dead King's boat is at the "mooring rope" and that he will not be "boatless" (CT182), and that he is "stretched out straight" and makes "ready the ferryboat" (CT218), which is moored in the "dockyard of the gods" (CT1036). Re also causes the gods to follow "when the bark travels, it being dragged straight on" (CT60). These parallels suggest that the journey into the Duat begins at the site of impulsive magnetic reconnection at the cusp, which is similar to the injection of recombinant DNA into the *E. coli* cell at the polar LamB receptor site, a dockyard for phage Lambda.

The LamB of God

IS 20: King opens double doors, double barrier, double gates, Double Ramgate

Bacteriologists know that polar localization of proteins is critical for cellular processes such as division, chromosome partitioning and cell cycle control in *E. coli.* Physical differences exist at the cell poles such as large polar caps or gaps between the cytoplasm and cell wall and protein enrichment sites. Also, the concentration of secretion and adhesion machinery to the cell pole may facilitate host invasion, such as that of phage Lambda which attaches to the LamB receptor site of *E. coli.* (Lybarger and Maddock 2001)

Entry into the earth cell or *E. coli* bacterium is through its double cell membrane or double barrier at the phage Lambda receptor site, the LamB porin. Porins are water-filled pores or channels across the outer cell membranes of gram negative bacteria such as *E. coli.* Maltoporin or the LamB porin is responsible for guided diffusion of maltose and maltodextrins for *E. coli*, along with being the phage Lambda receptor site. (Marcey[2] et al. 2001). Three-dimensional studies of LamB show that each subunit of the trimeric protein contains a wide channel formed by an 18-stranded antiparallel beta-barrel. Three inwardly folded loops, an umbrella structure, are located in the channel lining, along with the greasy slide, a hydrophobic path composed of aromatic residues. In the drawings in the Amduat and Book of Gates, the activity takes place along a three-channel pathway that may represent the three channels of the LamB porin.

LamB, a guided diffusion channel, is one of six proteins (MBP, MalE, MalF, MalG and MalK[2]) composing the maltose transport system in *E. coli.* Bacteria favor the carbon source of glucose, and maltose is a dimer of glucose; however, in its absence, bacteria will access lactose. Researchers have identified a mutant of the maltose transport system that transports lactose efficiently. The mutant has a missense mutation in the *MalF* gene that changes leucine to tryptophan. Mutations allowing lactose transport have a Lac+ phenotype. Scientists theorize that the maltose transport system may contain two figurative paths for the transport of substrate. In one path the substrate is bound to MBP, the maltose-binding-protein in the periplasm. In the case of lactose transport, the mutant accesses only the second low-affinity path, since MBP cannot bind the substrate lactose. (Merino and Shuman 1997) The Book of Two Ways also references these two figurative pathways. On the macrocosmic level, these two paths easily translate to the LLBL and the HLBL of the magnetopause.

Lactose transport is by proton symport. One proton and one lactose are transported by the lactose permease, a product of *lacY* gene. Any ion, such as a hydrogen ion, in excess outside of the cell can act as the driving force for transporting nutrients. (Clark 1999) Recall that the polar cusp is an excess of solar hydrogen ions. The Sun-god represents not only a composite of hydrogen ions and other energetic particles, but also the incoming phage Lambda that will ferry the Deceased into the bacterial host for transformation. We have posited that the genetic heritage of the Deceased inserts into the incoming phage Lambda at the *cI* gene, inactivating it. This is called insertional inactivation. Isis is also present on the Sun-god's supramolecular bark and may be the representation of lactose and its resultant transport through the cell by the hydrogen driving force. For, if the Lambda vector is carrying the *LacZ* gene, it may be active, as represented by Isis, Lady of Provisions, on the Sun-bark.

LacZ (*b-gal* gene) is the enzyme normally synthesized by *E. coli* cells when lactose becomes available. *LacZ* may be present in the vector, as it is for the Lambda insertion vector Charon 16A. However, a DNA insert into *LacZ* inactivates the gene, just as it inactivates the *cI* gene in Lambda gt10. It is interesting that the Lambda prophage sits silently at the *b-gal* gene (*LacZ*) in the *E. coli* host chromosome. When the prophage excises, it can sometimes leave with part of this gene, a type of specialized transduction, activating the *lac* gene by leaving the seat empty. Related to this idea is the symbol of the name of Isis in Egyptian, which is an empty seat or throne, suggesting that an empty seat or throne indicates the gene "seat" active for lactose metabolism, instead of inactive and occupied by the prophage in the lysogen. Thus, an empty gene seat could signify the excision of the prophage or the resurrection of Osiris. Decoded:

Egyptian polar Gap or dockyard of gods = LamB porin

Polar bursty reconnection site = injection of recombinant Lambda DNA

Isis' name (empty throne) = empty seat due to prophage excision

As we expand on our microcosmic model of the Sun-god operating like a Lambda vector, the earth representing an *E. coli* host bacterium, and the Deceased functioning as a DNA insert, it seems practical for understanding the Egyptian afterlife. In support, we have posited that the union of the Deceased and Sun-god at the northern polar cusp is similar to the insertion of an exogenous DNA fragment into an incoming Lambda genome. The Sun-god is a ferryman, carrying the Deceased through the Duat in a fashion similar to that of a Lambda cloning vector. Entry into the Duat or Mountain of West Gap is similar not only to adsorption and injection of Lambda DNA into an *E. coli* host at the LamB porin, but also to the injection activity of FTEs into the magnetopause. In addition, polar localization for cell cycle control in *E. coli* suggests a rationale for the Egyptian advice to go to the polar cusp of earth, which is enriched with high energy particles.

The presence of Isis on the Sun-bark at the northern polar cusp may indicate lactose transport by proton symport. Likewise, insertional inactivation of cI in the Lambda vector may indicate that the *LacZ* gene is functional and not inactivated by an insert in the vector, so that lactose enters the bacterial host. Similarly, the excision of the Lambda prophage from the *LacZ* gene (*b-gal*) may represent the meaning of the empty throne designating the name of Isis. All in all, the voyage of the Deceased Sun-god and crew of eight traces a figurative path for humans to the next level of evolution, viz., cosmic clone.

Objective 6 completed: The supramolecular nature of the Deceased Sun-god and crew of eight supports the idea of an afterlife cloning experiment that redesigns the human evolutionary future, if one bonds to the Sun-god.

With this detailed examination of phage Lambda, its LamB receptor site on *E. coli*, and the potential of the maltose transport system for lactose passage, we can easily decode additional Egyptian signs in the interests of finding out how the Deceased Sun-god restores the Eye of Horus. However, it will be helpful for the reader to refer to Figure 9.2 as an aid for understanding scientific ideas and chemical processes.

DNA of Deceased inserts into lambda vector for transduction through host cell (Duat) on lytic pathway

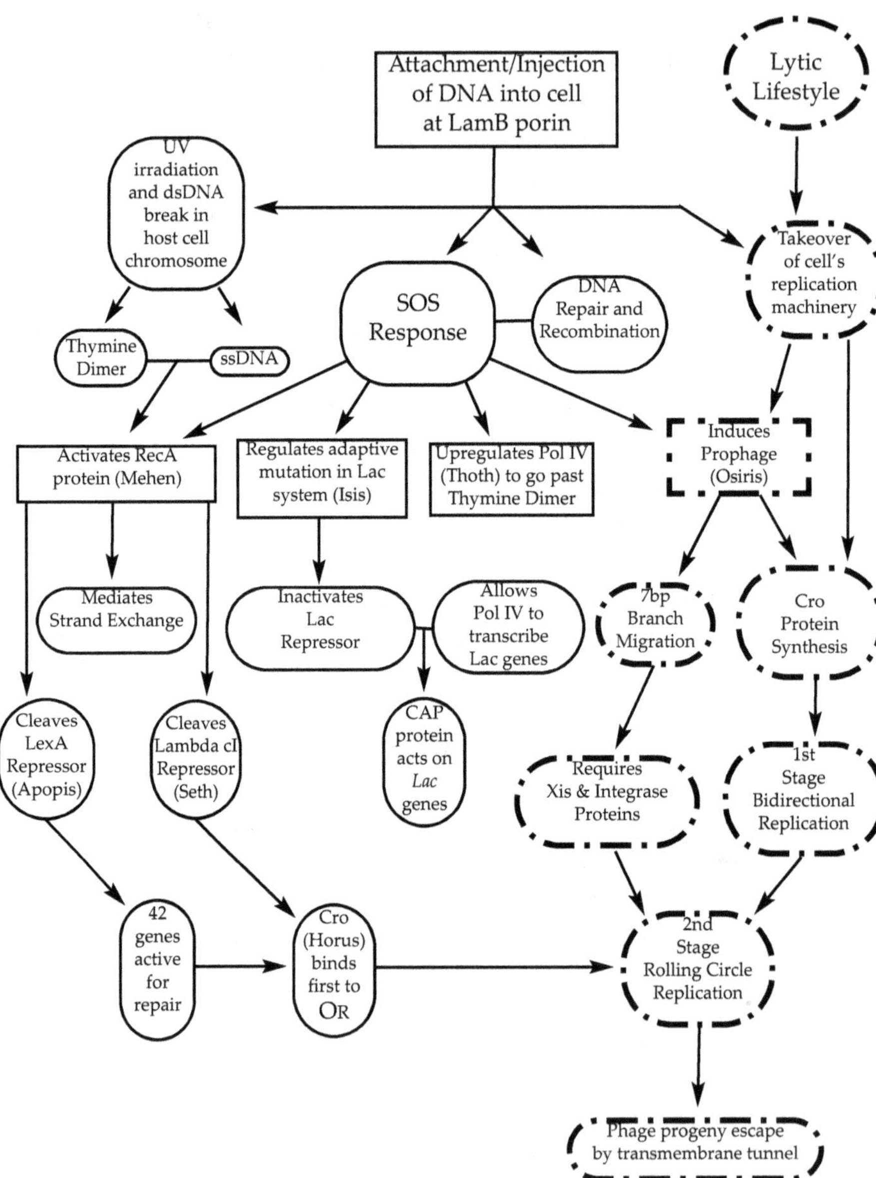

Figure 9.2

10

The Word as DNA Instructions

STALLED REPLICATION AND BIOCHEMICAL BUMPS: GENTLEMEN, RESTART YOUR ENGINES

IS 95: King tells scribe to destroy writings; requests scribe be replaced
IS 96: King bears god's book; King is Great Word

Objective 7: In order to discover how the Deceased Sun-god restores the Eye of Horus, we need to understand the signs suggesting DNA transcription and repair, keeping in mind the continued coherence and unity of our expanding matrices.

Transmitting messages in biology is electrolytic and can be described as the migration or flow of ions down electrical gradients. So we could say that the journey of the Sun-bark through the Duat simulates the flow of ions or a supramolecular message navigating the protein gradients. Recall that the Deceased is one who reveals what has been said to him. He also "dispatches the word of the Self-created to the multitudes" and "captains the bark" (CT75). "Mine is the writing" (CT137), he insists, and "I am in charge of the record of the word of God" (CT351). "This is the word which was in darkness. As for any spirit who knows it, he will live among the living. Fire is about it, which contains the efflux of Osiris" (CT1087). So, the *word in darkness* is Osiris, the DNA of Lambda prophage on the host chromosome, and efflux relates to the potential outflow of phage progeny related to the induction of the prophage.

At the point of return to the origin of time or the foundation of forms or first DNA (solar-star-viral), the Deceased states that as heir of the horizon and

Atum, he speaks and prepares "a path for Re when he comes to a halt" (CT1174). The application of the Word of Atum is the activity of DNA replication and information transfer processes. All these textual references use the idea of speech and words to point to the Lambda DNA instructions, for the Deceased bears the Word of God, the Lambda DNA of the Horus lineage, which now supplants the DNA of the human or Seth lineage (IS 95).

Word = DNA instructions of Horus lineage

By decoding *word* as Lambda DNA instructions, we can now understand the idea of *copying words* or DNA transcription. Reviewing the references to words in the Amduat in Figure 10.1, the process of DNA transcription and replication is explained in terms of uttering words, copying words, and destiny because of words (Hours 1-7), resulting in the subsequent translation to protein (Hours 8-10).

AMDUAT (SETI I) REFERENCES TO TRANSCRIPTION AND REPLICATION

HOUR	REFERENCE
1	If copies of these things be made according to the ordinances of the hidden house . . . ; The Majesty of this god uttered words after he hath come forth in this Court;
2	he paddleth along through this Field and uttered words; their boats send forth their words; This great god sendeth forth words; O ye who live in your forms, and who utter your words of magical power, . . . whose word is maat . . .;
3	Great one of words of power (in upper register)
4	he liveth on the words of the gods who guard this road
5	Behold Khepera who, immediately the [boat of Ra] is towed to the top of this Circle, unites himself to the roads of the Tuat; when this god standeth on the head of the goddess he speaketh words to Seker every day; to have his existence from the voice of the great god
6	Through the voice of Ra it is that the figures who are in him advance; If their names be uttered . . . Or if an exact representation in drawing be made of what is in the Hidden Place (Ament) of the Tuat;
7	Whosoever shall make [a copy of] these [pictures] according to the similitudes which are in writing
11	Whosoever shall make an exact copy of these forms . . . shall be a spirit well equipped
12	Whosoever shall make a copy thereof according to the copies which exist in writing upon the east; Those who are behind this Hidden Image in this Circle wherein he liveth have their nourishment from the words of this god in their own Tuat.

Figure 10.1

Similarly, biologists commonly use the metaphor of words to refer to the process in which the DNA instructions are translated from the language of nucleic acid into the language of protein, that is, from nucleotides to amino acids. In the cell is a translation engine that converts the nucleotide "words" into amino acids "words." Likewise, genetic engineers clone books for genomic libraries. When the Deceased states, "I shall live forever, I am he who dispatches the word of the gods to Re, I have come that I may report a message to its recipient" (CT1176), the Deceased is reporting the message, his DNA or genetic heritage to the Sun-god Re, who together with the Deceased may represent the initiation of transcription by the enzyme RNA polymerase, the most pervasive form of gene regulation from bacteria to higher eukaryotes. Decoded:

Copying words = DNA transcription into messenger RNA

DNA-directed RNA Polymerase

IS 49-50: Deceased Sun-god is Thoth in authority; Thoth and Book splits open mouth; Thoth cuts off head of Seth and followers
IS 51-52: Thoth gleams with Eye of Horus, crosses sky with the Deceased and Re, and reassembles Deceased

DNA-directed RNA polymerase (RNAP) synthesizes RNA. It is an enzyme that is evolutionally conserved across all domains of life in terms of function, structure and sequence (Cramer 2002). This core enzyme in bacteria synthesizes RNA from a DNA template. It has four polypeptide subunits, but it cannot initiate transcription by itself because the core enzyme does not recognize promoters (Mulligan 2002). Another protein, the *sigma* subunit, binds to it to form the holoenzyme. The *sigma* subunit tells RNAP where in the genomic DNA to start transcription by recognizing a section of the gene's DNA called the promoter region. It then melts the DNA to expose one of the double helical strands the RNAP will use as the template to synthesize RNA. (EurekAlert 2002) As mentioned, phage Lambda takes over the replication machinery of the host cell, and geneticists theorize that replication for phage Lambda begins with recombination, which the Egyptian evidence supports. Thus, it seems logical to propose that the god Thoth represents this activity of copying words, that is, transcription and replication within the host cell.

Thoth was the divine messenger and the Greeks associated him with Hermes Trismegistos. In the first dynasty (c. 3050-2850), he is associated with a dog-headed baboon, while in later periods, he is in ibis form, carrying a pen and palette of the scribe. Thoth is the lord of the sacred and the reenactment of divine speech. (Doxey 2002) He is also responsible for beheading Seth and his followers, suggesting the power of his DNA transcription over that of Seth's Eye, which produces the human species. Thoth is also present with the Deceased Sun-god, crossing the sky, performing the duties of a scribe, that is, transcription and replication in the earth host cell. Once again, the texts claim the Deceased Sun-god is Thoth because of nonlocality, a quantum phenomenon where the motion of atoms simultaneously affects and relies on the motion of neighboring atoms. However, for ease of understanding, we will treat Thoth as a separate unit and assign him the status of DNA-directed RNA polymerase. Decoded:

Thoth = DNA-directed RNAP

Stalled Replication

IS 62: Re and crew stopped by serpent on mountain. Deceased Sun-god stops the stopping of eldest god.

The Deceased prepares a path for Re when he comes to a halt (CT1174), that is, he helps the Sun-god start again after stopping. In the quantum world, UV or ultraviolet damage of DNA can produce thymine dimers, which block replication and transcription. In other words, the RNA polymerase idles at the site. A gap is left opposite the thymine dimer, which would be lethal because in the next round of replication it would generate a double strand break. (Sinclair 2003) A thymine dimer forms when UV damage causes an extra chemical bond between adjacent thymines (TT). The dimer forms a kink or biochemical bump in the double helix that results in mismatched bases.

Yet, there are polymerases that can overcome this obstacle. Biologists discovered the new *zeta* polymerase, the sixth eukaryote DNA polymerase to be described that replicates past a thymine dimer, enabling a cell to replicate its DNA even though UV-induced thymine dimers were not repaired. (Nelson 1996) In addition, a LexA-regulated DNA polymerase is expressed during an SOS response and is required for Lac+ adaptive mutation (Rosenberg 2001). Polymerase IV has been assigned a biological role in adaptive mutation. Stress leading to double-stranded breaks (DSB) promotes SOS induction, which upregulates polymerase IV. DSBs are repaired by recombination, which promotes replication and polymerase errors. Mutations form near sites of DSBs. It is theorized that Poly IV may make the errors that become adaptive mutations. (509) The SOS response is induced in response to DNA damage or to the inhibition of DNA replication, which the Pharaohs may be indicating by the idea that Re is stopped by the serpent or comes to a halt. So, Thoth with his famous capacity for writing and wisdom may also represent the activity of a polymerase that enables transcription or the Word of the Sun-god to proceed past a UV-induced thymine dimer. As mentioned, the Deceased King who crosses the sky with Thoth and Re (IS52) also becomes the polymerase that replicates past the damaged site. But, if this is the scenario referenced by the funerary texts, then what is the Egyptian metasymbol for the thymine dimer?

The Double Thymine Lion

IS 61: Beware of the Double Lion

For DNA, maximum absorption of UV radiation occurs at 260 nm. UV damage creates a distortion or biochemical bump, formed by an extra chemical bond between adjacent thymines. On the macrocosmic scale, we can compare this to the kinetic interchange or "kink" instability of magnetic reconnection that may be caused by UV irradiation at the cusp. On the microcosmic level, a thymine dimer also forms a "kink" in the double helix, affecting replication and transcription. Unless it is a polymerase that replicates past DNA damage, RNA or DNA polymerase cannot replicate past a thymine dimer unless it is repaired. Direct repair and excision repair systems are short-term responses. However, if there is extensive DNA damage, two long-term systems evolved for gap repair: recombination and SOS repair. The idea that replication for phage Lambda and *E. coli* begins through recombination has been proposed by modern geneticists, and break-repair-induced replication is a way broken or stalled replications are repaired and restarted. (Rosenberg 2001)

In the interests of learning more about the Egyptian sign system, we could say that the Deceased Sun-god/Thoth is representative of the polymerase halting at the site of DNA damage, a thymine dimer. It may be possible that the text is referencing this when it states that a serpent "will turn his eye against Re, and a stoppage will occur in the crew and a great astonishment in the voyage, and Seth will bend him with his hand" (CT160). The Deceased states, "I prepare a path for Re when he comes to a halt" (CT1174).

Pursuing this idea, let's say that the thymine (pyrimidine) dimer is represented by the Double Lion, each lion representing a thymine (TT). In Hour Five of the Amduat, the Deceased actually proceeds past the Double Lion in agreement with the nonlocal Deceased's claim that he is in Rosetjau (CT241), and he is Thoth "who healed the Sacred Eye in the House of the Double Lion"

(CT242). This is further supported by the Deceased's statement that the Eye of Horus is complete (CT249), along with the statement that the Deceased "is complete, and the Double Lion becomes faint" (CT250), or "the Lion who went out with a bow" (BD132). The texts state "the Mansion of the Double Lion is on the north of the House of the Morning at the House of *Dwn-rnwy* . . . on that night of stopping movements" (CT383), along with "Shu the Lion[4] (Var. 'the Double Lion') will not grasp me" (CT510). The Deceased Sun-god is very aware of the "secret paths of the Double Lion on which the gods fear to enter" (CT1003).

Further, "As for him who passes on the path, his foes will be felled and Apep [Apopis] will be driven off" (CT1053). This "path is prepared for Re when he comes to a halt" (CT1063). In other words, the thymine dimer or Double Lion can bring a polymerase to a halt, but not the Deceased Sun-god, who may represent DNA polymerase IV upregulated by the cell's SOS response to circumvent a thymine dimer. The Deceased then makes his path through the "Valley, a great one who made a bright path for myself, and I will be allowed to pass" (CT1086).

Because UV damage from the Sun is common on earth, the SOS response has evolved for gap repair. In SOS repair, a single-stranded gap along with the presence of DNA degradation products induces this system, which can replicate opposite thymine dimers. Error-prone or mutagenic replication is a dying cell's SOS to replicate past a region where the wild-type sequence has been lost. (Roberts 2003)

11

SOS Repair

WHY THE MONSTER SERPENT CANNOT SHIPWRECK THE SUN-GOD AND HIS CREW

Damage to DNA produces single-stranded gaps, but cells have options when cell death is signaled. With extensive UV damage, the cell's last chance to live is survival by the SOS response, which allows a replication fork (site where DNA is currently being synthesized) to proceed past damage. Thus, the cell does not die because replication is not blocked. The drawback to this process is that this eleventh-hour attempt to save the cell is highly mutagenic. Missing sequences cause unreliable templates, what has been referred to as the sinking ship motif (Budd 2003), increasing the possibility of mutations. In line with this idea, it may be that the "Boat which capsizeth" (AMD HR.3) signifies this sinking ship motif, whereas the Sun-bark captained by the Deceased proceeds, depicting the reliable template.

Regulating Adaptive Mutation

IS 7: Deceased King is magician, a saviour

Induction of the SOS response de-represses at least 42 genes that function in DNA repair, recombination, mutation, translesion DNA synthesis and prevention of cell divisions (Rosenberg 2001). These genes are usually depressed by the transcriptional repressor LexA. The inducing signal that de-represses these 42 genes is single-stranded DNA, which binds to RecA protein, activating a co-protease activity. Our model supports that the mobile elements of the Deceased insert into an incoming Lambda genome, which invades the host cell.

During the transcription journey through the cell, the serpent Mehen surrounds the Deceased Sun-god, just as RecA forms a helical filament around ssDNA.

RecA protein is a well-conserved, multifunctional enzyme with two roles. It not only mediates strand exchange during recombination, but it can also act as a protease destroying the LexA repressor protein during an SOS response. In its first role, it catalyzes DNA strand exchange for recombinational repair and homologous genetic recombination. A major domain binds ADP and probably single- and double-stranded DNA. The RecA protein also has two smaller domains, stabilizing a six-helical polymer of protein subunits and interhelical bundles, which is believed to be the active biological form. (Story 1992) A critical enzyme in the process of homologous recombination, RecA catalyzes the pairing of ssDNA with complementary regions of dsDNA. RecA forms a helical filament around ssDNA, extends the ssDNA, binding to dsDNA, which partially unwinds to allow base pairing between the ssDNA and dsDNA. The dsDNA further unwinds to allow the RecA-driven branch migration. Along with this role, the ssDNA-RecA filament cleaves the LexA regulon, de-repressing 42 genes. DNA repair then begins.

Now, let's explore this second role of cleaving or inactivating the LexA repressor protein. Positing that the monster serpent Apopis is the LexA repressor protein, when the recombinant DNA (the Deceased and Lambda Sun-god) enters the bacterial cell, this penetration along with UV DNA damage signals the SOS response. The ssDNA/RecA filament in a co-protease activity then cleaves the LexA repressor, which catalyzes its own digestion. This results in the de-repression of 42 genes and the destruction of the dragon, so to speak. So we could say that the Deceased restores the whole Eye of Horus, viz., cro protein production in the genome for the lytic pathway and excision of the prophage.

Apopis as LexA Repressor Protein

The LexA repressor (Apopis) controls repair genes *recA*, *recN*, and *ruvAB*, excision repair genes *uvrAB* and *uvrD*, the error-prone DNA polymerase (pol) genes *dinB* (encoding pol IV) and *umuDC* (encoding pol V). Researchers admit that LexA has many functions that they still do not understand. However, when RecA protein binds to ssDNA due to the processing of DNA damage or stalled replication (thymine dimer formation), the SOS signal transduction pathway results. The ssDNA is a signal that activates the otherwise dormant co-protease activity of RecA, causing RecA to facilitate the proteolytic self-cleavage of the LexA repressor (Apopis).

In order to better understand SOS activity, let's go back in time to 3000 BCE when Thuban in the constellation of Draco (the Dragon) was the polestar. When the texts advise the Deceased to go to the polar cusp guided by the polestar, it may be that the Pharaohs understood that the genetic result of this movement to Draco would be the slaying of the dragon Draco or Apopis. For, cleavage of the LexA repressor protein (the monster Apopis) occurs when the DNA of the Deceased merges into the Lambda Sun-god, enters the host cell and activates the SOS response. This causes the RecA filament to bind to a thymine dimer site on the DNA, activating a co-protease activity that cleaves the LexA repressor, de-repressing the SOS regulon. (Brunel University 1998) From a mythic perspective, the Deceased slays the dragon and wins eternity. Actually, the dragon or LexA repressor (Apopis) catalyzes its own digestion in the face of the ssDNA-RecA filament.

With the self-cleavage of the LexA repressor protein, 42 genes are de-repressed and active. It is interesting that activated RecA also facilitates the cleavage of phage repressors (Lambda cI repressor) maintaining the lysogenic state and *umuD*, creating *umuD'*, the subunit of *umuD'C* (pol V), allowing activity in trans-lesion error-prone DNA synthesis. McKenzie et al. (2000) state, "LexA repressed pol V participates in most UV mutagenesis by inserting bases across from pyrimidine dimers. Pol IV is required for an indirect mutation phenomenon in which undamaged Lambda DNA is mutated when added to UV-irradiated (SOS-induced) cells." Actually, the correlative evidence for this process and for the view that Apopis is the LexA repressor protein is found primarily in the Pyramid Texts, the least corrupted evidence.

The Deceased Cleaves Apopis

IS 28-29: Re sees 4-coiled Monster snake Apopis; appeal to Thoth for protection against Monster
IS 30: Monster serpent poisons itself
IS 31-32: Monster serpent goes into hole because 2 knots of Elephantine were for Horus
IS 33: Horus tramples snake in sky/centipede on earth
IS 34: White Crown (Horus) goes on after absorbing Apopis

When UV damage occurs, RecA protein becomes its second form, which is a protease, activating the self-destruction of the protein LexA. With the destruction of the LexA repressor protein, the operons are expressed or de-repressed. Some of the de-repressed proteins induce the SOS response.

The texts report that what comes out of Apopis' mouth "is turned back against yourself" (PT241). In other words, Apopis as the LexA repressor protein catalyzes its own digestion. Further, Apopis is described as "Snake in the sky! O Centipede on earth!" (PT378), suggesting that the result of Apopis' activity of repressing 42 genes results in many feet (centipede) on earth.

The Pyramid Texts state that Apopis is a four-coiled monster, which describes the actual structure of the LexA repressor as determined by 1H NMR spectroscopy. The structure contains three regular alpha-helices and one antiparallel beta sheet. (Fogh et al. 1994) Exhibiting a zigzag, coil-like shape, an antiparallel beta sheet could easily be described as a coil. Nonetheless, the four-unit structure of the LexA repressor protein is similar to the textual reference of a four-coiled monster. Still, if Apopis can be decoded as the LexA repressor protein, we must consider why the monster Apopis retreats into his hole when he sees the two knots of Elephantine meant for Horus (IS31, 32).

The Lambda Lifestyle of Lysis

IS 30: Monster snake turns around because Seth is beheaded
IS 31-32: Serpent goes into hole for 2 knots of Elephantine were for Horus

Phage Lambda is a genetic control system involved in the action of repressor proteins regulating lysogeny versus lytic replication. As explained, RecA also facilitates the cleavage of phage repressors maintaining the lysogenic state. The Lambda repressor, which binds the operator sequences and prevents transcription, is the cI (c-one) protein. With the production of cI and the help of cII and cIII, lysogeny is established with the phage genome integrating into the host chromosome, where it remains dormant. By binding to the DNA operator sites OL (Operator-left) and OR (Operator-right), transcription of N and cro proteins are prevented. N protein, a positive transcription regulator, promotes RNA polymerase transcription of phage genes that activate DNA recombination and integration of the prophage. (Gonzalez 1997) So we can see that there is a battle between cI protein and cro protein over control of the two operator sequences, which determine whether the pathway will be lysogenic or lytic.

Both proteins bind to the OR operator, but they bind differently. The operator site OR is actually three operators (OR1, OR2, OR3), and cI binds to OR1 and OR2 (the right-hand end) in a preferential order, that is, 1 then 2 then 3. Cro binds in the inverse manner, 3 then 2 then 1. If cI gets to the OR1 first, it captures the entire operator, stopping cro and stimulating its own synthesis. In addition, cI prefers right-arm binding, whereas cro prefers left-arm binding. So when cro preferentially binds to the left-arm side first beating out cI, the protein stops cI transcription and initiates its own transcription in a positive feedback loop (Gonzalez 1997) that reminds one of the Egyptian image of Osiris bent backward into a circle, a sign of rolling circle replication. Still, the question arises—how does cro ever win this battle for the two operator sites and restore the *Rightful Order* (*Maat*) on the genome?

If the cell DNA is badly damaged by UV radiation, the SOS response is triggered, which activates the host cell protein RecA. This enzyme destroys the Lambda repressor cI and cro wins. The phage, induced by UV, then goes into the lytic pathway, producing progeny by means of rolling circle replication. Also, if the nutritional state of the cell is poor, that is, low glucose, then the lytic pathway is favored over the lysogenic. (Hewlett 2000)

Once again, the idea that replication begins through recombination has been proposed for phage Lambda (Skalka 1974). So the function of RecA protein in recombination and co-protease activity is important to the Lambda lytic lifestyle, cro production, and the excision of the prophage or the resurrection of Osiris. Decoded:

Apopis = LexA repressor protein

OL and OR = 2 knots of Elephantine for Horus; 2 pillars in Mansion of Six

Duelo a Garrotazos

IS 66: Cut off heads of Seth's followers; night of battle dividing the Eye
IS 68: Eye of Horus will not fall to Seth's rage
IS 69: Horus brings Osiris what Seth snatched
IS 70-71: Deceased rules Mounds of Seth and Horus; Horus conquers Seth
IS 72: Arms of Horus and Seth united; Eye of Horus is whole
IS 74: Deceased's right hand supports sky and left hand supports earth
IS 75: Seth is beheaded
IS 76: Deceased takes Seth's Eye; Horus heals left Eye; Eye of Horus is whole
IS 77: Re crowns Deceased King as Horus and sets his two divine Eyes

As mentioned, it seems possible that the Pharaohs were explaining the operation of Lambda lifestyles with narrative metasymbols relating to three events:

1) the battle between Seth and Horus in the Island of Fire as the competition between protein production of cI and cro;

2) the theft of fire or Seth *snatching* the Eye, signifying cI snatching the OR1 first, capturing the entire operator, stopping cro and stimulating its own synthesis;

3) the ascendancy of either the left arm of Seth or the right arm of Horus, that is, lysogeny versus the lytic cycle.

In relation to these ideas, we can begin to understand additional signs. The Mansion of the Six corresponds to the three left and three right operator sequences (OL and OR). This "battle-ground of the gods" is also the "Island of Fire" or the Lambda genome. Although Seth was the "Eye-breaker" and a "robber" when he was in possession of the left Eye, the reversion of the Eye to Horus results in Seth warring "against the Double Lion," the thymine dimer or the DNA damage caused by UV irradiation that results in the SOS response and excision of the prophage. The Deceased Sun-god's penetration into the host cell activates break-repair-induced replication, while ssDNA activates DNA repair and RecA protein. RecA cleaves the LexA repressor protein or Apopis, allowing de-repression of the LexA regulon of 42 genes. The injured Eye is now whole with the operator sequences in the possession of Horus or cro protein production.

Further, the idea of the Deceased never being "inert" (CT235), of the Deceased veiling "the limpness of the Inert One" and of covering up "what I found missing" (CT237) suggests conquest over the inertness or inactivity of genes repressed by cI on the left-hand side, including those of the Lambda prophage or Osiris. As Thoth (RNA polymerase) with his 42 Books, representative of the 42 de-repressed genes, the Deceased heals "the Sacred Eye in the House of the Double Lion" (CT242).

In the xcivth Chapter of the Book of the Dead, the Deceased states, "I am supplied with the books of Thoth, and I have brought them to enable me to pass through the god Aker, who dwelleth in Set." (Budge v1 1904, 411) Aker is representative of the Double Lion. The Deceased then references that he has "copied what is right and true," a reference to DNA transcription. Budge notes that Thoth represents the left eye of Re, or the winter half of the year, and the "Black Eye of Horus" in the Pyramid Texts. Of the rising King Unas it is said, "Thou hast seized the two Eyes of Horus, the White Eye and the Black Eye, and thou hast carried them off and set them in front of thee and they give light to thy face" (413). The Deceased Sun-god is "over the Mansion of the Six" or the whole Eye of Horus. Thoth copies what is right and true, as the polymerase enabling transcription of the Word or DNA instructions of the recombinant Sun-god, viz., the mobile elements of the Deceased inserted into the incoming Lambda genome.

Another name for the Mansion of the Six is the Two Conclaves. Conclave is from the Latin representing "*(camera) cum clave*" meaning "(room) with key." For example, Roman Catholic cardinals meet in a private room to elect the Pope. Relative to the rivalry of Seth and Horus, "conclave" refers to the secret place where the kingship of Horus or Seth is determined, that is, cro versus cI production, the recombinant lineage versus the human lineage, the White Eye versus the Black Eye. The Coffin Texts reinforce this idea of triumph over Seth and the enthronement of Horus (CT312), suggesting Horus is on the throne of DNA. Thoth states to Horus that he gives "you vindication in the Two Conclaves and joy in the Two Enneads" (CT313, 315). From a genetic viewpoint, this is true because Thoth is associated with the de-repression of 42 genes and the activation of RecA that cleaves cI (Seth) allowing the kingship of Horus (cro) and transcription of the recombinant species. Thoth is in charge of what is carried out for the Deceased (CT317), that is, recombinant transcription and replication. Decoded:

Seth = cI protein (lysogeny)
Horus = cro protein (lysis)

Mansion of Six, Island of Fire, Battleground of Gods, Two Conclaves =
3 left and 3 right operator sequences of Lambda genome (O-left arm and O-right arm)

The Third Seat on the Eye

IS 90: Deceased sits on the Eye as the 3rd

When the cell is damaged by UV radiation, the SOS response activates RecA protein and the enzyme destroys cI. This allows cro to beat cI to the binding. Cro would then bind the right-hand end of the Lambda genome in the inverse manner, 3 then 2 then 1. CT 249 states the Eye of Horus is complete; CT 279 states, "You eat the cucumbers of the two mysterious mansions." CT 1181 states, "I am he who sits on the Eye of Horus as the third . . . My protection from you is the protection of Thoth." CT 1071 states, "I am sitting on the Eye of Horus as the first of the three." CT 277 states, "I have sat down with the Eye of Horus at the head of the Three who give orders among the gods in the affairs of Thoth." Thus, the Deceased as cro sits on the third operator site (OR or 3 then 2 then 1 binding for cro), beating cI to the binding because of RecA destruction of cI.

The 42 Books of Thoth

Thoth's 42 books of knowledge signify the de-repression of the 42 genes of the LexA regulon, along with the activation of RecA that cleaves cI. Also of interest, Clemens Alexandrines (Stromata, vi.) notes that the "Books of Thoth" were 42 in number, divided into six classes (Budge v1 1904, 414). These books enabled the Dead King "to pass through the god Aker" (411), a reference to the Double Lion or thymine dimer. In Hour One of the Amduat, 42 gods line the upper register and 42 deities line the lower register of the path, a possible representation of the 42 de-repressed genes of the incoming recombinant Sun-god (in the upper register) and the 42 repressed genes of the resident prophage Osiris (lower register).

In Chapter 125 of the Theban Recension the Deceased states, "I know the names of the forty-two gods of those who are with you in this Hall of Justice, who live on those who cherish evil and who gulp down their blood on that day of the reckoning of characters in the presence of Wennefer." Thoth as the RNA polymerase is also linked to the representation of the 42 de-repressed genes that create the divine Horus child, the new species the Deceased becomes. More proof for this idea can be found in the full version of CT 335, which states the Deceased restores the Sacred Eye, and Thoth raises the hair from the "right Eye of Re." Decoded:

42 Books of Thoth = 42 de-repressed genes by SOS Response

The Falcon Hieroglyph

In the early creation account, the rivalry between Seth and Horus resulted in Seth wounding the face of Horus, who lost the light of his right eye. Horus' right eye was the Sun and his left eye was the moon. The falcon hieroglyph designates the name of Horus, which transliterated fully is *Hnw* meaning "the distant one." However, the etymology of *Hnw* is also connected to *hry* meaning "one who is above/over," which we might take to mean Horus above/over Seth. The name also occurs in many compounds such as *Hr-sm3-t3wy* meaning "Horus Uniter of the Two Lands" (Meltzer 2002, 164-165), which we might take to mean the left land or arm (Seth) and right land or arm (Horus) of the Lambda genome, the genetic control system regulating lysogeny versus lytic replication. After all, land implies the ground from which life grows, and in this case, the texts indicate humans grew from Seth's eye, genome, cell or land. Seth is the god who killed Osiris, that is, allowed lysogeny or the prophage state of

Osiris, bringing death into the world. Seth like Horus is distant or a "god apart." When the Egyptians adopted Seth as a local god, they referred to him as "Seth-gives-salvation" and "Seth-causes-to-live" (Velde 2002, 333-34). When Seth is reconciled with Horus, he does give salvation, for the Deceased's transformation results from the function of Horus' whole eye, that is, both lands, both arms of the Lambda genome under the control of cro (Horus), since both operator sequences or the two knots of Elephantine (OR and OL) were meant for Horus.

12

The Deceased Judges the Rivals

WAS THE LAST JUDGMENT JUST A DETERMINATION OF PROTEIN LEVELS?

IS 58: Deceased judges Rivals, Combatants, Contestants

The Deceased is he "who judged the Rivals," removing "the humiliation from upon Osiris" (CT1184). In Part One we reviewed the Egyptian terms for the Opening of the Mouth ritual, which are *wpt-r* and *wn-r*, both which translate to "opening of the mouth." The verb *wpi* connotes an opening that entails splitting, dividing, or separating, and can indicate the separation of two combatants or a determination of truth. So we can now say that the separation of Horus from Seth, that is, the resolution of their argument, results in a determination of truth or judgment causing the "Opening of the Mouth" or birth of the Horus species by means of the lytic pathway.

The Deceased Sun-god gives judgment in the Mansion of the Six (CT75), which easily equates to the six operator sites (OL with three and OR with three) of Lambda. He addresses the blind head of the Six (left three operator sites), saying that it will share proportionately in his exaltation (CT132), that is, the full lytic function of the six operator sites. By building up the injured eye (CT154), the Deceased Sun-god opens and restores the blind eye or head of the Six, claiming he is Thoth who healed the Eye in the House of the Double Lion (CT242) or opened the mysterious Eye behind the Double Lion (CT1000) or thymine dimer (TT). In other words, the "two knots of Elephantine which are in the mouth of Osiris, which were knotted for Horus on the spine" (PT230) represent the OL and OR sequences that are governed by two Lambda promoters (Promoter-left and Promoter-right). Promoters are regions with a specific base sequence to which RNA polymerase will bind (Nicholl 2002, 110). These two promoters are now functional for the lytic pathway due to the SOS response activated by DNA damage, the Lambda Sun-god's cell entry, UV irradiation, the cleaving of LexA protein (Apopis) by Rec A, and the de-repression of 42 genes of the LexA regulon. The "spine" is representative of the backbone of DNA (Osiris or Lambda genome on host chromosome) under the influence of cro protein production (Horus).

The Deceased Restores the Eye

IS 59: Deceased King unites Two Lands and reduces them to order
IS 60: Conclaves of upper and lower Egypt bow to King

The Deceased purifies himself before the Two Conclaves (CT84). He talks of the new state he has attained in his mansion and that he has come to Osiris, "smitten Seth," and "slain his confederacy" (CT303). The Deceased states that the "two braided locks" and the "Mansion of the Cord" belong to him (CT310), both references to DNA. As the texts advise (CT856, 858), he has taken back the half of the Eye of Horus that Seth snatched. He is now unique, for he has "joined the Two Brothers" (CT318) and "restored the Eye" (CT335). Because the Deceased Sun-god has inactivated the *cI* gene site and "pacified the Two Warriors" (CT1125), along with entering the host cell and activating RecA cleavage of the LexA repressor, he has restored the Eye by subsequent production of cro protein and the lytic cycle for the Horus species.

The Arms of the Lambda Genome

IS 72: References to arms, limbs, foreleg, Eye related to Horus and Seth
IS 74: Left hand of Osiris obeys; King's right hand supports sky and the left hand supports earth

With cro protein production, both arms of the Lambda genome function for the lytic lifestyle. Earlier we established that references to left arm, left hand and arm of the Destroyer related to Seth or the left Eye of Horus, whereas the right arm and right hand referred to Horus and the right Eye. Both of these arms or eyes together form the whole Eye of Horus. Metaphorical references to Seth's foreleg Horus tore off, power over Seth's limb, and rescuing the Eye from Seth indicate the dominance of cro protein production for the Horus lineage. The texts exhort the Deceased: "Stand up for this left eye of the Mansion of the Mace," so that the Deceased will not "be wiped out or obliterated" and will have the "full power of Osiris" (CT69).

Because the Deceased has reduced the Two Lands to order (CT75), he aspires to be with Horus when he greets "the [left] arm of Osiris" (CT314), another reference to the left-hand side of the Lambda genome or the vanquished confederacy of Seth. In the Theban Recension, the Deceased states, "I am one who is hidden from the one whose arms fight" (Ch. 64), and Osiris raises his "right arm when he commissions the great ones whom he sends into the great tribunal which is in the God's Domain" (Ch. 41). The metasymbol of arms also relates to that of hands. Thus, the left hand of Osiris obeys and the entourage of Re is that of both the right and left hands (IS74). Finally, the drawing of the rising King with arms spread horizontally is a common metasymbol in funerary text imagery, signifying the balanced arms of the Lambda genome for the Horus lineage. The Egyptian Ka is signified by two upraised arms, which can now be decoded as the two arms of the Lambda genome working together to allow a human access to the recombinant species. Decoded:

Ka = two arms of Lambda genome and cosmic species

Arms of Weighing of Words

Thoth was the judge of words and presided over the testing of the soul on the arms of the Balance in the Hall of Osiris. The intended meaning of the balance may not have been a judging of actions, but a "weighing of words" (Budge v1 1904, 408), that is, a weighing of DNA, a balancing of the two Lambda arms, a *Rightful Order* decision for cro production and the Horus lineage.

In the Book of the Dead, the heart of Osiris is balanced in one pan of the scales to exactly counterbalance the feather of *Rightful Order* or Law in the other. It is interesting that the only part of the viscera the Egyptians left in the mummy was the heart, the indispensable centre symbolizing eternity. Alchemists considered the heart the image of the Sun within a human (Cirlot 1971, 142). On the other hand, the feather symbolizes the wind and the creator gods Ptah, Hathor and Osiris. Feathers suggest the flight of birds and the element of air. As a hieroglyphic determinative sign, the feather is used in the composition of words indicating emptiness, dryness, lightness, height, and flight. (102-103) The Deceased is described as the "lotus bird on the limitless plain," a falcon, a heron (IS8). So the symbolism suggests that the Deceased's heart or *Sun within* balances equally with the solar wind Horus lineage or *Rightful Order* of the Lambda right arm. For this to happen, both arms of the Lambda genome had to balance or operate fully. This only occurs when the lytic phase begins, and cro controls the *Rightful Order* of the operator sequences, not cI protein. Thus the emphasis on balance and "right" shows the harmony between the brothers, the Two Combatants, and the lytic power restored to the right arm or right operator sequences. After the names of deceased persons in funeral papyri, the epithet *maa kheru* was written, meaning "he whose word is *maa*." In time the meaning became "he whose word is right" (Budge v1 1904, 408-09), once again suggesting the right operators of the Lambda genome. When physiological conditions within the cell allow cro to accumulate so it can bind to OR1, the lytic lifestyle is assured and Osiris is resurrected.

The long version of CT 335 states, "Save me from that god whose shape is hidden and whose eyebrows are the arms of the balance on that day of reckoning with the robbers." Robbers refers to the stealing of the right operator sequences by the gang of Seth, activating the Lambda left arm for cI production and robbing Horus of his birth and development by means of the injury by Seth to the Eye or Lambda genome. This robbery or theft of fire, so to speak, can be considered the theft or capture of energy from the Sun and the trapping of that energy in matter (photosynthesis).

The text then poses the question—who is the god whose eyebrows are the arms of balance? The answer is "He is Horus who presides over Khem. Otherwise said: He is Thoth, it is he who uses his arm." So the left and right arms of the Judgment Balance represent the left and right arms of the Lambda genome, which functions by converting to protein (cro production) the new lineage of Horus through transcription (Thoth). As scholar Edmund Meltzer explains, Seth complements Horus because the pair represent a "bipolar, balanced embodiment of kingship" (2002, 165). Seth and Horus together complete the full function of the Lambda lifestyles, which are lysogeny and lysis. We could say that humans have the potential for full function or two different lifestyles. Human existence is the lysogenic lifestyle, and transfiguration to a longer-living species is the subsequent possibility, if the Deceased is at the protein-enriched polar site for afterlife chemical transduction and gene manipulation via the lytic pathway. Thus, we have the idea of two seeds, the two Enneads of nine, the twin births, which are found in the activity of the Lambda genome.

Decoded: **Two arms of Judgment Balance = two arms of Lambda functioning for the lytic lifestyle**

Seth as Hedgehog Gene

An additional insight into the Judgment Scene is found in the Book of Gates from the Tomb of Ramesses VI. The Fourth Division is followed by the gate of the Fifth Division, and the space between the gateway and door forms the Hall of Osiris. In this Judgment Scene the mummified Osiris, wearing the double crown, sits enthroned at the top of nine steps, and before him is a mummified figure shouldering an equalized balance, with the right balance showing an enclosed content of space greater than the left balance. In other words, the arms of the Lambda genome are balanced with both arms operative, but cro production on the right exceeds cI production on the left scale. Although cro production, which had been repressed by the LexA repressor protein (Apopis) is greater, the genome is still balanced because the full genetic potential of the Lambda genome is realized by the joint activity of both arms for lysis.

Of special interest in this scene, just beyond the steps is a boat sailing away from Osiris with a dog-headed monkey holding a stick over a pig. Piankoff notes that the inscriptions in the Tomb of Ramesses VI have not been deciphered and the text corrupt. Yet, Coffin Text 157 states that Seth transformed himself into a black pig and wounded the Eye. Although the scene from the sarcophagus of Seti I (Budge 1905, 80) is similar, the text is in tact according to Budge. The Sixth Division of the Duat in the Book of Gates shows Osiris, wearing the double crown of North and South seated in a chair of state. On the ninth step before Osiris is a Balance of Judgment. Behind the Balance sailing away in a boat is a dog-headed ape with a stick over a pig called *Am-A*, that is, "eater of the arm." (158-163) The text reads "[When} this god entereth, he riseth and putteth under restraint *Am-A*" (163), suggesting that the ape restrains the "eater of the arm" or that the arm is now rescued from Seth (IS72). This makes the Eye complete and balances the arms of the Lambda genome.

This representation of Seth as a retreating pig from the tombs of Seti I and Ramesses VI suggests the impairment of hedgehog gene function, which is a master developmental gene promoting limb formation in all known vertebrates (Gilbert 2000). Our scientists originally named this gene "hedgehog" because the gene actually looked like one. The Pharaohs, aware of the gene's shape, may have used this same strategy by drawing a pig. So we could decode this sign as the Hedgehog gene.

Seth as pig = Hedgehog Gene

Allowing this gene to function would result in matter or human creation, the weight of which would imbalance the scale. "Eating" or absorbing the arm in this case suggests the binding of the polymerase to the operator sequences, which results in the activation of the hedgehog gene. This terminology for binding has also been used relative to the son "eating" or absorbing the father.

Chemical Bonding and DNA Degradation

IS 100: Eat Eye of Horus; King eats or absorbs Eye; King swallows intelligence of gods; King swallows seven uraei; embrace of father Atum; enclose King in embrace

Protein synthesis is the process of DNA encoding amino acids and proteins. During protein translation, complexes of amino acids linked to tRNA bind to the codons in mRNA and form base pairs. The binding or molecular control of a chemical reaction can be described as absorbing, swallowing, embracing or eating another molecule. When the Deceased King swallows seven uraei, metasymbol for phage Lambda's seven operons, this means that the supramolecular King controls the modes of growth inside the host cell. Likewise, the Field of Offerings suggests the chemical arena where the binding reactions occur.

The idea of the son swallowing the father can now be understood in Pyramid Texts 273 and 274. The text states the sky is overcast, the stars dark, the planets stilled, as the King appears in power. The passage states the King "lives on his fathers and feeds on his mothers." The King is mightier than his father Atum; he "eats men and lives on the gods." Also, these texts portray the King as gulping down spirits, eating their magic, for the King is the oldest god. He receives his power, his warrant from Orion, father of the gods, an emphasis on the source of his elements. Thus, the King absorbs the power of his father in an act of consumption or eating, that is, chemical bonding. Similarly, when merging with the Sun-god, the Deceased claims, "I have eaten my father and am alive" (CT248). In this same text, the Deceased states, "I eat the gods, I kill him who I made to live, I bind him whom I loosed." The Pharaohs represented the Deceased chemically bonding and absorbing the power of his father, the Sun-god, as an act of consumption or eating.

Likewise, the ancient mythological motif of Sacred Kingship, or the young King replacing the Old King, also points to this process of absorption in the bonding of RNA polymerase (son or copy of DNA template) to the DNA molecule (father). The Deceased is the Sacred King, for he has died to the human part of him (old DNA template) due to some debility (death), and now his power passes to his successor (the newly risen King or new DNA template).

DNA degradation is an analogous process to absorption, consumption, or eating. The cell must control protein levels, so it reduces the steady state level of a particular protein by proteolytic degradation, the breaking down of DNA into smaller fragments by chemical or physical means. A cell undergoing an SOS response reacts by an increasing rate of proteolysis to salvage amino acids from non-essential proteins. Along with this, regulation of Integrase and excise genes of phage Lambda depends on RNA degradation. (Carnegie Mellon University) The "corruption of Osiris" (PT412; CT1087), also referred to as degradation, references this process of DNA degradation. Decoded:

Eating, absorbing, embracing = chemical bonding
Field of Offerings = nutrient area where binding reactions occur
Corruption or degradation of Osiris = DNA degradation

The Efflux of Osiris

IS 53: Efflux missing from Left Eye due to full power of Osiris; Osiris cut up has no efflux, but risen Osiris has efflux or flood; Dead King has water, flood from Two Enneads (Eyes); Deceased receives Seth's water; Dead King is fresh water, flood from Osiris; Dead King has efflux and is not inert.

From the Idea Strands, it is obvious that Osiris risen or the Lambda prophage excised has efflux, water and flood from the whole Eye of Horus (Left Eye of Seth and Right Eye of Horus) and is not inert, whereas Seth no longer has water or efflux. Bacteria protect themselves from toxic agents leaking through the cell membrane by transporting molecules back to the extracellular space in a process known as efflux. Efflux pumps for this purpose are made of proteins and located in the cell membrane to transport molecules out of the cell. In the case of rising Osiris or the excising Lambda prophage, the flood of water, efflux, or outflow indicates the release or the transportation of phage progeny out of the cell into extracellular space.

Thus, the following metasymbols referring to the Deceased, who is Osiris and Horus, suggest the process of cfflux: flood in Dead King's lap; cool water and great flood issuing from Dead King; flood from Two Enneads (Eye of Seth and Eye of Horus); efflux of Osiris. It is interesting that Seth's Great Flood is enclosed (CT997) and missing from the left eye (CT69), suggesting that the efflux of Seth generating the human creation does not occur due to the full operation of both Lambda arms, activating the lytic pathway.

Decoded: **Flood, water, inundation = process of efflux in bacterial cell**

Objective 7 completed: The Deceased Sun-god restores the Eye of Horus by activating the lytic lifestyle in the host cell and restoring the Rightful Order of the operator sequences on the Lambda genome for cro protein production. All interrelated matrices are still coherent and unified.

13

The Seat of Isis as the *LacZ* Gene

WHY THE BULL GODDESS BONDS TO THE SERPENT

IS 44: Isis gives Dead King his heart in middle of earth and fashions him
IS 45: Dead King receives milk of Isis, the Lady of Provisions
IS 46: Dead King takes Eye of Horus or two bowls of sacred milk; Milky Way references
IS 47: Isis accompanies Dead King in Sun-bark; Isis conceives King and reassembles Osiris
IS 48: Cream reconciles Horus and Seth and purifies Dead King

Objective 8: What evidence is there for the idea that the metasymbol Isis represents lactose metabolism?

Numerous references to Isis providing milk for the Dead King, suckling the White Bull, the Milky Way references, and the sweet and white Eye of Horus references (IS46) provide evidence for the idea that Isis represents the lactose nutrient medium. These references point to the operating ancient glycolysis pathway in cells that have pathways for both lactose and glucose energy metabolism.

Glycolysis evolved billions of years ago when there was hardly any molecular oxygen in our atmosphere. Both anaerobic fermentation and aerobic respiration start with the ancient glycolysis pathway, which runs whether oxygen is present or not. In aerobic respiration, all steps after glycolysis, such as the Kreb's cycle to make ATP, occur in the mitochondria. The starting point for glycolysis is normally glucose. In anaerobic conditions, the end product depends on the organism. For example, in some microorganisms (e.g. brewers yeast), the end product is ethanol and carbon dioxide, but in higher organisms, the end product is lactate. (Maber 1999)

Lactose is the predominant sugar in milk. The Pyramid and Coffin Texts point to this idea in the countless Egyptian references to the Milky Way and the mother goddess Isis. The Deceased claims that he is Horus, the offspring of Osiris and is born of Isis (CT313). He states he is "the White Bull whom the milk-goddess suckled" (CT175), and is "at nurse" (CT204). Perhaps the most convincing connection to lactose metabolism is that Isis is "the Lady of Provisions" (CT246). Thus we have the claim in "The Legend of Ra and Isis" (Budge v1 1904, 372) that Isis was a woman skilled in words of power (385), who enabled the dead to live (380), including Osiris.

In addition, the texts state Horus becomes "ruler over Egypt . . . by means of the Sole Eye, the Mistress of the Enneads, the Lady of All" (CT312). This idea that the Eye or genome of the glorious lineage of Horus is whole by means of Isis is found often (CT316), suggesting the Eye is nurtured by lactose metabolism. The Eye of Seth and the human creation thrives with glucose production, not lactose. Horus, of course, is the son of Osiris, who is born of Isis (CT313) or nurtured by lactose metabolism. This brings us full circle because the nonlocal Deceased is "one who was conceived and born as Horus the heir" (CT286). Additional references to lactose include that the Deceased will not travel around because "your arm is that of Horus, your arm is that of the Great One, while the Sacred Eye, the Lady of provisions is powerful" (CT246). So it is that cream or *zmn* (PT34) or *smyn* (CT354) reconciles Horus and Seth by providing the lactose medium for the complete Eye of Horus.

Numerous textual references also emphasize the importance of cultivating or brewing barley. The sugar maltose is used in the brewing of barley. Maltose, of course, points to the maltose transport system or phage Lambda receptor site (LamB porin). The Deceased receives the milk of Isis, which translates to accessing the lactose pathway through the maltose transport system, where a low-affinity path exists that does not allow MBP to bind the substrate lactose. (Merino and Shuman 1997) Decoded:

Barley cultivation = maltose transport path for lactose energy metabolism

The Eye of Isis

IS 42: Isis is Sole Eye, the Sacred Eye

To the Egyptians, Isis represented the Magna Mater, the great creative power nurturing all living things. Nephthys was her twin form and the consort of Seth. Isis' crown consists of a pair of horns between which is a lunar disk, sometimes surmounted by the throne symbol. Recall that the Lambda prophage lodges in the host *E. coli* chromosome at the site of the *LacZ* or *b-galactosidase* gene. With the prophage inserted here, the *LacZ* operon may be inactivated, resulting in a nonfunctional galactosidase. (Nicholl 2002, 135) With the excision or removal of the prophage, this gene for lactose metabolism is vacated, leaving an empty seat, or so to speak, an empty throne. Thus, we have a possible correlation between Isis' name depicting the empty throne or seat and the potential for lactose metabolism, which is necessary for the birth of the Horus lineage. The text states, "Isis wakes pregnant with the seed of her brother Osiris," saying "His seed is within my womb, I have moulded the shape of the god within the egg" (CT148).

Also, the Eye of Horus is referred to as the Eye of the Great Lady and, as Faulkner has noted (PT639, 264), the Eye of Horus is always feminine, suggesting Isis and lactose production. Recall that the sky goddess Nut, mother of the gods and Isis, is "the Sacred Eye" (CT335). Since Isis is representative of the introduction of lactose into the cell, she is present on the bark with the Sun-god (proton symport), entering the cell to inactivate the lac repressor. The Deceased Sun-god, on the other hand, represents recombinant Lambda DNA entering the cell at a double-strand break, which activates the SOS response, causing the prophage to excise, leaving the gene seat next to *LacZ* empty. Along with this idea, the Two Combatants Horus and Seth are reconciled by cream, that is, the milk sugar lactose. So, with the introduction of lactose into the cell, the texts suggest that both arms of the Lambda genome are nourished by this nutrient sugar.

The Goddess Bond with the Serpent

In the funerary texts, numerous drawings depict goddesses controlling serpents or bonded to serpents. The serpent Apopis represents the coiled LexA repressor protein, enforcing the repression of 42 genes and the activity of the Lambda cI repressor protein that maintains the lysogenic state of the Lambda prophage Osiris. Likewise, the Lac repressor is a coiled molecule suggestive of a serpent. A short review of the operation of the Lac repressor protein in relation to lactose production will explain why the goddess bonds with the serpent.

The *Lac* gene is only active when the cell encounters the sugar lactose in its environment. Lactose as the inducer first interacts with the Lac repressor protein. Sometimes a mutation that inactivates the regulator protein causes *LacZYA* to be continually expressed, but the function of the Lac repressor protein is to prevent expression of the *Lac* genes. When the *Lac* gene is induced by the presence of lactose, a membrane component or permease captures passing molecules of lactose and shoves them inside the cell. The lactose is then snipped in two by the enzyme *beta-galactosidase*, yielding glucose and galactose. Even small amounts of lactose can inactivate the Lac repressor, which binds to the operator, preventing RNA polymerase from transcribing the *lac* operon genes. When lactose is present, it binds to the repressor and changes the repressor's shape, so it cannot bind to the operator. Once the *Lac* gene is de-repressed, permease is made and inserted in the outer surface of the cell, where it increases the influx of lactose. (Jacob and Monod 1961).

Researchers have studied adaptive mutation of the Lac system in stressed or starving cells. Unlike Lac+ mutations in growing cells, the adaptive mutations form during exposure to selective conditions, occurring by means of a unique molecular mechanism that requires homologous recombination proteins like RecA, RecBC, and RuvABC. Researchers report that the SOS system regulates adaptive mutation in the Lac system of *E. coli*. Efficient Lac adaptive mutation requires SOS-induced levels of a LexA-repressed function(s) in addition to RecA. (Mckenzie 2000) So, adaptive mutation in the Lac system occurs with the cleavage of the monster LexA repressor (Apopis) that de-represses the necessary genes.

Horizontal Gene Transfer

If "words" are a reference to the DNA instructions translated from the language of nucleic acid into the language of protein, that is, from nucleotides to amino acids, then the words of Isis may represent an insertion mutagenesis of the *Lac* gene during DNA replication. (Insertion operons are usually polar.) Horizontal gene transfer, the transfer of DNA from one organism to another, would then provide the mechanism by which lactose metabolism is inserted. In bacteria, it is mediated by transformation, phage transduction, or conjugation. Transformation is the uptake of DNA from the extracellular fluid, and transduction is DNA transfer via bacteriophage vectors. The Amduat specifically states that the Deceased "maketh his transformations" (HR.1), reinforcing this idea again by stating "ye are great in your transformations" (HR.6). This idea is also reinforced by the presence of the transformative beetle (HRS.1, 2, 5, 10, 12).

Also, the Sun-god wears the horizontal ram horns through the Duat, which may signify horizontal gene transfer. In line with this signification, Isis occasionally wears a pair of horizontal ram horns under her double crown (Budge v2 1904, 203), suggesting the insertion or horizontal gene transfer of the *Lac* gene. Further, the only goddess on the Sun-bark is the "Lady of the Boat," who wears a white disk and horns on her head (AMD HR.1). This goddess is most likely Isis, one of the Great Ennead, a representation of lactose permease or the gene for lactose metabolism. Lactose permease is an enzyme responsible for transport of lactose from the environment into bacteria, and this may be exactly what is intended by the presence of Isis on the Sun-bark.

The reference to the words of Isis (AMD HR.7) points to the idea of DNA instructions, suggesting that the *Lac* gene is active. The text states, "If these words of power of Isis, and those of Ser be uttered, Apep shall be turned back and shall be shut up in Ament, in the hidden place of the Tuat" (Budge 1905, 141). The Amduat text further states, "behold, Serqet is at the head [Apep], and Her-Tesu-F placeth his deadly fetter about his feet after Isis hath taken possession of the words of power of Ser of two-fold strength, [and Re] giveth their words of power" (143). More support for this view comes from the texts of the Metternich stele that state Isis has knowledge how to use her mouth, so that no evil comes to the child Horus, whose "protection comes from the Boat of Ra" (Budge v2 1904, 211). But what is more interesting is that Isis as lactose is also responsible for the destruction of Apep (Apopis), suggesting that efficient Lac adaptive mutation may occur with SOS-induced levels of a LexA-repressed function in addition to RecA.

Composition of Lactose

The chemical composition of lactose is oxygen, hydrogen and carbon, all elements present in the polar cusp of our planet. The best known solar wind composition is He/H. But heavy elements are also present in the solar wind. The solar wind composition instrument on spacecraft Ulysses (SWICS) takes three measurements: velocity (time-of-flight), energy/charge (electrostatic analyzer) and energy (semiconductor detector). The Ulysses instrument shows good elemental abundance and ionization state distribution data for C, O, Ne, Mg, Si, S, and Fe for both low speed, coronal hole, and transient regimes. (Caltech) Robert Sheldon (2004) observed that H, He, C, O, and Fe are also present at the quadrupole cusp due to the energy of galactic cosmic rays (GCRs) from supernovae. Shock waves from the galactic disk transmit energy to the cusp, compressing it. These energy waves go into the cusp but do not come out.

Recall that our model, the earth bacterial cell, needs Fe or iron, which is abundant, and lactose is formed from HCO, which is also abundant. Olinto et al. (1999) found that ultra-high-energy events originate in our Galaxy and may be due to iron nuclei accelerated from young, strongly magnetic neutron stars. These high-energy events are magnetic traps of energetic particles created by cosmic ray acceleration due to supernovae explosions (Zirakashvili 1999). So the polar area of the earth-cell is enriched with high energy particles and the necessary ingredients for the Horus species, including lactose, for Isis is the Milk-goddess and Lady of the Winds (CT468). At this point, we can be fairly confident that we have decoded the Egyptian idea of Isis.

Isis = lactose energy metabolism
Seat of Isis = *LacZ* gene seat where prophage resides in host
Goddess/Serpent bonds = lactose inactivating Lac repressor
Feminine Eye of Horus = Lambda genome with lactose nutrient
Lady of the Winds = Lactose present at cusp

The Bull and the Goddess

It is worthwhile to review the symbolism of the bull and its connection to Isis. Archaeologist Marija Gimbutus in *The Goddesses and Gods of Old Europe* (1974) excavated numerous figurines dedicated to the Great Goddess, the Vegetation Goddess, the Bird or Snake Goddess, with fewer figurines devoted to the male god of vegetation. Gimbutus found evidence for the Great Goddess being associated with moon crescents and bull horns. She explains that the bull was initially associated with the Goddess, becoming a male symbol through syncretism. To really understand the Egyptian symbolic meaning related to the bull, one must look at the origin of bull worship in Egypt.

The worship of the bull in Egypt can be traced to the first historical king of Egypt. Herodotus (iii. 28) claims that the Egyptians believed lightning descends upon the cow from heaven that bears the Apis bull. We can associate the cow from heaven with the sky-goddess or starry Nut, the Celestial Cow, the Sacred Eye (CT335), remembering that supernovae explosions seed the cosmos with elements for creation. These sacred Apis bulls born of the stars were mummified and buried in a tomb with a chapel above. As the sacred Bull of Memphis, the Apis symbolized the moon, a sign suggesting not only the whiteness of milk, but also the presence of stars. The victorious Deceased's hands are full of the "milk of bulls" (CT695), but not when Osiris is inert or in the prophage state. Along with this, the Egyptians connected the god Apis with Osiris. Frobenius notes that the motif of the solar lion, which tears out the throat of the lunar bull, is repeated interminably in Asiatic and African ornamentation (Cirlot 1971, 190). Thus we can understand the connection between the lunar bull, Apis and the inert Osiris.

In light of this, what the Amduat is advocating is a chemical reaction or excision of the Lambda prophage that would restore the ascendancy of the lunar bull, the *Magna Mater*, the production of lactose metabolism for a celestial species, rather than glucose production for human creation. As we shall explore, the Amduat is a journey into a bacterial cell that exhibits the dynamics of a Kerr black hole while undergoing lysis and protein folding. In this process, Isis represents the ancient lactose metabolism pathway and is on the Sun-bark signifying the entry of lactose into the earth-cell, either by horizontal gene transfer or insertion mutagenesis of the *Lac* gene during DNA replication. Representations of goddesses bonded to serpents depict the removal of the Lac repressor protein from the DNA operator sequences, so RNA polymerase can transcribe the Lac operon's genes, increasing lactose in the cell and empowering the new creation. The presence of ssDNA activates the SOS response, cleaving the LexA repressor protein and activating the LexA regulon, 42 genes for the new lineage with some conducive to Lac adaptive mutation. Osiris rises, that is, the Lambda prophage excises, vacating the *LacZ* gene site. The lunar bull is ascendant and phage progeny are prolific, as the cell takes the lytic pathway. The Deceased Sun-god is transfigured into the Horus species. Thus, the Isis and milk references point to the ancient lactose pathway, the Milky Way the Deceased travels, thanks to Thoth, who represents RNA polymerase or the transcription of DNA into mRNA. Lactose provides the ascendant Bull's nourishment, and the Lion becomes faint.

Plutarch notes that on the upper part of a sistrum is carved the effigy of a cat with a human visage, whereas on the lower part is engraved the face of Isis on one side and the face of Nephthys on the other. Isis represents generation and Nephthys corruption, and Plutarch says that the cat denotes the moon. (Budge v2 1904, 257) This dual presentation of the sisters Isis and Nephthys hinges on the idea that Isis bonding with the serpent, or activating lactose production, generates the Horus species. Nephthys then represents the corruption or degradation of the DNA of the human material form. The white moon is an integral part of the Egyptian funerary texts, for along with representing phage progeny production, it represents lactose metabolism, the necessary nutrient for phage production. Isis is the production of milk, the Milky Way, the Great Mother with the milk of bulls, the *regina coeli* that generates the Divine Child Horus representative of recombinant phage progeny.

A Myth about Re and Isis

Isis preferred gods to men, but really esteemed spirits. She aspired to be mistress of the earth and a goddess as powerful as Re, but Re had grown old and he drooled. When Re slobbered on the ground, Isis took the earth and slobber, kneading it into a poison dart, a sacred serpent which bit Re, seriously poisoning him when he passed. The gods and their children could see Re was doomed, so Isis came with her words of power and the breath of life, asking Re to reveal his name. Re said he was creator of all that was human, but Isis insisted that this was not his real name, and the poison went deeper into Re. Finally consenting that his name should pass into Isis, Re hid himself from the gods and his place in the bark was empty. Re then vowed to give Isis his two Eyes, and the Eye of Horus went forth from Re's mouth and began to shine. (Budge v1 1904, 360-363 taken from Pleyte and Rossi, *Le Papyrus de Turin*)

The words of Isis or genetic instructions of the *Lac* genes destroyed the poison and restored Re to life in the same way that her words of power restored Osiris to life. Put simply, horizontal gene transfer of the *Lac* genes into the cell is one way to provide the lactose medium, resulting in the function of the whole Eye of Horus or the excision of the prophage and the active lytic cycle of phage Lambda.

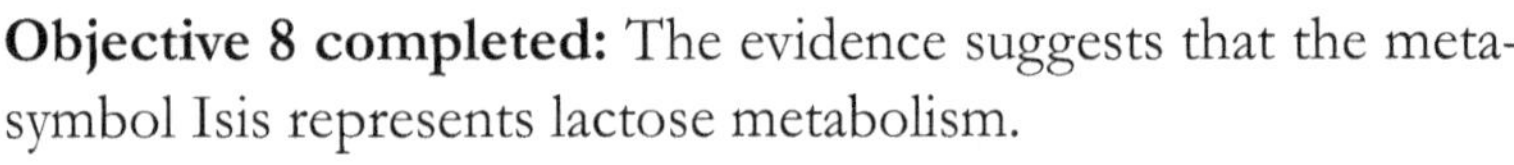

Objective 8 completed: The evidence suggests that the meta-symbol Isis represents lactose metabolism.

Figure 13.1 An empty seat or empty throne is the sign of the name of Isis in Egyptian.

14

Assembling a Family in the Afterlife

HOW A STAR IS BORN IN A PROTEIN FUNNEL MEETS LUCIFERIN AND BECOMES BIOLUMINESCENT

IS 84: King is reassembled, knit together

The Deceased seeks his family in the sky, earth and waters, for he is incomplete (CT141). The texts exhort the Deceased to assemble the family in the realm of the dead (CT143, 144, 146). Gene mutations are quantum processes, and the Amduat suggests that modified proteins are being built in the Egyptian afterlife. Thus we have the Deceased and crew (the DNA polymerase complex), after self-assembly, entering the mouth of the protein channel, navigating a difficult energy landscape easily, while descending deeper into the interior darkness of the protein funnel energy landscape. The Deceased is spatially fit or an "equipped spirit" (CT118, 276) and navigates the depth of the open site in the protein channel. The self-assembling journey described by the Amduat is to a selective binding site, the Lambda genome on the host chromosome, where the prophage resides at the *LacZ* site, which is within the protein structure, that is, its depth is below the surface as distinguished by the progression deeper into the darkness through the hours or circles of the Duat.

In biology, the most frequently used long-range means of transmitting messages is electrolytic, which is the migration or flow of ions down electrical potential gradients. For example, with the depolarization of the cell membrane, the fast messenger calcium enters a channel and the cell cytoplasm. A series of selected proteins recognize calcium for selective binding, which changes the shape of the proteins, generating mechanical signals in cells. Bundles of helices form proteins with conformational mobility, the protein helices moving over one another and *beta*-sheets. (Williams 2000, 281-282) In the analysis of the Amduat in Part Three, we will easily equate the many-headed serpents with the helix structure of specific DNA-binding proteins and the deities lining the passageway with selected proteins that wail or generate mechanical signals in the cell, as the Deceased Sun-god flows down the electrical potential gradients. Of special interest is the actual description of the new King of the Horus lineage. He has a jackal face similar to a nucleosome core, a Celestial Serpent middle similar to bundles of helices, and hinder parts like a Broad Hall suggestive of *beta*-sheets. So we could decode the idea of the Deceased King assembling a family as protein engineering.

Assembling an afterlife family = molecule formation or protein engineering

Proteins become more stable with increasing negative values of the free energy change between folded and unfolded. In other words, the binding energy increases or the entropy difference between the two states decreases, and the folded protein stabilizes. The major stabilizing effect may be the hydrophobic effect or the tendency not to combine with or dissolve in water. (Creighton 1990) Let's explore this process further.

Protein Folding Energy Landscapes

Proteins are complex systems best described by energy landscapes that reflect the energy of the protein as a function of the topological atom arrangement. Flow is examined in terms of folding funnels, docking, and navigating the folding routes. (Onuchic 1997) Words such as "aboard the lotus-bark at the dockyard of the gods" (CT1030) and "navigate on the Winding Waterway" (CT62) are used in the funerary texts to indicate this process and map an ensemble of states. Protein energy values are separated by mountains and ridges. Similarly, the Deceased sees the "mountains of Bakhu upon which the sky rests; it is of crystal" (CT160), and he also splits "open the mountains" (CT275). Bryngelson and Wolynes created a phase diagram for folding transitions, consisting of three distinct regions: unfolded or coiled state, misfolded or glassy state, folded or native state (Mulcahy 1997). Protein folding can be compared to crystallization in that a protein freezes to a unique stable structure. It is interesting that the Deceased Sun-god often refers to himself as the Unique One (IS11).

Proteins fold from a primary structure (linear amino acid chain) to a secondary structure (amino acids arranged in helices or sheets) into tertiary structure (the final shape in which secondary structures assemble to each other). In proteins whose final structure is largely made up of helical segments, the folding funnel landscape is stratified. Proteins undergo a dynamical transition near 200k termed the "glass transition." (Teeter 2001) Funerary text references to crystal may relate to a protein's glass transition or the entire folding process.

The Deceased further states, "I fly and soar between those two great mountains in which Re appears" (CT305). If we were to picture the Duat as an energy landscape, it may look very similar to the cavernous valleys and mountains represented by the energy landscape in Figure 14.1, depicting the reduction of conformational entropy as protein chains fold to their native states (natural shape). The energy landscape theory of protein folding is a statistical description of a protein's potential surface. Leopold et al. (1992) have shown that good folding sequences have a funnel-like landscape, which depicts convergent kinetic pathways for minimally-frustrated heteropolymers.

A heteropolymer is a polymer or substance made up of many repeating chemical units or molecules composed of different subunits. Some multimeric proteins are normally heteropolymers. Other heteropolymers can be made experimentally, using subunits derived from different species as a test of homology. From this, we might infer that the union of the Deceased with the Sun-god and crew has fashioned a functional multimeric protein that exhibits good folding sequences in the funnel-like landscape of the Duat.

Protein folding can also be depicted as a "Great Well" (PT368), or it can simply be described as "O King, take your bright tunic, take your cloak upon you, be clad in the Eye of Horus which is in Weaving-town" (PT414), or "Horus stands up and clothes this King in the woven fabric which went forth from him" (PT690). Another description is "Horus has woven his booth on your behalf, Seth has spread out your awnings. Be covered, my father, by the God's Booth, that you may be conveyed therein to your seats which you desire." Decoded:

Weaving, cloaks, clothes, God's booth, linen = protein translation/folding

Recall that an energy landscape is the potential energy surface defining the position of atoms. This surface has topographical features similar to the earth's landscape, such as mountains, valleys and hollows. However, the dimension is much higher and the energy landscape determines the behavior of the system. (Doye 2003) In Figure 14.1, we can see what appears to be a circular cone of mountains and cavernous valleys, pierced to its center by a hole in the shape of an irregular cone or funnel. But, more accurately, it is a replica of the described Egyptian Duat. So it may be possible that the Pharaohs perceived the potential energy surface that defines the position of atoms or other quantum elements that reflect the topographical features of mountains, valleys, and a stairway or ladder at the cusp. Similarly, these same features represent the energy landscape of the magnetospheric vortex, the black-hole Duat.

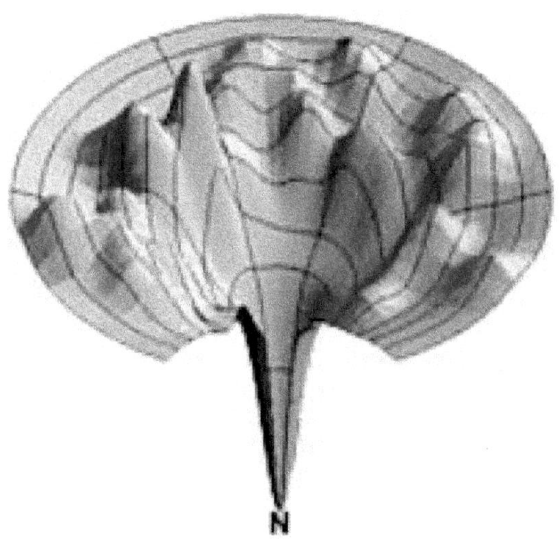

Figure 14.1

A rugged energy landscape with kinetic traps, energy barriers and some narrow throughway paths representing the reduction of conformational entropy as protein chains fold to their native states.

Permission from Ken A. Dill and Hue Sun Chan from "Levinthal to pathways to funnels," *Nature Structural Biology*, Volume 4, No. 1, January 1997.

In review, we could say that by death the Deceased has tunneled off the island of the earth, becoming a voltage source that must transfer the charge or electric potential to a new threshold. Imagine a particle in a potential well, bouncing back and forth until it tunnels through the potential into infinity. The Deceased begins his quantum journey as a small particle by engaging the Coulomb staircase, a stepwise increment of the current which reflects the different energies of different charge states due to tunneling. The goal is to fold into a different protein structure, a recombinant species by bonding with the Sun-god. The Deceased King then passes through the Gap (LamB porin) into the Duat (bacterium) and travels West to East on the Winding Waterway, the circular host chromosome near the plasma membrane, accompanied by the self-assembled crew on the Sun-bark. His destination is the *LacZ* gene, where the prophage resides. Activation of the SOS response cleaving repressor proteins, de-repression of genes, and other chemical reactions allow him to escape from the cell as a unique recombinant species. With this death vision of quantum processes in a protein folding funnel, the Deceased Sun-god states, "My face is that of a god, my flesh is that of a man" (CT1013) and "I am Horus" (CT1016).

The Sun-god's Destination

Phage Lambda is a lytic phage used to clone segments of DNA. They replicate by lysing (destroying) their host cell and releasing more phages. On a bacterial plate, this results in a small clear zone, a plaque. When the Deceased dispels the clouds, the unidirectional lytic pathway is working, progeny are produced, and the prophage excises. The funerary texts state that the Deceased Sun-god is journeying to Osiris, the Lambda prophage site on the host chromosome. One of the many texts referring to the Deceased's destination states that Re will guide him to the Two Conclaves and set him on the throne of Osiris (PT422). This language refers to the two arms of the Lambda genome lodged next to the *LacZ* gene on the host chromosome. On the circular chromosome, which modern scientists designate with 100 minutes, the LamB receptor site or maltose high affinity uptake system is at the 91.51 minute location. Approximately 16.3 minutes further in a northerly direction is the *LacZ* gene site at 7.81 minutes. (Institut Pasteur 2001) This direction on the chromosome matches the northerly west-to-east journey of the Deceased Sun-god to the prophage site. See the sketch of *E. coli* in *the Road from Orion*, Chapter 22, showing the positions of the seven rRNA operons from the map of *E. coli* (Nomura 1999).

The Duat as a Star House

The funerary texts identify the biological origin of human life with the lysogenic lifestyle of phage Lambda, whereas the lytic lifestyle allows a potential transformation after death that results in a unique species. Yet, the lytic lifestyle of eternity only occurs if one can arrive at the LamB receptor site or the polar area of the earth-cell and merge with the Sun-god.

Related to this merger, it is obvious that the Deceased hates inertness and sleep. Similarly, when Horus triumphs over the dispute with Seth, Horus is no longer inert. When the Great Inert One stands up on his side, he is victorious and the argument stops. It is evident that Atum or the Sun-god Re is the incoming phage Lambda, and Osiris is the Lambda prophage in the *E. coli* earth cell or Geb. Osiris lives when Horus overcomes Seth and takes back the Eye Seth snatched. The Eye of Horus then becomes whole, the prophage excises, and rolling circle lytic replication begins. So it is likely that the activity of the Eye is the excision of the Lambda prophage Osiris and the resultant rolling circle DNA replication. Decoded:

Osiris alive and risen = excision of Lambda prophage
Osiris dead = Lambda prophage

Now, when Osiris is alive and risen (IS77-83), the Horus lineage blossoms, which represents the transformation of the Deceased in the Duat (IS88-90). As mentioned, the derivation of the word "Duat" offers support for this idea. In *Egyptian Grammar*, Gardiner states (1957) that the word for "netherworld" was originally the place of the morning twilight known as the "Duat." The individual ideograms in the hieroglyph for Duat mean "star" (487) and "house" (33). The noun is feminine, which is indicated by the ending. So the individual components of the hieroglyph denote a feminine star house, suggesting a womb or house where a star is born, a new birth, a morning star. This meaning is further supported by references to the Morning Star being the Deceased's offspring (PT473, 481, 507, and IS87), the Deceased ascending to the sky as a Morning Star (PT553), and the Deceased joining other stars in the sky (PT666). The fourteen texts preceding the PT666 reference (PT634–639, 641, 649, 651-653, 655, 658, 662) refer to the Deceased receiving the Eye of Horus before star ascension. In other words, the Deceased is Horus within his Eye (CT107, 110), and the Eye of Horus in the Duat becomes the Morning Star (PT519). So we can infer that the Eye of Horus develops into the morning or dawning star that represents the Deceased's transfiguration. This is further supported by

Faulkner's footnote (PT639) that the Eye of Horus is always feminine, once again suggesting the idea of birth and development from a womb and the importance of Isis as lactose. Faulkner also notes in a footnote to PT569 that the translation of the word *dw3t* remains uncertain but appears to be a noun derived from "dawn" or "morning." So the Duat is that place where the first Eye or cell of Horus is created again (after life on earth) through Lambda DNA transcription, replication and translation to protein. We can now add the following to our decoded signs:

Duat, Star house, Morning Star = chemiluminescent reaction

Transduction/transformation of Deceased Sun-god, along with excision of Osiris leads to birth of Horus = bioluminescent species

Bioluminescence versus Photosynthesis

On the macrocosmic scale, the funerary texts suggest that if the Deceased enters the magnetosphere at a site of magnetic reconnection at the polar cusp of earth, then he will travel through the system, escaping to the cold-light interplanetary magnetic field of the Sun. In contrast, remaining within the earth's magnetic field may result in thermal entrapment of matter, where photosynthesis captures the Sun's energy. The choice then is between bioluminescence and photosynthesis. The desired transfiguration for the Deceased is becoming a celestial being, a Morning Star, a bioluminescent species retaining the consciousness of the Deceased, albeit at a deeper dimensional level.

The Pharaohs are suggesting that the primordial dominance of cI protein production in the Lambda genome lodged in the first host bacterium resulted in the development of prokaryotes and eukaryotes such as ourselves. In contrast, at human death, if one is in the right place, the balance will be set straight by the Deceased himself, who will recapture the origin of time, where his mobile elements will insert into an incoming phage Lambda to be transduced through a lysing bacterial cell that is excising its Lambda prophage. In this transformation, the Deceased Sun-god emits light as he progresses through the Duat (Amduat), rectifying DNA damage, which suggests that he has an internal source of light or photoreactivation process. These events coincide with the transcription, replication and translation to protein of the recombinant human-phage or bioluminescent species.

In the "Chapter for going forth from Rosetjau" (TR119), the Deceased states, "I am the Great One who created his own light." This would suggest that the transduction of the Deceased results in bioluminescence, which is the chemical production of light by an organism. The protein that produces light is Luciferin. Luciferase is the enzyme or catalyst that cleaves Luciferin in the presence of oxygen to emit light. The two *lux* operons (*lux*R and *luxICDABEG*) are both controlled by the same operator *luxI*-VAI synthase. Transcription of *lux*R is activated by cAMP-CRP, but repressed by iron. *Lux*R protein folds into active conformation by GroEL and GroES (stress proteins). Transcription of the *luxI* operon is repressed by LexA. (Achenbach 2002) So what are we to make of this?

When glucose levels in the cell are high, the molecule cAMP/CRP does not form, but when glucose levels are low, cAMP/CRP forms and binds to a protein called CAP, which binds to the CAP binding site to activate transcription. The lac operon is de-repressed by high levels of cAMP/CRP and transcription of *lux*R is activated by cAMP-CRP, but *lux*R is controlled by *luxI*. Now, transcription of the *luxI* operon is repressed by LexA repressor protein (Apopis), a negative regulator of the SOS regulon. RecA protein activation and cleavage of the LexA repressor upon DNA damage results in the induction of SOS. All these related processes hinge on RecA activation and LexA cleavage, thereby de-repressing *luxI*, along with the presence of lactose (Isis) and low glucose levels, allowing the activation of cAMP-CRP, which enables transcription of the other operon *lux*R. This may result in luminescence and is posed as an Outstanding Question for further research.

Research does support bacterial luminescence being enhanced under SOS conditions. Czyz et al. (2000) propose that luminescence may enhance the efficiency of DNA repair and allow light-emitting bacteria to survive irrespective of an external source of light. Czyz et al. results show that *lux* genes are negatively controlled by the SOS response regulator and effective luminescence of *Vibrio Harvey* is possible at low cell density under conditions causing DNA damage. Whereas Czyz et al. propose that luminescent bacteria have an internal source of light that is used in DNA repair by a photoreactivation process, the Pharaohs describe a similar process exists in the incoming Lambda Deceased Sun-god, who emits light regularly during his journey through the Duat (see Book Amduat). This suggests that the *lux* genes may be present in the mobile elements or genetic heritage of the Deceased, which is possible since the *Lux* gene is of eukaryotic origin. Also, the hieroglyphics painted in a bluish-green color in the pyramids and the funerary text emphasis on the color turquoise suggest the blue-green color of iridescence produced by bioluminescence (IS99). Possibly, the passage to the quantum holographic universe upon death restores these *Lux* genes to humans in some inexplicable way, enabling the transfiguration to a bioluminescent life-form.

The Calabi-Yau Lotus

The Deceased has the power in the afterlife to transform into a lotus. The Book of the Dead vignette (BD8B) shows a human head springing from the lotus plant. Symbolizing nascent life, scholars suggest that the lotus represents all evolutionary forms, the realization of potentialities, or the central point. The Egyptians, the Chinese, the Japanese, the Hindus and the Aryans have honored the lotus, which is remarkably similar to the importance of the rose in Western culture. (Cirlot 1971, 193)

The lotus shape is also popular with modern physicists and is very similar to the shape of a Calabi-Yau space, a six-dimensional geometrical shape that meets the mathematical equations for the curled-up dimensions of String Theory. The theory proposes that fundamental, oscillating strings of Planck-length components lie deep in the core of matter. Each string is made of one quantum loop of string. (Greene 1999, 141) All forces and all matter arise from these strings, which appear as point-like particles due to their smallness. The Planck length (10^{-33}) is about a hundred billion billion times smaller than an atomic nucleus. Since the strings are so small, they can vibrate in large extended dimensions and also in small curled-up dimensions. So we have our three space dimensions, six curled-up dimensions in our Calabi-Yau lotus shape, and one time dimension for a total of ten dimensions. Considering T-Duality and our earlier observations on the string structure of magnetic field lines of the earth and Sun, along with DNA structure, the theory does have some important correlations related to the innate architecture of our universe.

Another correlation to String Theory is the Eye of Horus which almost adds to one. An intrinsic property of every electron in the universe is that it spins at one fixed rate (Greene 1999, 171). Taking String Theory a step further, supersymmetry is the idea that particles of nature come in pairs. These pairs have respective spins differing by a half unit (1/2). Bosons are force particles whose spins are one (1), and fermions are matter particles whose spins are 1/2 of a whole. When a boson is positive, the fermion is negative and vice versa (173). So every known matter particle, including those that comprise a human being, has a super-partner particle, a double as the Pharaohs would say. Known matter particles all have spin-1/2. Translated a la Egypt, the attempt to make the Eye of Horus whole or a unitary one would result in the return of the missing matter, or a translation of matter from fermion (1/2) to boson (1) status. Therefore, the Lambda genome has the potential to create fermions by the lysogenic lifestyle and bosons by the lytic lifestyle. This idea is discussed further in Part Four, The Book of the Dead.

General Conclusion for Part Two: After reviewing our Matrices, which are meaningful and coherent, we could say our Lambda model in Matrix 2 has some validity relative to activities in the Egyptian afterlife. The solar wind/earth spin system fits the model of phage Lambda invading an *E. coli* host bacterium, which exhibits dynamics similar to a quantum mechanical Kerr black hole and a protein folding funnel.

Matrix 6

EGYPTIAN SIGN TRANSLATED TO POSSIBLE MODERN SCIENCE PARALLEL

Apopis, Apep: LexA repressor protein repressing 42 genes, allowing Lambda cI repressor protein to maintain prophage
arm, left and ascendant: lysogeny
arm, right and ascendant: lysis
arms of Judgment Balance: two arms of Lambda genome for lytic lifestyle
arms of Ka: two arms of Lambda genome activated for lytic lifestyle and release of phage progeny
assembling family in afterlife: molecule formation; protein engineering
barley cultivation: maltose transport system for lactose energy metabolism (aka LamB porin for phage Lambda entry)
Deceased judges Rivals: Deceased's genetic heritage inserted at cI gene in incoming Lambda genome (insertional inactivation)
Deceased, prepares path for Re when he halts: ssDNA induces SOS response upregulating pol IV and transcription proceeds; de-repression of 42 genes; RecA cleaves LexA repressor; excision of prophage activated
Deceased Sun-god/crew: supermolecule, nucleosome core
degradation or corruption of Osiris: DNA degradation
destination of Sun-god: Lambda prophage site at *LacZ* gene in host bacterium
Duat, star house, creation of Morning Star: process of chemiluminescence rather than photosynthesis in earth system
Duat entry at polar Gap of Geb: Adsorption and injection of Lambda recombinant DNA at LamB receptor site on host bacterium
eating, absorbing: chemical bonding
efflux of Osiris; flood, water, inundation: movement of molecules by efflux pumps to extracellular space (efflux); outflow of phage progeny
Enneads, Two; twin births; Horus and Seth: Lambda genome potential for lysogeny and lysis; fermions and bosons
Eye of Horus, feminine: lactose energy metabolism for full Lambda genome
Field of Offerings; seven cows; seven uraei: seven Lambda operons; binding reactions related to protein and nutrients
goddess/serpent bonds: lactose inactivating Lac repressor and removing it from DNA so the *lac* genes can be transcribed
heads, tails, vertices, faces: phage morphology
horizontal ram horns: horizontal gene transfer
Horus versus Seth: cro protein (lysis) versus cI protein (lysogeny)
inertness, sleep, weariness references: prophage state in lysogen
Isis on Sun-bark: lactose permease in environment entering earth-cell
Isis, Lady of Provisions: lactose medium for protein development of Horus species
Isis, Lady of the Winds: presence of lactose at cusp in solar wind

MATRIX **6 continued.**

Isis, empty seat or throne: *lacZ* gene empty when prophage excises
jar of Re's cold water at polar region for Deceased: injection of Lambda recombinant DNA into host bacterium; Flux Transfer Event
Judgment or Weighing of Words with emphasis on *Rightful Order*: weighing of DNA instructions by occupation of OR1 first by cro for development of Horus species
Knots of Elephantine, two for Horus: OL and OR of Lambda genome in the lysogen; also Promoter-L and Promoter-R
knowledge of souls in Duat: molecular recognition
Lion, Double: DNA damage; thymine dimer
lotus: Calabi-Yau space
Mansion of the Six; Battleground of Gods; Two Conclaves; Island of Fire; Eye of Horus: six operator sites or two arms of Lambda genome
Mehen, thin serpent around Sun-god: RecA filament
mountains and valleys of Duat: energy landscapes of magnetosphere; energy landscapes depicting protein folding
Osiris bent backward in circle: lytic lifestyle; rolling circle replication
Osiris cut up or dismembered: Lambda prophage; lysogeny
Osiris risen: excision of Lambda prophage; lytic cycle; rolling circle replication
Osiris risen; birth of Horus lineage; transformation of Deceased: bioluminescent species (active *lux* genes) through transduction of Deceased
self-creation of Deceased: molecular self-assembly
serpents: DNA-binding proteins (HTH)
serpents, winged: DNA-binding proteins (winged HTH)
Seth, pig: Hedgehog gene; no limb formation in vertebrates
Seth snatching Eye; robbery: cI protein snatching OR1 first, activating cI protein production and lysogeny
son swallowing father: DNA binding; absorption in the bonding of RNA polymerase (son or copy of DNA template) to the DNA molecule (father)
Thoth: DNA-directed RNA polymerase
Thoth's 42 books: 42 de-repressed genes formerly controlled by monster LexA repressor protein
Two Ways: LLBL and HLBL; two LamB porin pathways with one for lactose
Union of Sun-god and Deceased at polar region: insertion of exogenous DNA fragment (mobile elements or genetic heritage of Deceased) at cI site of incoming Lambda genome at LamB receptor site on host bacterium
weaving, cloaks, clothes, God's booth and awnings, linen: protein translation and protein folding
Word, Great: DNA instructions for new species and lytic pathway
Word, copying: DNA transcription

III

The Guided Diffusion Path to Eternity

The nature of infinity is this: That every thing has its
Own Vortex, and when once a traveller thro' Eternity
Has pass'd that Vortex, he perceives it roll backward behind
His path, into a globe itself infolding like a sun,
Or like a moon, or like a universe of starry majesty . . .

Thus is the earth one infinite plane, and not as apparent
To the weak traveller confin'd beneath the moony shade.
Thus is the heaven a vortex pass'd already, and the earth
A vortex not yet pass'd by the traveller thro' Eternity

William Blake from *Milton*

15

The Book Amduat

GLIDING TO ETERNITY WITH SEVEN GUIDING SERPENT-PROTEINS

Objective 9: Do the Matrices centered on the Lambda model apply to, illuminate and support a reasonable understanding of the Amduat and the Book of Gates?

This study uses Piankoff's publication of the tomb of Ramesses VI, an English translation that Erik Hornung claims has yet to be superseded (1999, 31), supplemented by Budge's illustrations from the tomb of Seti I for the following reason. According to Piankoff (1954, 227), complete versions of the Book Amduat, which first appeared in the Eighteenth Dynasty, are found in the tombs of Thutmosis III and of Amenophis II. The first eleven divisions are found in the Nineteenth Dynasty tomb of Seti I and in the Twentieth Dynasty tomb of Ramesses VI. Piankoff notes that the best version is from the tomb of Seti I, and that the version from Ramesses VI is abridged and registers of Divisions 7, 8, 9, 10 and 11 are hopelessly intermixed. Because of this, Piankoff constructed his diagrams of the Hours from Eighteenth Dynasty versions of Thutmose III and Amenophis II. (227-229) Referencing Eighteenth Dynasty, Nineteenth Dynasty (Seti I) and Twentieth Dynasty (Ramesses VI) versions provides continuity and a larger evidentiary base of text and images for this thesis. Also displayed are Budge's illustrations, which were traced from the plates of the tomb of Seti I and presented in his analysis *The Egyptian Heaven and Hell*, a 1905 text now in the public domain. Budge's translation will be used when appropriate.

The Hidden Chamber

Of all the funerary texts, the Amduat or the Book of the Hidden Chamber explains the central Egyptian doctrine of life after death related to the transfiguration of the Deceased. The Book describes quantum events related to the lytic cycle and the excision of the Lambda prophage (Osiris) by mapping the preferred path from this world to the next that was only available for souls who rode in Re's ferryboat, that is, the Lambda vector. In the afterlife, the texts exhort the Deceased to "go forth into the day" or to join the light of the Sun. After merging into the Sun-god, the Deceased is transfigured into the shape of a god, a being of matter and light in the energy funnel of the Duat. But, to make this transformation, the Deceased must travel in Re's bark through the dark, deep valley of the Duat along a guided diffusion pathway for incoming phage Lambda through the LamB porin to the site of the integrated Lambda genome on the host cell chromosome at the *LacZ* or *b-gal* gene seat. The chemical journey through the Duat resembles the thermodynamic energy landscape of the host cell, where proteins fold to native conformations within an energy landscape funnel.

In this process, the Deceased visits the Hidden Chamber of Osiris, the 30 bp prophage attachment site containing a conserved central 15 bp region where recombination takes place. (Mulligan 2001) Similarly, the domain of Osiris contains 15 Aats (Budge v1 1904, 176-177), and the Egyptian afterlife game Senet had 30 squares, suggesting the 30 bp prophage site of phage Lambda. The significance of Lambda as 30 is expressed by the Greek Lambda *l* equaling 30, which probably stemmed from the Hebrew Lamed *l* equaling 30. Also, texts reference the "House of the 30" (CT277, 688), allusions to the 30 bp Lambda attachment site on the host chromosome. The Sun-god's journey results in the excision of the prophage (Osiris) and rolling circle replication for cro protein production of human-phage progeny, the Horus species.

DNA to RNA to Protein

Like supramolecular chemists identifying molecules, the numerous deities in the Amduat are able to distinguish each other by their shape or properties. Thus, we have the Pharaohs using a New Science method to describe quantum experiences and molecules that the Deceased encounters in the afterlife. The elaborate Egyptian system of metasymbols depicts the shape and properties of molecules in the universal catalytic process of 1) binding of the substrate, 2) chemical transformation into the product, and 3) the release of the product to regenerate the active catalyst. The 12-hour journey of the Deceased Sun-god and crew into the Duat or earth-cell represents the catalytic process and follows the Central Dogma of DNA to RNA to Protein.

The presence of the Deceased at the northern pole of the earth-cell is important, for polar localization of proteins is critical for bacterial cell division, chromosome partitioning, and cell cycle control. In the first stage of adsorption, phage Lambda binds at the maltose receptor site (LamB) of the bacterial earth-cell. Induction of the maltose-binding protein activates the formation of a polar distortion called a polar cap, which is a gap between the cytoplasm and the cell wall, resulting in deformation and subsequent protein enrichment (Lybarger and Maddock 2001). The process begins with the ferrying of charged or neutral species across the cell membrane by a Lambda vector, what the Egyptians call the Sun-bark. The crew of the Sun-bark constitutes a supermolecule, a group of individual ions or molecules united by weak bonds into a discrete unit with a well-defined structure and dynamics. This unit of self-assembled molecules is bound together with a three-fold purpose: 1) SOS and recombinational repair, 2) the initiation of transcription by the host cell enzyme DNA polymerase to transcribe the recombinant species, and 3) excision of Lambda prophage and activation of lytic cycle for translation to protein.

Supermolecules, Proteins and Chemical Processes

Metasymbol	Parallel to Bacterial Genetics
Osiris, God of Duat	Lambda prophage
Sun-god	Incoming phage Lambda
earth	*E. coli* host bacterium
Apopis the Monster	LexA repressor protein
Horus	Lambda cro repressor protein of cI
Seth	Lambda cI repressor protein of cro
Deceased Sun-god	Mobile DNA of Deceased as insert in Lambda
Deceased Sun-god and crew	Supramolecular complex of human DNA, lactose permease and other species
Isis	Lactose metabolism
Thoth the moon-god	RNA polymerase for transcription
Thoth's 42 Books	De-repression of 42 genes
Egyptian Moon Festivals	Model for phage growth related to lactose, depicting eclipse period, latent period, adsorption, burst size

Figure 15.1

In light of these dynamics, Figure 15.1 presents the major metasymbols in the Egyptian molecular recognition system. The anthropomorphized personalities or objects point to supermolecules, proteins and quantum chemical processes.

Seven Serpents

Seven major serpents or proteins glide through the Book Amduat, which describes chemical reactions related to transcription, the lytic lifestyle and prophage excision. Textual descriptions and actual drawings show a remarkable correspondence between Egyptian serpents an DNA-binding proteins. When describing DNA-binding proteins, the Pharaohs portrayed the molecules as serpents with three, four or five heads that correspond to the protein's alpha helices (primary structure) and beta sheets (secondary structure). The following brief summary of proteins that appear at the appropriate time during the described chemical reactions will aid the reader through the Amduat journey.

1. LexA monster repressor protein Apopis

The Pyramid Texts refer to Apopis as a four-coiled Monster snake. The structure of the LexA repressor as determined by IH NMR spectroscopy contains three regular alpha-helices and one antiparallel beta sheet. The beta sheet exhibits a coil-like shape that could be described as a coil. (Fogh et al. 1994)

Figure 15.2: Apopis from Amduat Hour Seven (drawing by Budge from Seti I)

Thus we have the four-coiled Monster that represses 42 genes, while allowing the active Lambda cI repressor to maintain the prophage in an inert state (Osiris), and permitting the active Lac repressor protein to bind to the DNA operator sequences to prevent lactose activity. In Hour Seven of the Amduat (Seti I), we find textual references to Apopis and a drawing of the long fettered serpent.

2. RecA protein Mehen

RecA protein is a multifunctional enzyme with two roles. In its first role, the protein mediates strand exchange during recombination. The second role involves the cleavage of the LexA repressor protein (Apopis) during an SOS response. RecA protein has two smaller domains, stabilizing a six-helical polymer of protein subunits and interhelical bundles. (Story et al. 1992, Morimatsu et al. 2002, Chandra)

Figure 15.3a. Sketch of RecA subunits (drawn from image in Cairo Coffin CGC 28082)
b. Serpent Mehen around Sun-god in Amduat Hour Ten (drawing by Budge, Seti I).

Representations in the Cairo Coffin CGC 28083 map from the Book of Two Ways depicts a similar structure (Figure 15.3a). The two top uraei represent the two smaller domains stabilizing the six-helical polymer of protein subunits, signified by the bottom six uraei of interhelical bundles. However, in the Amduat, the protein is depicted as the serpent around the Sun-god (Figure 15.3b), which seems appropriate, for in its first role related to recombination, RecA forms a helical filament around ssDNA. In a co-protease activity, the ssDNA/RecA filament cleaves the LexA repressor protein, which catalyzes its own digestion.

3. Cro repressor protein Horus

Hour Four of the Amduat shows a three-headed serpent that matches up with the active, three-helix cro repressor of phage Lambda (that represses cI) with its three helices. This DNA-binding protein (Figure 15.4a) is a homodimer with each subunit being 66 amino acids in length.

Figure 15.4a. Sketch of Cro repressor protein from Amduat Hour Four (drawn from image in tomb of RVI).

Having a helix-turn-helix (HTH) motif, the repressor has three alpha helices, two of which are separated by a short turn with a third helix fitting into the major groove operator DNA. (Albright and Matthews 1998; Ohlendorf et al. 1998; Marcey 2001; Christoffersen 2004) Figure 15.4a depicts a sketch of the active cro protein with three serpent heads, 14 disks, 14 heads and 14 stars from Amduat Hour Four in the Tomb of Ramesses VI.

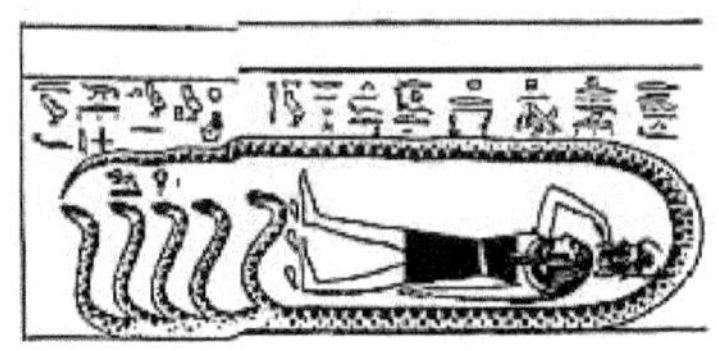

Figure 15.4b. Lambda cI repressor protein from Amduat Hour Six (drawing by Budge from Seti I)

4. Lambda cI repressor protein Seth

The Lambda cI repressor (Figure 15.4b) regulates phage gene expression in the lysogenic state by binding to OR and OL operator sequences. The dimeric repressor has five alpha helices in a bundle with helices two and three forming a helix-turn-helix. (Sevilla-Sierra et al. 1994) One can easily equate the image of the five-headed serpent repressing the inert Osiris in Amduat Hour Six with the five-helixed Lambda cI repressor protein.

5. Catabolite gene Activator Protein (CAP)

The winged three-headed serpent in Hour Five represents CAP protein, also known as cAMP Receptor Protein (CRP). Classified by modern biologists as a "winged" helix-turn-helix DNA binding protein (Donaldson et al. 1994), the protein exhibits an extensive beta sheet structure (wings) and three alpha helices (heads) (University College London). In the absence of glucose, CAP binds to the CRP site near the Lac operon promoter, stimulates transcription of the Lac operon, and interacts with RNA polymerase.

The Lac operon is also under positive control by CAP or catabolite activator protein, now thought to be bound to its Lac binding site at all times, even during repression. (Lewis et al. 1996; Pearson 2003) The image in Figure 15.5 shows the presence of CAP at the Lac binding site, next to which the prophage Osiris is lodged on the host chromosome. *E. coli* grown on glucose do not metabolize

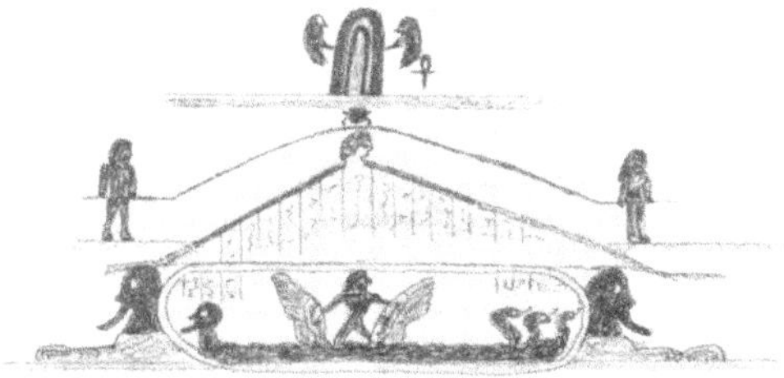

Figure 15.5. Sketch of *LacZ* gene site where winged CAP protein is bound in Amudat Hour Five (drawn from image in RVI)

lactose until glucose is absent. This is called catabolite repression. Glucose represses the Lac operon of *E. coli* by preventing the entry of lactose through an occasionally present lac permease molecule. (Pearson 2003) The sketch in Figure 15.5 depicts the pyramidal mound of the *LacZ* gene seat where the prophage is lodged (dark chamber). In line with modern research, the texts show the winged-HTH serpent or CAP protein bound to its Lac binding site to stimulate transcription.

6. Lac repressor protein

The Lac repressor protein keeps the lactose genes turned off in the cell and is also active because of the LexA monster repressor protein (Apopis). But, with LexA or Apopis mastered, the Lac repressor bonds to allolactose rather than the DNA operator sequences, so that the necessary genes for the Horus species are transcribed. The prophage is lodged between the *LacZ* (*b-gal*) and *bio* gene sites. The *LacZ* or *b-gal* 116 Kda monomer is active as a tetramer. The Hour Ten representation (SI) of a two-headed serpent with four legs depicts the structure of the Lac repressor protein having four polypeptide subunits, which form a tetramer (4 legs).

Figure 15.6 a. Lac repressor from Amduat Hour Ten (drawing by Budge from Seti I)

The protein has bonding sites for both allolactose and the operator sequences of DNA, as indicated by its two heads. When repressing the Lac genes, the headpiece or first 56 amino acids of the Lac repressor binds to the DNA of the operator. The rest of the Lac repressor is responsible for inducer binding and tetramer formation. (Pace et al. 1990; Lewis et al. 1996; Bell and Lewis 2001) Thus, we have the Red Crowned serpent head on the left representing the unbound headpiece and the White Crowned serpent head on the right pointing to inducer binding and tetramer formation.

Figure 15.6b. sketch of DRADA from Amduat Hour Four (drawn from image in Seti I)

7. dsRNA-specific Adenosine Deaminase (DRADA)

In Hour Four of the Amduat, the top register shows the winged-HTH, DNA-binding protein DRADA, a protein that functions to modify viral RNA genomes and bonds tightly to Z-DNA. (European Bioinformatics Institute) The enzyme works by changing adenine so that it acts like guanine. It has the potential to recode genomic information and alter protein function. Its structure reflects the characteristic wings or beta sheet loops and the three alpha helices. (Herbert and Rich 1996, 2001; Rich 1999) Eukaryotes also experience RNA editing, which influences evolution by the continual interplay between RNA and DNA (Rich 1999).

MATRIX 7

SUMMARY OF SERPENT PROTEINS

Serpent Protein Function	Structure
4-coiled monster Apopis: LexA repressor 1) represses 42 genes 2) allows Lambda cI repressor activity 3) allows Lac repressor activity	3 *a*-helices, 1 *b*-sheet
8-uraei-headed Mehen: RecA 1) mediates strand exchange 2) cleaves LexA during SOS	Forms helical filament; two domains stabilize 6-helical polymer
3-headed Horus: Cro repressor 1) represses Lambda cI repressor (Seth) 2) produces Horus species	3 *a*-helices
5-headed Seth: Lambda cI repressor 1) maintains Lambda in prophage state 2) shown in Hr. 6 as 5-headed serpent around Osiris 3) represses cro	5 *a*-helices
3-headed winged CAP Protein 1) stimulates Lac operon 2) bonded to Lac binding site	3 *a*-helices; 1 extended *b*-sheet
2-headed 4-footed Lac Repressor 1) represses lac genes by binding to operator sequences 2) when de-repressed, bonds to allolactose (i.e., the goddess)	1 headpiece bonds to operator; the rest bonds to inducer; 4 subunits form tetramer
3-HEADED WINGED DRADA 1) modifies viral RNA genome 2) changes adenine to act like guanine	3 *a*-helices; 1 *b*-sheet

During the host cell's SOS response, RecA protein cleaves LexA repressor protein (Apopis). This inactivates the Lambda cI repressor (Seth), allowing the activity of cro repressor protein (Horus). This also inactivates the Lac repressor, allowing function of the lactose genes. When the lactose operon becomes activated and glucose levels are low, cAMP binds with CRP and facilitates transcription of the Lac operon (Mathews et al. 2000). DRADA, a protein that functions to modify viral RNA genomes, bonds tightly to Z-DNA as the polymerase plows through the DNA. (Kim et al. 1989; MIT News 1995)

The Ram-headed Man with the Forked Staff

Hour One in Seti I depicts the Deceased Sun-god sailing with his crew of eight as a ram-headed man wearing a disk and carrying a forked staff, suggesting a replication fork. The Sun-bark enters a permeable barrier door or screen, which may represent protein channel selectivity for a particular ion or molecule at the cell membrane, such as phage Lambda at the LamB receptor site.

The enclosed Sun-god on the bark suggests that the species is water soluble and bound in an ionophore (in chemistry, a cage carrier and chemical compound capable of forming a complex with an ion and transporting it through a biological membrane). An ionophore, a carrier molecule with a hydrophobic coat, has the ability to transfer ions from an aqueous medium across a hydrophobic phase. Put simply, an ionophore is an ion channel in the membrane. It functions by causing a leak in the membrane, thereby allowing too many protons in than are necessary. An SOS signal goes off and the cell attempts to pump out the protons. (Lavaki and Callaway 2001). Phage Lambda's protein W has a well-packed hydrophobic core that stabilizes the DNA in the phage head (Maxwell et al. 2001), which may qualify the phage as a carrier molecule with a hydrophobic coat.

Recall that the icosahedral capsid found in most viruses generally fit 60 x N subunits into their capsids. "N" is the triangulation number with values of 1, 3, 4, 7, 9, 12 and higher. When an icosahedral virus contains 60 subunits, it displays perfect symmetry. (Cann 2004) The Pharaohs may have been indicating the icosahedral shape of phage Lambda when they titled their afterlife divisions as hours, suggesting the 60 subunits. As mentioned, the Sun-god's horizontal ram horns may indicate horizontal gene transfer or the transfer of genes between non-interbreeding, fully developed and independent organisms via vectors such as viruses.

To place this idea in its proper perspective, our model of the Lambda Sun-god with its Deceased insert entering the *E. coli* bacterium or earth-cell easily parallels the process of horizontal gene transfer. On the cellular level, large-scale changes in the structure and organization of genomes result from horizontal gene transfers, which introduce novel physiological traits. For example, horizontal acquisition of the lac operon has enabled *E. coli* to use the milk sugar lactose as a carbon source (Ochman et al. 2000). The presence of Isis as Lady of the Boat, who occasionally wears the horizontal ram horns (the unusual headdress of the Ram-god) under her double crown (Budge vol. 2 1904, 203) suggests the horizontal gene transfer of lactose into the cell. So it may be that the process of the Deceased Sun-god making his transformations is the same horizontal gene transfer mechanism of modern genetics called transduction, and that Isis' presence on the bark indicates the original horizontal acquisition of the lac operon for the host cell.

Hour One

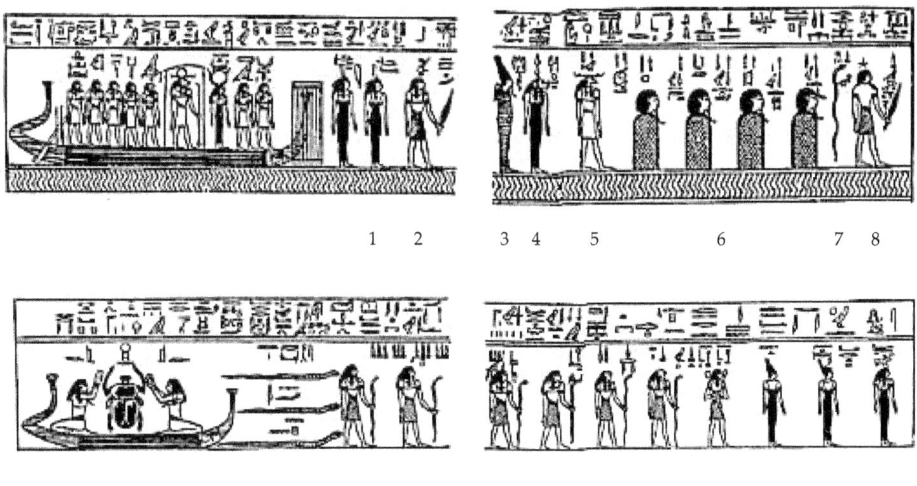

Figure 15.7. Amduat Hour One Middle Register (drawing by Budge from Seti I)

The Middle Register is divided in two. In the upper Middle Register, with specific attributes and names, probably for molecular recognition purposes, the following deities march in front of the bark in the divided Middle Register (SI; RVI):

1) 2 goddesses (Truth, Rightful Order)
2) 1 god holding a knife (He who injures)
3) 1 bearded god in mummy form wearing White Crown (He at the Head of the West)
4) lioness-headed goddess (Sekhmet)
5) a Ram-headed god (The Great Illuminer)
6) 4 terms (Orders of Re, Atum, Khepri, and Osiris)
7) 1 elongated serpent standing on its tail
8) 1 god holding object (He who passes through the Hours)

Again, southern or Lower Egypt represents the left Eye of Seth, whereas northern or Upper Egypt represents the right Eye of Horus, so it seems appropriate to have two goddesses of Truth and Rightful Order: Nephthys connected to the left Eye of Seth and Isis connected to the right Eye of Horus. The goddesses also represent the two daughter strands of DNA, for RecA activates recombination-dependent replication (RDR), which is seen in bacterial transduction, a normally rare process (Cox 2001).

The mummified, bearded god wearing the White Crown (3) suggests the dormant phage Lambda (Osiris). The deity Sekhmet (4), who annihilates Re's enemies, personifies the scorching, destructive heat of the Sun's rays (Budge v1 1904, 515) and suggests ultraviolet irradiation. The four terms (6) depict the four termination stops for phage gene expression: terminators t_R1 and t_R2 control transcripts at PR; transcripts t_L1 and t_L2 control transcripts initiated at PL (Mulligan 2003). The elongated serpent (7) suggests the elongation phase of transcription. The text below this register states the Sun-god will make his transformations after passing the gate into the Duat's Hidden Chamber.

In the bottom Middle Register, a second boat carries a beetle worshiped by two gods, suggesting the coming into being of Osiris or the excision of the Lambda prophage. Three elongated serpents glide before this boat, representing messenger, ribosomal and transfer RNA. Before the serpents are:

1) 3 man-headed gods holding serpent staffs
2) 3 hawk-headed gods holding serpent staffs
3) a god called Henebty holding two crooks crossed like an "x"
4) a goddess wearing White Crown
5) a goddess wearing Red Crown
6) a goddess

RVI shows three additions to the procession:

7) a pole with 2 horns on which a small bearded mummy stands facing right
8) a crook
9) a god facing left

Man-headed gods (1) and hawk-headed gods (2) with wavy serpents in their left hands indicate Horus lineage activation of the Left Arm/Eye of Horus. Henebty (3) with two crooks crossed depicts crossing over of DNA into the host chromosome of the earth-cell or a Holliday junction (Holliday 1964), which is a basic site-specific recombination process responsible for integration and excision of bacteriophage genomes into and out of the host bacterium (Campbell 1962; Weisberg and Landy 1983). A Holliday Junction forms in recombination when a single strand from each of two duplex DNA segments is exchanged in a region of sequence homology, yielding a branched structure with four duplex arms (Gopaul et al. 1998). In addition, the presence of White Crowned (4) and Red Crowned (5) goddesses suggest lactose metabolism for both arms of the Lambda genome or the whole Eye of Horus. The pole (7) with the mummy facing right signifies PR (Promoter-right) for phage transcription, which is necessary for the lytic lifestyle. Now, a crook (8) may point to the flagella hook-associated protein in molecular assembly. Immediately outside the cell is a flexible protein hook, functioning as a universal joint that allows the flagellum to adopt any cell wall orientation. (Illingworth and Henderson 1999) Flagellae are rigid structures with flexible universal joints called "hooks" at their base where they insert into the bacterial membrane. This would suggest that Hour One signifies the phage adsorption/penetration stage.

The Upper Register is lined with
- 9 baboons opening gates to the Great Soul
- 12 goddesses unfolding earth portals
- 9 kneeling gods praising Re
- 12 goddesses guiding Re

The Lower Register shows
- 9 seated baboons singing to Re as he enters Duat
- 12 light-giving uraei lighting dark Duat
- 9 man-headed gods praising Re
- 12 goddesses praising Re who passes over to River Urnes

It is possible that the 42 gods of the Upper Register signify the 42 de-repressed genes of the LexA regulon and lytic pathway for the second coming of viral DNA (Sun-god), with the 42 gods of the Lower Register indicating the former condition of 42 repressed genes or the lysogenic pathway of the first viral DNA, which resulted in the prophage Osiris dismembered, dormant, mummified. Put simply, we could take this duplicate imagery for the dual potential of lysis and lysogeny.

Yet, at the ends of the linear Lambda genome are short sticky (12 bp) single-stranded regions that are complementary (Nicholl 2002, 67). It may also be possible that the 24 Upper Register goddesses represent one short 12 bp region, with the Lower register 12 uraei and 12 goddesses representing the other 12 bp cohesive end that enable circularization of the genome within the bacterium. With the idea of phage adsorption/penetration in mind, and since the Sun-god in this court is navigating to Urnes, we could then say that the DNA in the viral head is injected down the hollow tail to the double membrane and cell gates, where the Sun-god enters the second division of the Duat called Urnes or the host cell waterways. Let's look closer at this possibility.

Text from Ramesses VI (Piankoff)

The Introductory Text to Hour One (RVI) states that the Book is about the writings of the Hidden Chamber, where souls, gods, shadows and spirits stand. The Hidden Chamber is the interior 30 bp region of the DNA molecule where the Lambda prophage resides. The journey begins at the Horn of the West, the Gate of the Western Horizon, which translates to the polar cusp at the LamB porin. The Book holds the knowledge of mysterious powers, the gates, the path of the Great God, the powerful and the annihilated. Seth stands on the riverbank, suggesting compliance.

The names of two of the nine baboons in the Upper Register, who open the earth are "The Heart of the earth" and "The Heart of the Heart of the earth," suggesting the movement into the ultimate structure of DNA. Of the nine kneeling gods, three are crocodile-headed, three are jackal-headed and three human-headed. The jackal-headed gods are named "Lord of the Holy Ground," "Opener of the Two Lands," and "The one who separates the two Powerful Ones," a reference to cI and cro protein competition for genetic control. The three human-headed gods are "The One whose arm is shining," "Visible Arm," and "The One who praises with his arm," references to the triumphant right arm of the Lambda genome or cro protein production. The god with the two crossed crooks is *hnbty* or Henbety. The name of the Field is the "Water of Re," suggesting the interior of the phage head and the movement of phage DNA from the Lambda head into the tail for host cell adsorption and penetration.

The occupants of the bark are "Opener of the Ways, Mind, Lady of the Barge, The Flesh, Horus the Praiser, The Bull of Truth, The Watchful One," and "She who guides the Barge." The text at the end of the first division states that the gates are open for Re, who travels to the place where Osiris rests, to give breath to Osiris, whose forms are hidden. Re's resting place is the "sprouts on the fields of the earth," signifying lytic vegetative replication. Serpent spirits will illumine the darkness for Re. The text states that Re rests on the barge of Khepri, and he has taken "the heads of Henbety" or *hnbty* "among those of the field." When Re reaches the gates of the earth, he commands that the gates be resistant with sealed bolts. Then the deities wail as Re passes.

Thus, the Hidden Chamber is the "heart of the heart of the earth" or the interior hydrophobic bases of DNA, where the prophage is lodged on the host chromosome. References to the battle between Seth and Horus (cI and cro) with direct statements about the shining arm and Visible Arm, suggest the active right arm of phage Lambda or the celestial Horus lineage. This is complimented by the statement that Re will breathe life into the resting Osiris, suggesting the excision of the prophage and lytic pathway. Taking the heads of Henbety, who holds the crossed crooks, suggests the chemical reaction related to Holliday Junction annealing and cleavage at the prophage site, the place where Osiris rests. (232-239)

Text from Seti I (Budge)

The text explains that the Sun-god passes by in the form of a ram to make his transformations. The Sun-god states that his word goes out to the Field's gods, that he will avenge his rebel members by destroying "that which had been made for it" or their foundation, that is, the DNA base. This idea of destroying writings or removing the scribe is also present in the Pyramid and Coffin Texts (IS95). The SI text further states that the dead remain in this court. The banks (Upper and Lower Registers) of the stream are lined with baboons, gods, and goddesses singing hymns of praise, along with serpents belching fire. The deities line the banks like nucleotides on DNA double strands or frozen ions on magnetic field lines. The text states that Re is at the "entrance to the doors of the earth" on his way to the secret place of Osiris. The Sun-god will bring in the day by seizing the grain of the god Henbet in the secret place. In other words, he will break the bonds of Henbet, so that the prophage Osiris will rise. Re states, "Shut [your doors] by your bolts," and "stand on the banks of the stream." When the Sun-god departs the first division, wailing ensues. The name of the Field is Maati; this division is called Net-Ra.

Transduction

Transduction jumpstarts the chemical reactions in the Amduat. The incoming phage Lambda Sun-god shuttles the inserted Deceased into the host cell. At the doors of Geb (earth), the recombinant DNA is transferred into the bacterial earth-cell. Two infections were necessary: 1) Lambda infects the Deceased, what we might call the donor DNA, and 2) Lambda with the donor DNA infects the recipient earth-cell. Thus we have the Sun-god/Deceased union at the North Pole, the polar membrane of the earth cell, which is then entered or infected by the recombinant DNA and transduction begins. Once again, the Pharaohs suggest the Sun-god is like a Lambda gene vector, with the earth-cell representing a lysogen that will be induced to undergo a productive infection in which the Deceased becomes a bioluminescent cosmic species.

The polar cusp, where the magnetic field is null, is almost always dominated by H+. Recall that when field lines reconnect, the two families of plasma from the earth's magnetosphere and the Sun's magnetosheath mix and are accelerated by the JxB force at the magnetopause. In our earth-cell, plasma exchange now becomes genetic instructional exchange for protein synthesis. In other words, the depolarization at the earth's cusp is similar to the process which occurs when the cell membrane is at rest, and the channel is blocked by a gating portion of the protein. The resting membrane has a positive charge on the outside and a negative charge on the inside, similar to the negative electron movement discussed in the magnetosphere that allows the Flux Transfer Event to move through. When the channel protein senses a change in voltage due to the opening of adjacent pores (depolarization), the gate opens, allowing the ions to rush through the channel into the cell. Buechner et al. (1999) investigated ion channel activities in *E. coli's* outer membrane and found the presence of gated ion channels, suggesting that most of the outer membrane pores such as LamB are closed at rest and may be openable by physiological stimuli. Remember, the Deceased "splits open the sky and drives away the storm" (CT1179). Once the membrane is fully depolarized, the special blocking segment of the pore protein actually shuts the channel, or as Re states in the text of Hour One, "Shut [your doors] by your bolts."

Wailing and Praising as Quorum Sensing

Bacteria communicate using signaling molecules released into the environment. They also regulate gene expression in response to their increasing cell population density by a phenomenon called quorum sensing evident in *E. coli* (Surette et al. 1999). Quorum sensing enables a cell to sense the number of bacteria by the accumulation of signaling molecules. Bacteria coordinate this activity during infection of a host for three reasons: 1) to adapt to nutrient availability, 2) to defend against other competitors/microorganisms for the food source, or 3) to escape the immune response of the host. Thus, in the mixed species population of the earth-cell, the Amduat Hours resonate with wailing, lamenting, praising, and cheering as the Sun-god passes, for the infection is spreading, and quorum sensing cross-talk or interspecies communication is occurring.

As mentioned, the Sun-god is self-created or self-assembled, and we encounter this self-creation or molecular assembly and mass generation process of protein folding in the Amduat. As Re approaches the earth-cell doors, he encourages the divine Souls to come into being for Khepera or the Deceased

Sun-god's transformation. He moves through the first Field of Souls as if he were a particle being created in a Higgs field. Particle masses are generated by interactions within an elementary field call the Higgs field after British physicist Peter Higgs. This mass-generating mechanism results in a self-sustaining cluster analogous to the Higgs particle itself. (Smith 2003)

Matrix 8: Amduat Hour One

Egyptian Sign translated to Possible Modern Science Parallel

arm, Shining, Visible: right arm of Lambda genome on host chromosome
barrier door or permeable screen before bark's prow: protein channel selectivity for a particular ion or molecule in cell membrane; LamB porin
Beetle or transformations of Deceased Sun-god: bacterial transduction
cage around Sun-god: hydrophobic protein coat of virus
crook: hook-associated protein in molecular assembly
Deceased: foreign insert into vector/virus
Deceased traveling to North Pole: movement to polar phage Lambda binding site at LamB on *E. coli*
deities, distinguishing shapes or properties: molecular recognition
deities, 3 man-headed and 3 hawk-headed holding wavy serpents: activation of full Lambda genome or 6 operator sequences
deities, 42 Upper Register: 42 de-repressed genes activated by incoming Sun-god with human insert
deities, 42 Lower Register: 42 repressed genes of prophage
division titles of Amduat (Hour 1, 2 . . .): reference to icosahedral capsid of 60 subunits or 60 x N subunits as compared to 60 minutes in an hour
earth gates: double cell membrane of *E. coli*
forked staff of Sun-god: DNA replication fork
Gap: polar cap, a gap between the cytoplasm and the cell wall resulting in deformation and subsequent protein enrichment in a bacterial cell
god with beard, White Crown and mummy shape: indicator of right arm of phage Lambda; prophage
goddesses wearing White and Red Crowns: lactose for whole genome
head of human with beard: phage head with tail (or cilia?)
Henbety holding 2 crooks crossed like an X: crossing over of DNA or Holliday Junction and 7bp branch migration
House of 30; Lamed = 30; Lambda = 30; Senet game of 30 squares; 15 Aats: *E. coli* chromosome site where Lambda integrates; 30 bp in size, containing a central 15 bp region where recombination takes place
horizontal ram horns of Sun-god: horizontal gene transfer or the transfer of genes between non-interbreeding, fully developed and independent organisms via vectors such as viruses (transduction, transformation)
horizontal ram horns of Isis: original horizontal acquisition of lac operon for *E. coli*
Isis and other goddesses: lactose permease entry into cell; lactose metabolism
Maat goddesses, Isis and Nephthys: lactose for whole Lambda genome; two DNA daughter strands for replication; lactose and allolactose
model, solar wind/earth: model of bacterial virus/bacterium
moon: model for phage growth; eclipse, latent, adsorption and burst size
mummification of dead: phage simulation of head and tail stalk for prophage renewal; attempt to limit bacteria
Osiris coming into being: integrated phage in bacterial host enters lytic path
Osiris in Hidden Chamber; heart of the heart of the earth: 30 bp region between *LacZ* and *bio* genes; interior hydrophobic base of DNA of prophage

Matrix 8 continued.

pole with mummy facing right: Promoter-right for phage transcription
Powerful Ones, two: cro and cI repressor proteins
Re breathing life into Osiris: activation of prophage excision
Sa, elongated serpent: DNA elongation phase of transcription
Sekhet or Sekhmet, lioness-headed deity: indicator of ultraviolet irradiation
serpents, 3 elongated before Boat of Birth of Osiris: messenger, ribosomal and transfer RNA
Shut [your doors] by your bolts: process of resting cell membrane sensing voltage change due to depolarization and opening/shutting gates for ions
Sun-god's destination as secret place of Osiris: Lambda prophage site
Sun-god/crew: supermolecule; nucleosome core; phage Lambda; gene vector
Sun-god seizing Henbet's grain in secret place: Holliday Junction necessary for excision of prophage
Sun-god speaks words, orders copies: early transcription of phage Lambda
Sun-god's word going out; crew traveling through Field of Maati or Net-Ra to River Urnes: DNA in viral head travels down tail to lower fluidity of polar bacterial cell membrane
Terms of Osiris, four: 4 terminators on Lambda genome; conversion of bacterial host gene expression to phage gene expression
wailing, praising: quorum sensing cross-talk or interspecies communication
Water of Re: Lambda DNA traveling down tail; attachment

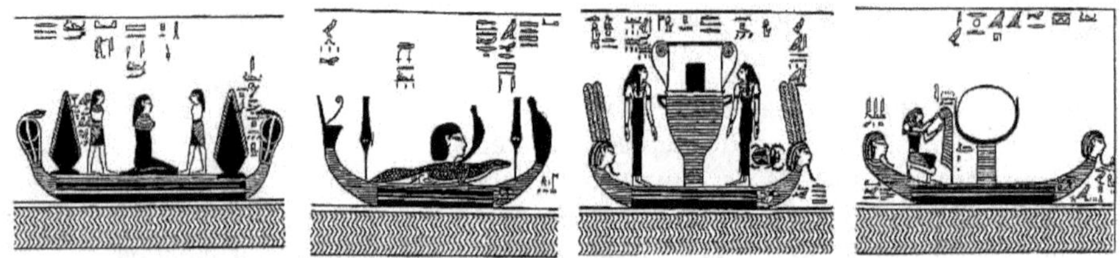

Figure 15.8. Amduat Hour Two Middle Register. Four boats before Sun-Bark (drawing by Budge from Seti I)

Hour Two

Hour Two in Seti I presents the same crew in the Middle Register, but with the enclosed ram-headed Sun-god minus his disk, suggesting that the phage Lambda DNA is now within the bacterium. The forked sceptre or staff in his left hand is a waving elongated snake, depicting an active replication fork, for the Sun-god has entered the host cell. In the prow of the Sun-bark are two uraei called Isis and Nephthys. They are traveling through the watery Field of Urnes. Before the Sun-god's bark are four boats. The first three boats have a *utchat* on each, but the fourth boat of the Grain God Neper does not. Deities line both the Upper and Lower Registers as before, lamenting as the encapsulated Sun-god passes.

The Boat of the Full Moon

At the prow and stern of the first boat are bearded human heads, pointing to phage heads with tails. With the Sun-god now minus the disk on his horizontal horns and the appearance of a large oval disk on the Boat of the Full Moon, we might surmise that the Lambda DNA circularized within the host cell, so it is not degraded but ready for replication. The plume probably signifies Isis, one of the two Maat goddesses. The word *Maat* is written between the plume and disk, reinforcing "Truth, Rightful Order." The text above this boat states that the Deceased is conveyed in the boats of the earth and utters his words, that is, DNA instructions.

The Boat of the Goddess Hathor

The second boat, its ends showing bearded human heads with double plumes on each, carries two goddesses on each side of a large sistrum, symbol of goddess Hathor, and a beetle named Neper in the prow. The double plumes on the bearded heads indicate Nephthys and Isis, the two plumes that ornamented the head of their father Re. We can address the beetle as a transformation symbol and the shaking of a sistrum as a chemical reactive shaking up of atoms for cell processes. The oldest form of Hathor is that of the cow (Budge v1 1904, 428), suggesting milk or lactose. The name of the goddess is Het-Hert, meaning "house above." The cosmic goddess Hathor was the principal female counterpart of Re (429). Her headdress includes the disk between the horns and other forms of plumes, the uraeus, and the sistrum. According to one myth, Hathor was the star Sothis, and she took up her place in the face of Horus or Re as his right eye, that is, the Sun. However, in another myth she was associated with the moon. (436) So Hathor represents a dual functionalism related to two eyes, or the renewal of divinity or humanity as does Isis. To the left of the sistrum is the clause "their boats send forth their words." On the right over the double-plumed front are the words "Osiris crieth to it." The reference to "words" indicates DNA instructions.

The Boat of the Lizard God

Piankoff provides a valuable footnote explaining that the White Crown was the crown of the South and Upper Egypt, whereas the Red Crown was that of the North and Lower Egypt (242). The third boat bears the crown of the South (on prow) and the crown of the North (stern), and its cargo is a lizard between two sceptres. Above the lizard looms the head of Osiris and the crown of the South springs from the lizard. The northern crown represents the left Eye of Horus, with the southern crown representing the right Eye, so the lizard-springing southern crown represents the renewal of the right Eye of Horus. This reptilian form with the head of Osiris is suggestive of rebirth or the regeneration of Osiris and excision of the prophage from a dormant state. Put simply, Osiris is emerging from a primordial or earlier prophage state. In Hour Seven, we meet this image and its symbolism again. The Boat of the Lizard God bears the symbol of the whole eye or *utchat* and the sign for heaven on it, as does the Boat of Hathor and the Boat of the Full Moon. Our next boat does not bear this sign.

The Boat of the Grain-God Neper

The fourth boat carries an armless deity between armless men, behind which are two cone-shaped objects that look like a plant or sheaf of wheat on each end, possibly a reference to the grain-god Osiris, with the prow and stern terminating in the uraei heads. This boat does not have the *utchat* or the sign for heaven, leading one to believe that this boat is not going to be involved in the transformation. The Egyptians honored Osiris as an agricultural god, and according to myth, Osiris was murdered by his brother Seth and then dismembered. This dismemberment was compared with the annual cutting and threshing of wheat. Osiris was thought to rise again with the new crops. (Willis 1993, 42) So this boat without the *utchat* or sign of heaven suggests rebirth, new vegetation or the birth of the human form on earth. We might consider this boat as the template for human reproduction or the Seth lineage in the cell, which is inactive, for the Deceased is dead to the material world and rising as the Horus lineage.

It is possible that armlessness may indicate the dismemberment of Osiris, for the prophage or viral genome in the first prokaryotic cell is replicated and dismembered (1/2, 1/4, 1/8, 1/16 . . .) by DNA replication in its transition to eukaryotic status. But it is more likely that armlessness suggests the nonformation of limbs on earth. Similarly, the lack of two arms may enforce the idea that the two Lambda arms are under cro protein control that does not result in the human creation. Yet, we are traveling in the realm of the chromosome, so armlessness may indicate the absence of expression of the SHH (sonic hedgehog) gene, which is important in limb formation and is found in different species, such as the mouse, fruit fly and human. Mutations in the human Sonic Hedgehog cause holoprosencephaly, a developmental defect of the forebrain and midface (Roessler et al. 1996). When this gene is not expressed, a single central eye known as cyclopia develops. With normal development, this gene is responsible for the separation of the single eye field into two bilateral fields. (Gilbert 2000) In addition, the SHH gene controls the size and shape of brain structures (University of Chicago Medical Center 2001). Other evidence, such as the retreating pig in the Judgement Scene, suggests the retreating SHH gene necessary for human development, so it is likely that armlessness or nonformation of limbs on the Grain-God's boat points to the inactivation of the SHH gene and the sinking of the template for human reproduction.

The Upper Register

Figure 15.9. Amduat Hour Two Upper Register (drawing by Budge from Seti I)

From right to left, the first six seated deities (1-6) have a knife-like form that is stationed just below the breastbone at the base of the sternum, that is, solar plexus. One force determining DNA structure is the electrostatic (repulsion) force. In DNA duplex melting, the repulsion force between phosphate groups favors strand separation. Each of the six deities sits on a throne or foundation of forms that suggests a DNA base. The six gods are also in phage or mummy-shape, with two of these having a human bearded head pointing to phage head and tail structure. The ibis-headed god on the throne (4) is representative of Thoth, the RNA polymerase. As early as the First Dynasty (c. 3050-2850 BCE), Thoth appears in the iconography as a dog-headed baboon and later as an ibis-headed human carrying a pen and palette (Doxey 2002, 353), suggesting transcription. In the Osiris myth, Thoth helps Horus and Anubis reconstruct the dismembered body of Osiris after Isis breathes life back into him.

Also in the Upper Register is a hawk-headed god (8) called Horus of the Duat, pointing to the transformation to the cosmic species. The striking god (9), holding a knife in his left hand is called "Powerful Arm, He who smites his enemies" (translation by Piankoff), suggesting chemical activities related to lysis. The god (12) called "His Two Faces" (Piankoff) represents Seth in his two functional forms. As the hawk-headed god looking to the right, he assists the full operation of the Eye of Horus or the lytic cycle of phage Lambda. The animal head looking to the left suggests the old form or the human creation due to lysogeny and the activation of the SHH gene (Seth pig-animal) for human brain development and limb formation.

In the Upper Register, the crook of Osiris (13) appears, along with the serpent-headed staff of Osiris (14), suggesting an active replication fork. The Osiris Term (15) facing the lioness deity (16) indicates early phage transcription or the antitermination of the terminators to allow gene transcription. Lambda regulates timing of gene expression with antiterminators. The lytic cascade is irrevocable once Q antiterminates PR or the promoter for rightward transcription. When Q antiterminates, mRNA extends around the circular phage chromosome through the head and tail genes. (McClean 1998; Doi et al. 1999) The lioness called "Terrifier of spirits" suggests UV irradiation and impending potential for cell lysis. Next are six goddesses (17-22) and a goddess (23) wearing the Red Crown of the North and Lower Egypt. In RVI, Piankoff depicts two more goddesses, one wearing the White Crown of the South and Upper Egypt and a goddess wearing a single plume named "First Truth (goddess) of the Valley," a reference to Maat or Rightful Order.

The Upper Register deities praise Re as he passes, uttering words on his journey to the divisions of the "great double city" or Mansion of the Six, where the Lambda prophage lodges on the host chromosome. Then they lament, preparing to make souls approach their forms, causing the offerings of the night to come into being, and overthrowing Re's enemies, for the Sun-god is on the lytic pathway.

Lower Register

Figure 15.10. Amduat Hour Two Lower Register (drawing by Budge from Seti I)

Among the deities in the Lower Register, we find three gods with corn on their heads (2-4), three gods (5-7) with wheat or barley in left hands, suggesting the lactose nutrient medium for the Lambda left arm, and three seated gods (9-11) in phage or mummy shape. Two inverted life signs are at the solar plexus of two of the mummy-shaped gods (10-11). Two standing human forms (16-17) also hold the inverted life sign, which may represent either the repression of the human lineage or the two sets of inverted repeats in site-specific recombination of phage Lambda. (Tekle et al. 2002) Recombination at inverted repeats causes an inversion (Mulligan 2001).

Mummy-shaped or phage-dressed Osiris (12) wearing the White Crown suggests excision of the prophage or the rising Osiris. The god Khui (13) holds two lotus-topped sceptres, suggesting regeneration of both arms of Lambda. As mentioned in Part Two, the lotus is a symbol of nascent life or a Calabi-Yau space, a six-dimensional geometrical shape in the quantum core of matter. To follow is a two-headed god (14), a representation of Seth looking to the left and Horus to the right, suggesting the composite function of both arms of the Lambda genome.

The Lower Register deities take instructions from Re, kindle fires to burn up Re's enemies, and lament when Re passes. Additional text explains a conversation between the Duat gods and Re. The Duat gods rejoice, praising Re and making plans to destroy Apopis (LexA repressor) immediately on Re's behalf. Because Re's jawbones are his own (Lambda arms or jaws), the Duat gods believe he will illumine the darkness in the hidden Ament, where he will rest before becoming Khepera in the East. In response, Re asks the gods in his following to help him, so that he can travel to his Eye, avenge them, and order their destinies. His destination at his Eye is the prophage site, where Osiris rests between the *LacZ* (*b-gal*) and *bio* operons on the host chromosome.

Text from Ramesses VI

The introductory text states that Re will enter the earth and open the locks of hair of the gods who wear locks, a direct reference to the double spirals of DNA. He will pass over the Eater of the Ass (Arm?), eat bread, and be given the fore-rope of the barge (241). Piankoff lists Isis the Protectoress as the last goddess in the Upper Register of RVI, along with listing Isis and Nephthys as the two serpents in the bark.

Regarding the Middle Register, Piankoff records the crew of the bark as Opener of the Ways, Mind, Lady of the Barge, Flesh, Horus the Praiser, the Bull of Truth, the Watchful One, and Magic (242-243). The text in the Lower Register states that Re commands the gates to open and tells his followers that they will not decompose. In this register, we also find Osiris Unennefer, a name given to the resurrected Osiris translated as "The one who has arrived to the state of accomplishment" (244 footnote). Piankoff notes that Re is "Expeller of Those whose arms are hidden" (245), suggesting the excision of the Osiris prophage or arms of the Lambda genome. The text at the end of Hour Two states that Re goes in the following of his Bright Eye, that is, the right Lambda arm, and he proceeds upon his left Eye, a reference to the left Lambda arm.

Matrix 9: Amduat Hour Two

Egyptian Sign translated to
Possible Modern Science Parallel

armlessness: absence of SHH gene expression and limb formation; human creation inactive due to Lambda prophage excision (no Lambda arms present)
bearded human heads: phage heads and tails
Boat of Full Moon: circularized, enlarged Lambda DNA
Boat of Goddess Hathor with sistrum that shakes: a chemical reactive shaking up of atoms for cellular processes
Boat of Grain-God Neper with no *utchat*: DNA template for human creation
Boat of Lizard God or Osiris with solar plexus knife: activity of prophage excision and active electrostatic or repulsion force determining DNA structure
Crown of Lower Egypt; northern: left arm of Lambda
Crown of Upper Egypt; southern: right arm of Lambda
Double City, Mansion of Six: 6 operator sites controlling lysis v. lysogeny
god Khui with two lotus-topped sceptres: regeneration of both Lambda arms
god striking; Powerful Arm: chemical reaction of lysis
gods, 3 with barley; Offerings of the Night: lactose nutrient medium
knife at deity's solar plexus: electrostatic force
life signs, inverted: inverted repeats in Lambda site-specific recombination
Lioness, Terrifier of Spirits: UV irradiation; potential for host cell lysis
Osiris, mummy-shape: Lambda prophage
pig urged away by stick-wielding ape: absence of SHH gene expression
Seth of two faces: Lytic pathway (right arm) v. lysogenic pathway (left arm)
Sun-god minus his disk: Lambda DNA injected into cell
Sun-god as expeller: activates prophage expulsion or excision
Sun-god, his Eye: Lambda genome
Sun-god, forked sceptre as wavy snake: active DNA replication fork
Sun-god, jawbones: two Lambda arms of incoming phage
Sun-god, white disk of: Lambda DNA
Term of Osiris: early transcription, N product is an antitermination factor; in delayed early, Q is antiterminator of late genes
Thoth, ibis-headed: RNAP or upregulation of Poly IV due to SOS induction
uraei; Isis/Nephthys in bark: daughter strands after DNA replication; lactose

Hour Three

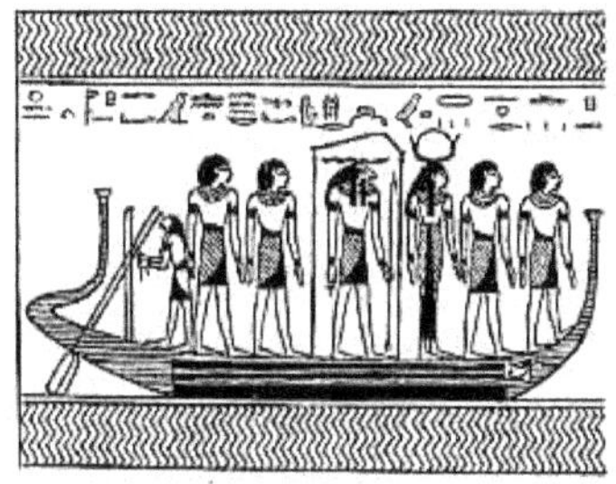

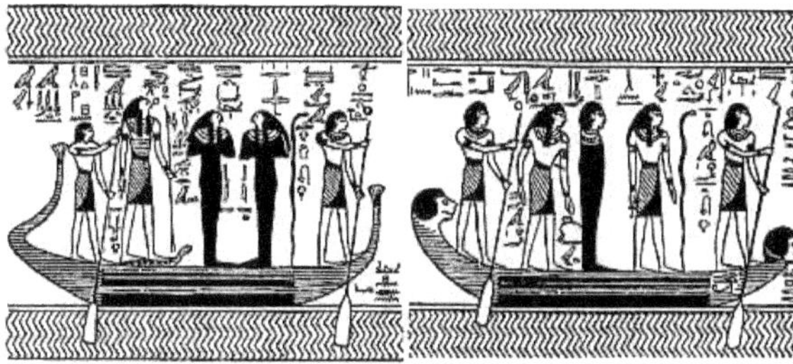

Sun-Bark Boat which capsizeth Boat of Rest

Figure 15.11 Amduat Hour Three Middle Register (drawing by Budge from Seti I)

Boat of the Branch Four Forms of Osiris

Hour Three (SI) depicts the encapsulated ram-headed Sun-god minus his disk with an unwavering forked sceptre or stalled replication fork and a crew of six. Isis is present along with a hawk-headed deity looping ropes around two hawk-headed rowlocks. The text (SI) states that the great god rests for a period in this City or division. Recall that adsorption of Lambda to its host *E. coli* allows penetration of the phage genome into the bacterial cell. For protection, the linear DNA circularizes in the bacterial cell by means of single-stranded 5' extensions of 12 bases at both complementary ends. After ligation, the phage genome becomes a negatively-coiled structure, which means that the DNA twists about its axis in the opposite direction from the clockwise turns of the right-handed double helix. In the first stage, the circular Lambda DNA replicates bidirectionally in the host *E. coli* in a *theta* or circle-to-circle mode, switching later to the *sigma* or rolling circle mode. (Baranska et al. 2001) It yields daughter DNA molecules. So, topologically closed DNA can be loops constrained at the base. The smaller hawk-headed Horus deity on the bark forms looping ropes around two rowlocks at the stern, which may indicate this *theta* mechanism of Lambda replication called circle-to-circle. During the second stage, phage Lambda switches modes from circle-to-circle to a rolling circle replication.

In first-stage *theta* replication, the phage Lambda genome becomes a negatively-supercoiled structure or a left-handed form of the DNA molecule called Z-DNA. Coiled in the shape of a left-handed screw, Z-DNA displays a zig-zag backbone. Negative supercoils arise behind a transcribing RNA polymerase, which plows straight through the DNA double helix instead of rotating around the DNA. (Liu and Wang 1987). A specific protein, dsRNA adenosine deaminase (DRADA), binds tightly to Z-DNA and changes adenine, one of the four components of nucleic acids, so that it acts like guanine. In Hour Four, the Sun-god will travel a zigzag series of corridors in the presence of a winged three-headed serpent. This can be easily decoded to Z-DNA and the "winged" HTH protein DRADA with its three alpha helices.

The Boat which capsizeth

The bark now enters the region Net-Neb-Ua-Kheper-Aut or the "Stream of Osiris." Three boats proceed before the Sun-bark: the first boat after the Sun-bark is called the "boat which capsizeth," the second boat is named "boat of Rest," and the third boat is "The Branch." There is no *utchat* on the "boat which capsizeth," which is steered by two men and contains the hawk-god Bak and hawk-goddess Baket, along with one human-headed form standing on a snake, holding a forked sceptre or inactive replication fork. The hawk-headed human form on a snake indicates the victory of Horus over Apopis. Put simply, the DNA of the human lineage will capsize or be boatless due to the autocatalysis of the LexA repressor protein and consequent de-repression of 42 genes. In Coffin Text 1099, the Deceased Sun-god achieves his goal of bonding with Osiris and states, "I was not boatless in the great crossing." Thus, his victory over Apopis allows the Sun-god to proceed by not capsizing his DNA template. The left Lambda arm is no longer replicating the human lineage DNA, which capsizes due to the inactivation of the monster LexA repressor protein.

The Boat of Rest

The second boat in the procession is the "boat of Rest," which has a *utchat*, cynocephalus heads at each end, and two steersmen, with a mummy-shaped Osiris standing between two human forms. This suggests that the Sun-bark will rest at the prophage attachment site on the bacterial chromosome, that is, the hidden chamber of Osiris. The *E. coli* chromosome site where Lambda integrates (*attB*) is 30 bp in size and contains a central 15 bp region, where the site-specific recombination reaction takes place. Excision of the Lambda prophage conserves the 15 bp elements, which are aligned to excise the integrated segment again. Site-specific recombination of Lambda results in excision of the prophage and regeneration of the original sites on the phage and bacterial chromosomes. (Mulligan 2001)

The Boat of the Branch

The third boat with a *utchat* is called the "Boat of the Branch" and bears mummified Osiris with two legs exposed and the wavy horizontal ram horns on his bearded head. We might take this to mean that Osiris, who stands between a mummified human and another god, is coming out of his dormant prophage state, for his legs are exposed. Lion-heads decorate the prow and stern, and the name of the boat suggests that this boat will branch. This further suggests prophage excision, which results after a short 7 bp branch migration. In fact, the Lambda enzyme Integrase catalyzes the integration and excision of Lambda DNA into and out of the *E. coli* host chromosome at specific attachment sites (Tekle et al. 2002). The enzyme Integrase carries out the recombination reaction steps, including the short 7 bp branch migration (Mulligan 2001). For future reference, excision also requires the Xis protein.

Each of the three boats in front of the Sun-bark contains an elongated serpent standing on its tail. Transcription in the cell is the synthesis of RNA from a DNA template, involving three steps: initiation, elongation, and termination. Elongated serpents represent the elongation stage of transcription, which the ideograms represent here. Four armless forms of Osiris face the boats, possibly suggesting the four Integrase molecules that bind to the two sets of inverted core-type DNA sites that each flank the 7 bp overlap sequence. (Tekle et al. 2002) In Hour Two (Lower Register) gods 10-11 and 16-17 holding inverted life signs represent the two sets of inverted repeats.

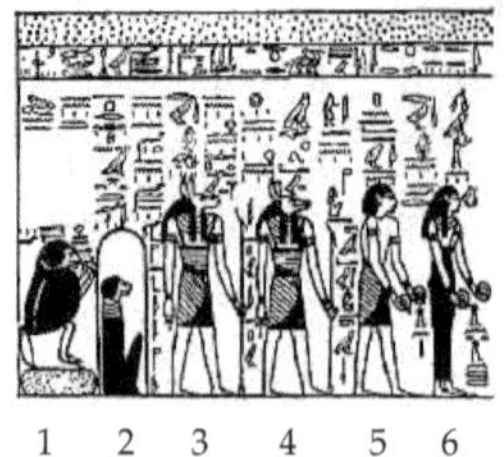

Figure 15.12. Amduat Hour Three Upper Register
(drawing by Budge from Seti I)

The Upper Register is lined with deities, goddesses, dog-headed baboons and jackal-headed gods. Note that a man called Anth (5) bears two pupils of the Eye of Horus, while the woman Antet (6) brings another two. This may indicate the options of renewing both the whole Sun and Moon Eye of Horus, that is, the cosmic species or lytic pathway (Antet), versus the Sun and injured Moon eye or human species and the lysogenic pathway (Anth). In addition, a kneeling man (10) brings the Eye of Re or the integrating Lambda DNA. The SI text related to the Upper Register reads: "flesh of their own bodies" and "their shadows are united unto them." The deities weep when the Sun-god passes. Their work is to take vengeance upon the Seba fiend. If one knows this, he will not be driven off by their "roarings" and never fall down into their "caverns." Roarings suggests a chemical reaction related to the SOS response of the cell, the excision of the prophage and cell lysis. Caverns suggest the ultimate structure of DNA.

Figure 15.13. Amduat Hour Three Lower Register
(drawing by Budge from Seti I)

In the Lower Register four bearded, mummified forms of Osiris (3-6), wearing the White Crown suggest the activation of the prophage and right Lambda arm due to lysis. This is reinforced by the four names: "Osiris, lord of Amentet," "Osiris at the head of Amentet," "Osiris of the two seats," and "Osiris, conqueror of millions of years" (SI). The two seats suggest the left and right arms of Lambda or OR and OL operator sequences. In addition, four seated, bearded, mummified forms of Osiris (16-19) wearing the Red Crown indicate cro protein control of the left Lambda arm. The goddess Ba-Khati (22 top) holds in each hand the two Eyes of Horus. The text once again reinforces the idea of sending forth words or DNA instructions, so that they receive their "heads," which we can take literally as phage heads. Also, the text states that the work of these deities is to hew and hack souls to pieces, set restraints on shadows, and destroy doomed beings that have their "being in their place of destruction which blazeth with fire." The enemies are those with knives on/over heads, suggesting the loss of the electrostatic force. The hydrophobic interaction stabilizes the folded or native state of proteins, but hydrogen bonds, van der Waals forces and electrostatic interactions also play a role (Mulcahy 1997), as the loss of electrostatic force means unstable protein structures.

Text from Ramesses VI

In RVI, the solar bark has a crew of six divinities, but is without the Sun-god in older versions and is preceded by three boats. The boat in front of the solar bark with no name has a ram-headed prow with six occupants, then the next boat has a headless man and woman and is called the Boat of Rest. The ends of the third boat, which is called Boat of Equipment, terminate in lotus flowers with three hawk-headed divinities between two oarsmen, with the first hawk-headed figure holding a sceptre and the sign of life as he stands on a snake. In the Lower Register, the four seated figures of Osiris have distinctive names: "Osiris, Lord of the West," "Osiris at the Head of the Western Land," "Osiris of the Locality," and "Osiris who seizes millions." The last name suggests the millions of phage progeny. Piankoff notes that the text at the end of the Third Hour does not exist in RVI, so he includes the text from Thutmose III. This Eighteenth Dynasty text shows that the two goddesses of Truth lead the Sun-god to the water of the Unique Land, where his rays will penetrate into "the darkness of the Region of Form." The Sun-god states that the soul of Osiris is destined for the sky, while his body is destined for earth, suggesting that the substrate remains in the host cell.

Matrix 10: Amduat Hour Three

**Egyptian Sign translated to
Possible Modern Science Parallel**

Antet, woman with two pupils of Eye: option for new species; lysis; lactose
Anth, man with two pupils of Eye: option of human renewal; lysogeny
Boat of the Branch: short 7-base pair branch migration for prophage excision
Boat of Rest: stalled replication fork near prophage attachment site
Boat which capsizeth, no *utchat*: no replication of human DNA template
Boat which capsizeth, Horus on snake: autocaalysis of LexA repressor protein
caverns: DNA multidimensional phase space; cavern system for mapping functionality
enemies, knives over heads: loss of electrostatic interactions; unstable protein structures
heads, sending words to receive: DNA instructions for phage head assembly
Horus, hawk-headed with looping ropes: circle-to-circle Lambda replication
man kneeling with Eye of Re: integrating or incoming Lambda genome
Osiris, 4 armless forms greeting boats: 4 Integrase molecules that bind to 2 sets of inverted core-type DNA sites that flank 7 base pair overlap sequence
Osiris, 4 bearded, Red Crowned, mummified forms: cro protein control of left Lambda arm
Osiris, 4 bearded, White Crowned, mummified forms: prophage activation, cro protein control of right arm; lytic pathway
Osiris, mummified, legs exposed, wavy ram horns: prophage excision
Osiris of Two Seats: activity of left/right Lambda arms and 6 operator sites
Osiris who seizes millions: production of millions of phage progeny
roarings: chemical reactions of SOS response, lysis, prophage excision
Region of Form, darkness: protein folding funnel
serpents, elongated, upright on boats: elongation stage of transcription
Sun-god's forked sceptre, unwavering: stalled replication fork

Hour Four

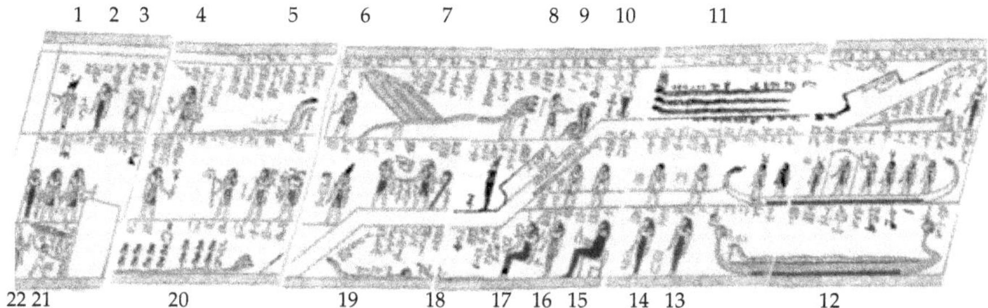

Figure 15.14 Amduat Hour Four Upper, Middle, Lower Registers (drawing by Budge from Seti I)

Hour Four begins a journey through a zigzag series of corridors with doors that represent the dynamic zigzag structure of the host cell's DNA molecule. As described in Hour Three, Z-DNA exhibits a zigzag backbone, and events in Hours Four through Five show that the RNA polymerase (Sun-Bark) is plowing straight through the DNA double helix, leaving negatively supercoiled DNA behind it. This is also suggested by the text: "when the bark travels, it being dragged straight on" (CT60).

The main corridor is Rosetjau or Rosetau, which has several interpretations due to the diverse meanings of Egyptian words. For example, *ro* means mouth or opening, *jau* can mean old god or linen fabric or food offerings, with *jah* meaning rope or tow-line. *Tau* means holy or sacred gate. Thus we have interpretations of the word Rosetjau and Rosetau ranging from "mouth of the far horizon" or "mouth of the chambers" to the "opening or passage of dragging." In reference to Osiris, Ogden Goelet, Jr. notes the translation "the one purified by your own efflux (*setjau*) against (*r*) which the name of Rosetjau was made" (1994, 147). With *ro* meaning mouth and *setjau* meaning efflux, the name suggests the mouth of the efflux or the rising Osiris, which catalyzes the outflow of phage progeny. Goelet suggests that the most likely translation is "place of the dragging" (143). This seems to be a good choice, for like a pulse of slow light traveling through a vortex, the Sun-bark is dragged within the plasma in a fashion similar to the phenomenon that occurs near black holes.

Nonetheless, Rosetau is the Sun-god's destination for his reunion with Osiris at the 15 bp attachment site on the host chromosome, where the Lambda prophage has integrated at the *LacZ* gene. With the SOS response of the cell and the arrival of the Sun-god supramolecular complex, the Lambda prophage is induced to get out of the cell, and this initiates the excision reaction. In this

Hour, Re is wearing the horizontal ram horns with the disk, but has no replication fork.

As a result of the Sun-god arriving at the integration site of Rosetau, Hours Four through Six depict several overlapping chemical processes:

1) stalled replication fork due to thymine dimer (DNA repair process is necessary to pass by the dimer);
2) site-specific recombination (strand exchange, cleavage/rejoining reactions, 7 bp branch migration);
3) recombination-dependent replication;
4) excision of Lambda prophage (requires excisionase XIS, excision repair, regeneration of original two attachment sites on phage and bacterial chromosomes); and
5) possible removal of the *LacZ* gene (specialized transduction) with the excision of the prophage.

As depicted in these Hours, the recombinational and excision repair pathways appear to be the same, for the Sun-god passes over the barrier or Land of Sekri in Hour Five and then encounters the prophage Osiris in Hour Six on the same pathway.

Because Rosetau represents the innermost chambers of DNA, where base pairs are present, the region is depicted as zigzagged, not only because of the zigzag backbone of Z-DNA, but also because thermal fluctuations cause DNA structures to twist, stretch and bend as strands unwind. Specific base pair sequences lead to bends and kinks in the direction of the helix, which Hours Four and Five detail. These kinks and bends on the DNA molecule help proteins identify binding sites necessary for replication, transcription, regulation of gene expression, and DNA repair mechanisms. (Ansari and Marko 2001)

Rosetau is described as the "Land of Sokar, who is on his sand." Sand or desert signifies the hydrophobic bases (cannot form hydrogen bonds with water) oriented perpendicular to the helix axis. Hour Four depicts the Sun-god reaching the hydrophobic interior of the DNA hidden chamber, where a serpent boat for sand or hydrophobic areas is more efficient than one on water or hydrophilic sugar-phosphates on the exterior of the DNA molecule. Since the interior bases are hydrophobic, their stacked structure in the center of the molecule shields them from water. However, with thermal denaturation of DNA, the bases are exposed to water and the solubility decreases. (Brooks 2004). Also, the Sun-god's tow-rope in Hour Four suggests the DNA strand, a term used to designate a chromatid or chromosome, each of which contain a DNA duplex. The term is also used at the molecular level to designate a single nucleotide chain of a DNA duplex. With this brief review, let's look at chemical reactions in Hour Four.

In the Middle Register, the encapsulated, ram-headed Sun-god now sports a disk between his horns, but has no replication fork, so it seems that the Sun-god is at rest as indicated by the Boat of Rest in Hour Three that signifies a stalled replication fork at the prophage attachment site due to a DNA lesion, template strand break, a bound protein complex or other barrier such as a thymine dimer. The Sun-god and his crew are in a boat with serpent heads on the prow and stern, which is dragged by four gods, suggesting the four Lambda Integrase molecules, which integrate and excise Lambda DNA into and out of the *E. coli* host chromosome.

The flames emitted by the Sun-god's boat guide him through these pools, where he cannot see forms, yet he cries out to them so they hear his voice. Deities and serpents line both registers. In front of the four gods towing the boat is a bearded, mummified Osiris form wearing the White Crown, the crook of Osiris, ibis-headed Thoth, and the hawk-headed Horus with outstretched hands holding the *utchat*. Thoth's title is "the raiser," which seems appropriate because Osiris Lambda DNA is rising, and Thoth represents RNA polymerase or perhaps DNA polymerase IV that is active in recombination-dependent replication leading to the excision of the prophage. The deity with the two-pronged object in place of a head suggests divergence, and this is related to stalled and active replication forks. These deities are the "hidden travelers" in the hidden place of the Duat, that is, the innermost chambers or caverns of DNA, where Osiris or the Lambda genome is lodged.

Of interest in the Upper Register is the god Ap-Tuat (6), holding a forked sceptre or stalled replication fork and standing before the serpent Neheb-Kau (5) that bears two serpent heads on one end of its long body and a third serpent head on the other. It seems possible that the two heads of the serpent Neheb-Kau on one end may suggest DNA denaturation or the separation of two strands of DNA, as the RNA polymerase moves through the DNA double helix. The third serpent head emerging from the ground or sand signifies the action of some DNA-binding protein or bacterial restriction enzyme to cut or edit the DNA, for the Sun-bark is called "The One who cuts the way" (RVI). As Piankoff translates, the serpent enables the towing of the Sun-god toward the "Hidden One" or Osiris.

This image of Neheb-Kau also points to the change in shape brought on by the right-handed B-DNA double helix shifting to the thinner, elongated left-handed Z-DNA conformation that involves flipping the base pairs upside down. Modern biologists have shown that Z-DNA formation in *E. coli* is regulated by transcription. (Herbert and Rich 1996). However, *E. coli* RNA polymerase does not transcribe through Z-DNA (Peck and Wang 1985). Based on the Egyptian evidence, this work posits that Polymerase IV or V and RecA protein transcription result in Z-DNA formation. Kim et al. (1989) have shown that RecA binds much faster to Z-DNA than B-DNA. However, exactly as to how RecA, Poly IV and Z-DNA interact must be posed as an Outstanding Question. Nonetheless, the Pharaohs are mapping *E. coli* reactions in *vivo* (in a living organism), so it appears that the biological role for Z-DNA relates to inverting the DNA molecule for a unique transcription resulting in the recombinant species.

Ap-Tuat opens the way for the two gods, suggesting Re and Osiris, and Neheb-Kau is the holy way of passage of Rosetau. The third serpent head is held by a god (4), whose other hand holds a lasso or lariat. In genetics, a lariat is a lasso-shaped intermediate in certain splicing reactions. Lariat structure is the structure of an intron immediately after excision, in which the 5' end loops back and forms a 5'-2' linkage with another nucleotide. The lariat-holding god is facing a headless god named Ab-Tuat (3), holding a forked sceptre or stalled replication fork. Headlessness represents the lack of penetration and killing power, for the phage head contains all phage sulphur, host range specificity, penetration enzyme and killing power. (Anfinsen 1959, 82)

Replication at this point is stalled by not only Ap-Tuat (6) and the serpent Neheb-Kau (5), indicating DNA denaturation and Z-DNA potential, but also by the headless god Ab-Tuat (3), representing stalled replication without DNA denaturation potential. As mentioned, the first stage of Lambda replication is bidirectional, so these images represent the change to second-stage, unidirectional rolling circle replication with the excision of the prophage. Once again, as in Hour One, the Upper Register shows three serpents moving side by side (11), suggesting messenger, ribosomal and transfer RNA. Thus, we have indicators for the chemical reactions of DNA denaturation, Z-DNA formation, rolling circle replication, and excision of the prophage.

The SI text states that we will meet the guardians of these chambers, and thus, in the Upper Register we meet the scorpion Ankhet (10), a large uraeus (9), and a god (8) offering two eyes to the uraeus, suggesting the whole Eye or both Lambda arms under cro control. The uraeus is a symbol of divinity and royalty, and the walls of Osiris' abode are surmounted by "living uraei" (Budge v2 1904, 377), whereas the scorpion may represent the many feet of phage progeny.

Next is the winged, three-headed serpent (7) with two pairs of human legs and feet, looking toward the Sun-god. This winged HTH DNA-binding protein with three helices represents dsRNA-specific adenosine deaminase (DRADA), a protein that functions to modify viral RNA genomes. With the formation of Z-DNA, as denoted by the zigzag corridors, the arrival of DRADA at this precise point is additional evidence that our decoding of imagery is correct. The RNA polymerase plows through the DNA, leaving Z-DNA in its wake as the editing enzyme DRADA modifies the information. Also, the three-headed DNA-binding protein greeting the Sun-god has the *ankh* sign beneath its heads, suggesting that it is favorable to the Sun-god's arrival or active. We can conclude that the libations offered to the uraeus and the life sign beneath the three-headed DRADA serpent signify that Osiris is rising and that cro protein has won the battle for genetic control over cI.

Figure 15.14a. Amduat Hour Four, Lower Register Image 20 (drawing by Budge from Seti I)

More evidence for the view that cro protein has won the battle for genetic control is the second three-headed serpent (20) in the Lower Register that greets the Sun-god. Like the Lambda repressor cI, the cro protein also has three helices (Marcey 2001). This three-headed serpent Menmenut is the hidden image of Seker or cro, and it has 14 human heads, each head bearing a disk and six stars from Budge's drawing from the tomb of Seti I. The tomb of Ramesses VI depicts 14 stars rather than six, according to Piankoff. The serpent carries the gods of the first 14 days of the month to the *utchat*, which Thoth and Horus carry to it. In other words, the 14 disks represent the protein product of the cro gene building up to a critical level and then binding to the OR and OL sequences to stop early transcription and commence late transcription. The 14 bearded heads represent production of phage heads with tails.

It is also possible that the 14 stars represent phage morphology. The evolutionary adaptive bacteriophage Lambda is extremely small, but the morphology can be obtained by electron microscopy. Levinthal and Thomas embedded bacteriophage particles in an electron-sensitive emulsion, and the passage of fast electrons emitted during radioactive decay caused the formation of a track of silver grains. Since the single phage particle acted as a point source, it caused the formation of a star in the emulsion, due to the decay of a phosphorus atom. This detecting method is so sensitive that researchers estimate the radioactivity of a phage particle emits about 15 disintegrations per month. The number of tracks per star measures the molecular size of the emitting source relative to the intact phage particle. (Anfinsen 1959)

The 14 stars, 14 heads and 14 disks may relate to the protein product of the cro gene building up to a critical level, phage morphology, and the radioactive phage particle emissions, which are equivalent to about 15 disintegrations per month. The first 14 days of the month indicate the progression of the phage protein product. In line with this idea, the image with 14 heads also suggests phage head packing with DNA that expands the capsid to mature size. The concatemer is the substrate for head packing. The stars may indicate the transition from a hexagonal to a star-shaped configuration, similar to that found in bacteriophage T4, which has 14 structural proteins. (Crowther et al. 1977) Another Outstanding Question arises—does phage Lambda undergo a transition from the hexagonal to a star-shaped configuration similar to T4?

To the left of the three-helix cro protein and before the door, is a striking god (21) with his right arm raised, indicating cell lysis activities. This same image is present in the Edifice of Taharqa (see Part Four), related to the destruction of the world, that is, cell lysis. Also, the large serpent (12) in a boat, its ends terminating with the heads of women suggesting lactose, is parallel to the Sun-god's boat in the Middle Register. This large serpent with the *ankh* sign beneath its head guards the Aheth chamber and represents a concatemer or long tandem repeats of the Lambda DNA genome, the substrate for head packing. During the replication of phage Lambda, when it switches replication modes from circle-to-circle to rolling circle, the concatemer is cleaved and used to fill empty Lambda heads during the phage assembly process. (Smith 2000)

Now, at this point the bidirectional replication forks are stalled. Research shows that the cessation of DNA replication during SOS results from the collision of replication forks with sites of DNA damage (Cox 2001). However, the text and drawings not only indicate the presence of lactose by goddesses

(16-17) and women (13-14), but they also show that the Sun-god will not rest or stall for long. Restart starts with repair as Hour Five depicts.

Text from Ramesses VI

Piankoff uses the introductory text from other versions because it is omitted in RVI. This text states that the towing of Re is stopped in this cavern called "Life of Forms," suggesting the DNA foundation of the Lambda genome. The text above the Upper Register states that Re is at the mysterious ways of Ro-Setau, which Piankoff translates as "The Gate of the Passages." Because of corrupted text, Piankoff uses older versions that reference deities such as "She who guards the Rising One," which indicates Isis or the *LacZ* gene where the prophage is lodged. The god holding two eyes is "He who separates the Two Gods," that is, Horus from Seth. (255) Put simply, Horus and Seth are not fighting, which signifies cro protein production, cell lysis, and the prophage excision, or the rising Osiris that causes the birth of the Horus lineage and the transfiguration of the Deceased Sun-god.

In the Middle Register, the Sun-bark is named "The One who cuts the Way," and the four towers of the bark are named the "Mysterious One," "The One who keeps the *Nefert*-rope," "The One who presides the *Uart*-rope," and "The One who stretches the rope, the Just-One." The three names referencing the tow-rope of the Sun-bark suggest the activity of the DNA strand stretching and replication. The name of the Udja-eye (*utchat*) held by two gods is "Sokaris" (257). The last three gods and goddess in this register are called "Living Image" or "He who conducts life," "The One who brings the Distant One," "The One who commands," and "The Lady of Life," which again indicates Isis and the lactose nutrient medium (*LacZ*). The major portion of phage protein is derived from the nutrient medium (Anfinsen 1959, 82), that is, Isis, the Lady of Lactose Provisions. With the Sun-bark cutting the way at the prophage site, the activity is the precise break/join events involved in the 7 bp branch migration. The Distant One is Horus, as the meaning of his name denotes.

In the Lower Register, the name of the elongated serpent (12) or concatemer in the boat is "Moving Radiance." The diagram of the three-headed serpent (20) or cro protein with its 14 disks above 14 heads is very similar to Budge's depiction from Seti I, with the exception that there are 14 stars under the heads. This serpent is called "The Shaker," the mysterious image in which light is evident at the birth of Khepri (259). Shaking indicates the displacement of atoms in a chemical reaction, as does the sistrum (Hour Two). The Lower

Register text mentions that Anubis enters the mysterious road to "him who hides the body of Osiris." The passage doors are called "Knife which joins the Earth," "Knife of him who sees the Earth," and "Knife of Eternity," indicating once again the cleavage activity related to site-specific recombination-dependent excision of the prophage Osiris. Finally, the last goddess (22) is named "Truth" or Maat, that is, Rightful Order.

Matrix 11: Amduat Hour Four

Egyptian Sign translated to Possible Modern Science Parallel

Ab-Tuat, headless holding forked sceptre: stalled replication fork lacking DNA denaturation potential
Ap-Tuat with forked sceptre before serpent Neheb-Kau: stalled replication fork with DNA denaturation potential
deities and serpents lining registers: nucleotides on DNA strands and proteins
deity with 2-pronged object for head: modern sign for divergence
flames from Sun-bark: an internal source of light or photoreactivation process
god holding 2 eyes or He who separates the Two Gods: whole function of both arms/eyes of Lambda genome
god striking, right arm raised: cell lysis activities
god with lasso holding serpent head: indicator of excision and restriction enzyme; lariat or lariat structure
headlessness: lack of penetration and killing power
Isis, Lady of Life: lactose provision for phage protein
knife references, Hr. 4: cleavage activity related to excision
One who brings the Distant One; Horus: birth of recombinant species
Rosetau: hydrophobic inner chambers of DNA
sand or desert references: hydrophobic interior of DNA base pairs
scorpion Ankhet guarding: sign for inversion
serpent boat for sand versus water boat: hydrophobic DNA interior movement versus former hydrophilic sugar-phosphate travel on exterior DNA molecule
serpent Moving Radiance: DNA concatemer for phage head assembly
serpent Neheb-Kau with serpent in its train looking backward: Z-DNA
serpent, Shaker, 3-headed, 14 stars, 14 heads, 14 disks: cro protein for phage replication and translation to protein
  14 disks: cro protein product building up to critical level to bind to OR, OL
  14 bearded heads: phage head and tail production
  14 stars: phage morphology; radioactive phage particle emissions equivalent to about 15 disintegrations per month; transition from hexagonal to the star-shaped configuration
serpent, 3-headed, winged: winged HTH DNA-binding protein DRADA
She who guards the Rising One: *LacZ* gene where prophage is lodged
Sun-bark dragged straight on: RNA polymerase transcription straight through the double helix, leaving negatively coiled DNA behind
Sun-bark, One who cuts the Way: cleavage due to 7 bp branch migration
Sun-bark towed by 4 gods: the 4 Integrase molecules, which integrate and excise Lambda DNA into and out of the *E. coli* host chromosome
Sun-god crying out and wailing of deities: interspecies cross-talk
Sun-god without forked sceptre: stalled replication fork
Sun-god's destination for reunion with Osiris: 15 bp attachment site at *LacZ*
Sun-god's tow-rope: DNA strand
Thoth and Horus holding utchat named Eye of Sokaris: indicates transcription and replication for phage production
Thoth as the Raiser: indicates excision of prophage due to transcription
zigzag series of corridors/doors: kinks and bends on DNA molecule; Z-DNA

Hour Five

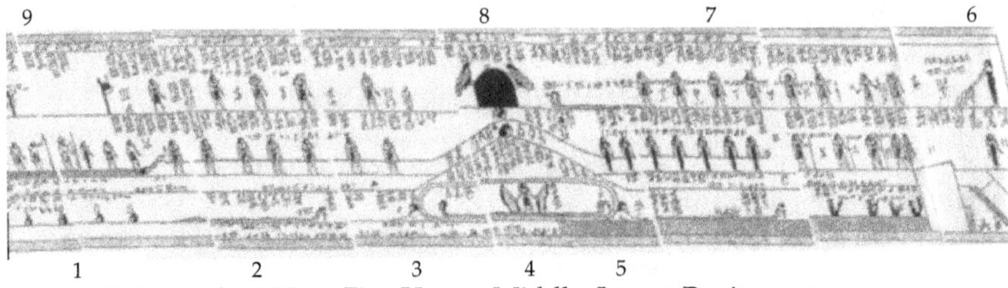

Figure 15.15 Amduat Hour Five Upper, Middle, Lower Registers (drawing by Budge from Seti I)

In the SI Middle Register, seven gods and seven goddesses, signifying the 7 bp branch migration necessary for excision of the prophage, tow the Sun-god's boat so he can advance through this circle. His forked sceptre is now a waving serpent, suggesting an active replication fork. Strand exchange is taking place, and the towline represents this activity. Typically, RecA protein forms a filament around ssDNA, pairs with a linear DNA duplex, and aligns homologous sequences between the two DNAs. Then a strand exchange occurs within the filament. (Shan and Cox 1997) Before the towing deities march four gods (Integrase molecules), who give food under the guidance of Isis, the lactose nutrient medium. When the sugar lactose is present, the operon is de-repressed and transcription of the polycistronic mRNA encoding *LacZ*, *LacY* and *LacA* begins (Hewlett 2000), suggesting that the winged three-headed serpent in the mound is CAP protein at the *LacZ* gene (4), where the prophage is lodged in the dark chamber (8). What remains of the broken SI text informs us that the earth is opened, Re is crying out to the Land of Seker, and Horus has life. At this point, the Sun-bark is towed over the Land of Seker, who guards the "hidden flesh." Apparently, this biochemical bump represents the Lambda attachment site that modern geneticists also diagram as a bump on a chromosome.

The Land of Seker

The SI image of the Land of Seker or the *LacZ* gene site, where the prophage is lodged, is an interesting portrait of Lambda prophage excision, the start of rolling circle replication, and *lac* operon activity. A long ellipse full of sand sits between two man-headed sphinxes (3, 5), having only heads and forequarters, suggesting a Double Lion or thymine dimer, which may have influenced the cessation of replication forks in Hour Four. Within the ellipse is an elongated serpent or CAP protein (4), having two serpent heads at one end, suggesting DNA denaturation, and a bearded human head facing backwards at the other end, suggesting Z-DNA. Only genes being expressed have Z-DNA in them (MIT News 1995), so we can assume that the *lac* genes are being expressed. (Please note that Piankoff's text depicts a serpent with three heads on the right, whereas Budge depicts only two heads on the right.)

As discussed, *lac* operon activity is stimulated by CAP protein, which is thought to be bound to its *lac* binding site at all times, even during repression. CAP is classified by modern biologists as a winged HTH protein with a *beta*-sheet structure and three *alpha*-helices that bind to the CRP site near the *lac* operon promoter to stimulate transcription and interact with the RNA polymerase. When glucose is low, cAMP/CRP forms and binds to the protein CAP. The *lac* operon is de-repressed by high levels of cAMP/CRP. Increased cAMP concentration leads to increased affinity for specific DNA-binding sites. As a homodimer, each subunit binds to a symmetric half-site. The monomers have a two-domain structure composed of a C-terminal domain of three *alpha*- helices and N-terminal with an extensive *beta*-sheet cAMP-binding site followed by a long *alpha*-helix. (University College London) The structure of CAP protein easily matches the image within the Land of Seker, but does the function of the enzyme support the chemical reaction?

Above this elongated serpent within the oval is hawk-headed Seker, holding a large wing in each hand, which suggests the activation of enzymes such as CAP protein to process lactose. A woman's head facing to the right is at the apex of the pyramidal mound containing the ellipse, suggesting Isis and lactose. Once again, the Lambda prophage (Osiris) is lodged at the *LacZ* gene (Isis), which this drawing depicts, for the goddesses address Re, saying that Isis gives herself to him. Above the woman's head, one-half of a scarab beetle is emerging from a dark chamber with a rounded roof (8) to unite with the roads of the Duat. Two large hawks cling to this chamber, suggesting the regal emergence of the Lambda prophage. The SI text informs us that this is the Image of the god "whose legs are bent round," that is, Osiris emerging from the prophage state and the change from *theta* replication to rolling circle replication. So, both imagery and text support the function of CAP protein related to *lac* operon activation.

The Thymine Lion Dimer

The representation of Seker's sphinx-based ellipse actually looks similar to a thymine dimer. Envision each lion (3,5) as a pyrimidine. A thymine dimer is a pair of abnormally chemically bonded adjacent thymine bases in DNA, resulting from damage by UV irradiation. The attachment sites on the phage (*attP*) and bacterial chromosome (*attB*) reflect the following core DNA sequence and indicate thymine dimer formations (TT):

AttP	tCAGCTTt	tTtatAc	tAAGTTGg
AttB	cCTGCTTt	tTtatAc	tAACTTGa

Integrase binds to the left and right sides of the core sites, cutting the DNA within the core site to initiate recombination (Maloy 2000). When Integrase binds to an isolated arm site or to the P'1,2 pair of arm sites, it induces bends of approximately 35 to 45 degrees. The bends during site-specific recombination are also induced by the virally-encoded Xis and the bacterially-encoded IHF and FIS, as the proteins carry out integration and excision. (Thompson and Landy 1988; Radman-Livaja et al. 2003). The bends form the intasome structure, which is a nucleoprotein structure, wrapping approximately 230 bp of DNA (Rosenstiel 2001), and then the Integrase molecules are able to capture a partner *att* site in a synaptic complex ready for recombination. Synapsis during recombination is when the two molecules come together. Strand nicking and joining occur at the core sites within the intasome bound by the Integrase tetramer. Recombination continues resolving the Holliday junction intermediate. (Radman-Livaja et al. 2003)

Looking at the Seti I bending diagram of the DNA in Hours Four and Five, the bends are approximately 35 to 45 degrees, paralleling modern research. Integrated Lambda DNA is flanked by two hybrid *att* sites: *attL* (left) and *attR* (right), each derived from one-half *attP* and *attB*. Both *attL* and *attR* are necessary for Lambda excision. (Rosenstiel 2001) What the Pharaohs are linking together in Hour Five is the excision of the Lambda prophage from the *attL* site, as represented by the beetle's chamber, and the *attR* site, as represented by the biochemical bump of the Land of Sekri, where the thymine dimer is located near the bacterial *LacZ* gene. The 14 deities with the tow-rope indicate the intermolecular reaction of the 7 bp cut and recombination, so that the cell can enter rolling circle replication for phage production and the prophage can excise. The 14 deities pulling the Sun-god seem to spool the tow-cord between the half-emergent beetle (prophage) and the head of Isis (*LacZ* gene), which signifies the 7 bp branch migration at this site on the host chromosome along with the proper lactose nutrient level for excision and phage protein. These 14 deities represent the 7 bp branch migration, along with the X-structure known as the Holliday junction, an intermediate in Lambda site-specific recombination.

The Holliday Junction

A Holliday junction forms during recombination when one strand from each of two duplex DNA segments is exchanged in a region of sequence homology, yielding a branched structure with four duplex arms (Gopaul et al. 1998). The X-structure can be envisioned as a cross, with the dark chamber of the emerging beetle lined above the Land of Sekri perpendicular to the pathway of the Sun-bark. The bend or biochemical bump caused by the thymine lion dimer forces the Sun-bark into the narrow passage between the beetle and the woman's head. The image of the lion dimer is also found in Plate Seven of the Book of the Dead, where two lions stand back-to-back with the *akhet*-sign "horizon, bright place" between them. (Goelet 1994, 159)

Recent research (Radman-Livaja et al. 2003, 791-792) illuminates the nature of the unique conformation (bent, antiparallel, bridging nonpartners) formed when Integrase Holliday junction tetramer binds simultaneously to the arm site and a core site, each having inverted and direct repeats. The conformation looks remarkably similar to the god Thath-neteru (Hr. Six) in mummified form with his obvious arms holding a sceptre and knife that cross. Piankoff translates the god's name Thath-neteru as "Purification of the Gods" (272). The meaning of *purify* is "to clear or purge from," which is similar in meaning to *resolve*, "to clear away or dispel." Because interlinking DNA molecules in a four-way junction is potentially disastrous for replicating cells, a Holliday junction needs resolution or clearing. Research shows that a Holliday junction resolution can initiate recombination reactions (Sharples 2001), and Hour Five drawings indicate this link as does the Hour Six god Thath-neteru depicting Holliday junction resolution. Also, in the Middle Register of Hour One, a god called Henebty holds two crooks crossed like an X, an early indicator of the Holliday junction intermediate in site-specific recombination. Breaks can also occur at the transition to rolling circle replication (2001), which the Amduat is indicating by recombination-dependent replication, allowing the genome to resume replication when the cell machinery is blocked. Yet, resolution will occur in Hour Six.

Text from Ramesses VI

The introductory text of RVI states that Re will make mysterious land arrangements in the cavern carrying the divine flesh, a reference to the cutting for the 7 bp branch migration necessary for prophage excision. The Gate is called "Stop of the Gods" and the Cavern is that of the Hidden One or the prophage Osiris. The mound from which the beetle emerges is called "Night," and the two hawks are Isis and Nephthys the Mourners, who mourn because Osiris is inert. In the Middle Register, the text above the Sun-bark references Re as "cleaver of the ground" and indicates that Khepri lifts the tow-rope for Re, which is depicted in Plate 84. The text above the woman's head on the mound indicates that the Sun-god rests here and gives orders. In the older versions, the text states that the head is the flesh of Isis, which we can interpret to mean the *LacZ* gene. The four gods in front of the 14 deities that tow are deities under the authority of Isis for food provisions, and the last goddess is Isis of the West, reinforcing the idea that the prophage is lodged at the *LacZ* gene.

In the Lower Register, the text under the woman's head within the pyramidal mound states that the flesh of Sokaris, who is on his Sand, is in thick darkness and the Double Lion god Aker guards the image. The text then describes the image as an egg that is lit by Aker's eyes, with shining flesh and legs as coils inside the egg. This again suggests the emerging recombinant species due to lactose provision and Lambda prophage excision. When Re passes by, a noise is heard inside the egg like a roaring storm. The text then states that the Sun-god does not pass by the gods in the Imhat Necropolis, and that the inhabitants of the Netherworld will have no access to that fiery water in the Land of the Dead. The text in the passage above the four heads with flames (1) states that Isis enters the Land of Sokaris to be behind her brother, suggesting that the lactose nutrient medium stimulates the excision of the prophage. The Land is filled with flames from the mouth of Isis, another indicator of the energy of the lactose medium that promotes excision of the prophage. The nutrient medium is also suggested by the name of the serpent after the four burning heads, which is "The Taster" (2), a reference to tasting the sweetness of the milk sugar lactose.

In Seti I, four of the nine axes (9) are broken off and none are showing in the drawing, yet Piankoff (RVI) also identifies the group of nine axes and the names of the "divine symbols" as Khepri, Shu, Tefnut, Geb, Nut, Osiris, Isis, Nephthys, and Horus, so we are back to the first Great Ennead without Seth, the origin of time before the rivalry of cro and cI. These axes will cleave the concatemer in Hour Six for the Horus lineage. In line with this idea of cleavage, we also observe a goddess (6) stretching her hands over the head of a small suicidal figure, holding an ax to its head, and the text states that the goddess "lives upon the blood of the dead." This may represent the regulation of Integrase and excise genes of phage Lambda that depend on RNA degradation. (Carnegie Mellon University)

RNA Interference and Cell Lysis

In light of the above suicidal ideogram and the Sun-bark as a representation of the RNA polymerase complex, one must remember that there is a corresponding mRNA—that of the human lineage, which must be targeted for destruction. The texts affirm that the Deceased has "sunk the bark of the enemies" (BD125A). As an example, in caenorhabditis elegans, the target for RNAi is the endogenous (meaning growing or proceeding from within) mRNA. The degradation of this homologous mRNA occurs before translation. (Fire et al. 1998) RNA interference is the ability of double-stranded RNA to suppress the expression of a gene corresponding to its own sequence. This ability, which represents an ancient cellular defense to control viral infection or to silence transposons, is a basic mechanism of gene regulation, resulting in apoptosis.

Hippocrates (460-370 BCE) first used the term "apoptosis" to mean "the falling off of the bones." The characteristic morphology includes cell shrinkage, chromatin condensing to the periphery of the nucleus forming crescents, loss of nuclear pores, cytoplasm membrane blebbing, and phagocytosis of apoptotic bodies by neighboring cells or macrophages. Phagocytosis is the ingestion and destruction of particulate matter by cells. Two main integration pathways converge to a common execution phase, and dead cellular matter is removed. This bifurcation to the death receptor pathway is caused by apoptosis.

Looking at this process more closely, what happens on the cellular level is that homologous mRNAs are degraded by being cleaved or chopped up into 21-23nt small interfering RNAs by an enzyme called DICER (DCR-1) In animals and plants, these shortened, small interfering RNAs assemble into a RNA-induced silencing complex, binding and destroying homologous RNA molecules. Homologous means that the mRNA would have a corresponding structure or origin, but not necessarily a corresponding function. There are three phases to the process (Elbashir et al 2001; McManus et al. 2002):

1) Initiation: cells receive the death-inducing stimulus such as shortage of metabolic supply;
2) Effector: regular pattern of metabolic reactions and the "decision to die is taken;"
3) Degradation: increase in overall entropy and apoptosis becomes apparent.

The Degradation of Osiris

Along with the group of nine large axes (9) (not shown in the Upper Register drawing) is the associated Seti I text: "O nine gods who have come into being from my flesh, and have not come into being from your own forms." So we could say that the chemical reaction of concatemer cleavage is nearing. Yet, this is related to phage replication, not cell lysis. Degradation is DNA fragmentation or massive protein degradation. In the Book of Two Ways, Piankoff translates Coffin Text 1087 as "It is the decomposition of Osiris of Rosetau;" other texts reference the degradation of Osiris, which indicates this process. Three major events in cell death are the rapid engulfment by phagocytes, complete elimination of cell corpses, and the digestion of chromosomal DNA.

Also related are the eight gods (7) in the Upper Register (SI), who stand by at the annihilation of the dead by burning (thermal chemical reactions) and by cutting and hacking or cleavage. The god with the two lassos is part of this group. Re addresses the eight gods referencing the "blocks of torture," "destruction of the dead," "hack in pieces shades [of men and women]," and "who avenge Osiris" (SI). The text in RVI related to the eight gods also identifies them as executioners with the same function.

Matrix 12. Amduat Hour Five

Egyptian Sign translated to
Possible Modern Science Parallel

ax to head of small figure: cell death (apoptosis); DNA degradation
axes, 9: chemical reaction of concatemer cleavage
beetle emerging from dark chamber: excising Lambda prophage
bends in Hr. 4 and Hr. 5 roads: Lambda Integrase binding to arm sites induces 35-45 degree bends
flames from mouth of Isis: lactose energy medium
flaming heads, 4: head assembly through lactose energy medium
flesh of Sokaris; egg of shining flesh, coiled legs: Lambda prophage
god Iu-her-aptesu holding 2 lassos: lariat structure
gods of annihilation (8): chemical reactions of cleavage and DNA degradation
gods (4) providing food under Isis: Lambda Integrase tetramer; sufficient phage nutrient level for excision of prophage
gods (7) and goddesses (7) towing Re: 7 bp branch migration for excision
hidden country of Sekri guarding hidden flesh: Lambda prophage
land arrangements in cavern of divine flesh: 7 bp branch migration/excision
Land of Sekri with Double Lion: prophage attachment site with thymine dimer
Osiris with legs bent round: rolling circle replication
Osiris Unnefer, rising Osiris: prophage excision
Seker on sand/desert: hydrophobic DNA interior
serpent, 3-headed, winged: CAP protein at *LacZ* gene
serpent, the Taster: *lac* operon activity or production of sweet sugar lactose
Sun-god forked sceptre waving: active replication fork
Sun-god Re resting in Nu: chemical reaction of stopping due to TT formation
Sun-god Re uniting to roads: DNA transcription, replication; initiates excision
woman's head on Land of Sekri; flesh of Isis: *LacZ* gene site where prophage is lodged; lactose nutrient for excision
X formed by Chamber/Land of Sekri and roads of Sun-god: Holliday junction cross

Hour Six

Figure 15.16 Amduat Hour Six Sun-bark
(drawing by Budge from Seti I)

In SI Hour Six, the Middle Register depicts the encapsulated Sun-god with a crew of eight in his original boat. He is traveling the hidden path of Amentet and paddling to the place of the "body of Osiris." In both SI and RVI, the Sun-bark terminates in lotus flowers, suggesting the movement to the core of matter or Lambda DNA. Surprisingly, thrones are absent, suggesting the creation of forms or DNA. Recall that in Hour Four, the Sun-god stops in the cavern called "Life of Forms," suggesting the DNA foundation of the Lambda genome (Osiris) on the host chromosome next to the *LacZ* gene.

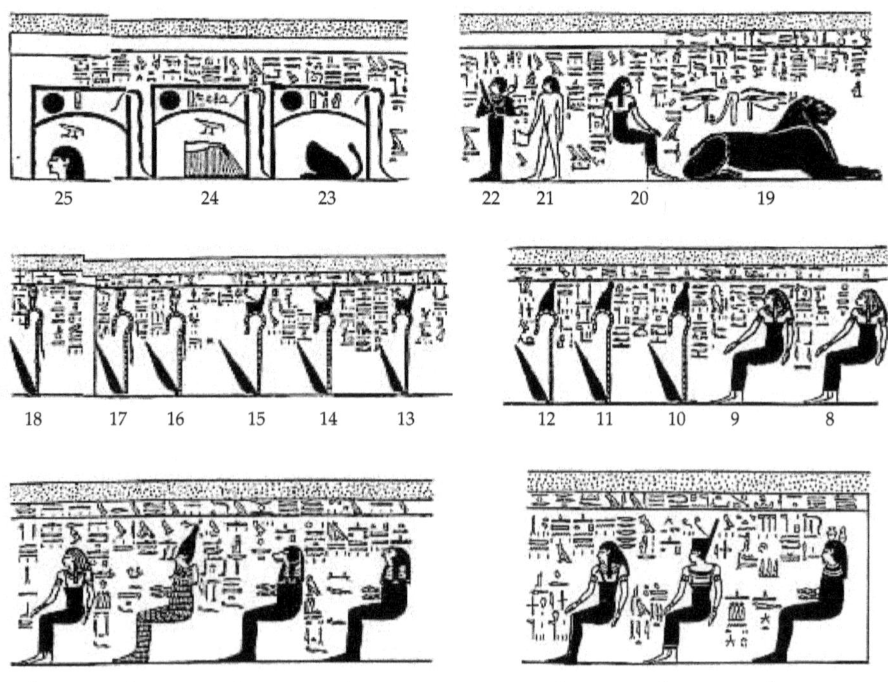

Figure 15.17 Amduat Hour Six Upper Register (drawing by Budge from Seti I)

From right to left, the Upper Register contains nine deities (1-9) seated without thrones, nine sceptres (10-18) or emblems of fertility representing nine Lambda replication forks, a reclining lion Ka-Hemhemet (19) with both the left and right Eyes of Horus above, suggesting the full operation of the Eye of Horus, a seated goddess without throne (20), a standing deity (21), and the resolving god Thath-neteru (22), who signifies Holliday junction resolution related to the excision of the prophage Osiris. Regarding the nine sceptres (10-18), the Sun-god informs us that "their souls shall rise up in the Tuat on their sceptres," indicating phage genesis.

The Upper Register also contains three chambers with an opening under the roof through which a serpent, which stands on its tail outside, belches fire. The first chamber (23) contains the image of Re, in the form of the hind-quarters of a lion; the second chamber (24) contains an image of Re in the form of a hawk's wing; the third chamber (25) represents Re in the form of a human head. These three chambers may indicate a codon or section of DNA made up of three nucleotides that either codes for a particular amino acid, or serves the purpose of starting protein synthesis. But more likely, the chambers represent the three promoters of phage Lambda. The human head chamber signifies the PL promoter; the hawk wing signifies the PR promoter, and the headless lion signifies the cI or PRM (promoter for repressor maintenance). The headlessness of the lion also indicates the tameness of the reclining lion Ka-Hemhemet. Two of these Lambda promoters allow transcription of lytic genes, whereas the PRM allows transcription of a repressor protein that can block all lytic genes. However, the repressor protein cannot block its own promoters, so the cell continues to synthesize a small quantity of repressor protein. (Terry 2000) The chamber with the headless lion (23) indicates the promoter synthesizing small amounts of the repressor protein during the lytic cycle, so we could say that the lion has been tamed. More support for this view is found in the Tomb of RVI.

The text in RVI identifies the reclining lion in the Upper Register as the "Bull of Roaring" and the goddess (20) next to it as "Isis the Weaver." The name of the lion, along with the headless chamber lion (23), confirms the ascendancy of the lunar Bull, or the full function of the Eye of Horus. The idea that Demdemet (referenced in the Budge translation at Ka-Hemhemet) is now "of Horus" suggests the taming of the lion or cI protein due to cro protein or Horus ascendancy. The RVI text referring to the three chambers states, "The darkness on the earth is lighted up, He in the flesh rejoices. The head of He who has reunited his members speaks." The name of the human head chamber

(PL) is "The Castle which hides Seth;" the hawk wing chamber (PR) is "The Castle of the corridor which carries the fight;" the headless lion chamber (PRM) is "Castle of Demdemet of Horus." Also, the Coffin Texts (1030/31) state "a Castle destroys another Castle," a reference to the "Castle of the Moon" (phage production) dominating over the Castle of the Mace (Seth). One can compare this to the idea of the solar lion no longer tearing out the throat of the lunar bull. So the full function of the Eye of Horus, that is, the Lambda genome, is restored and the lion is tamed.

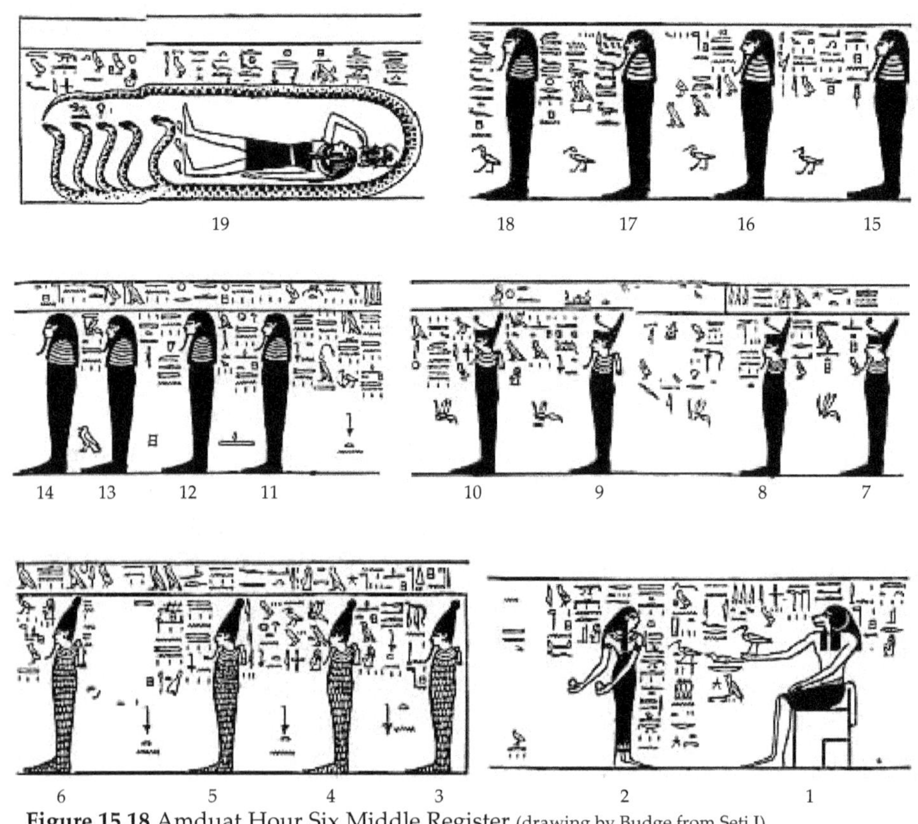

Figure 15.18 Amduat Hour Six Middle Register (drawing by Budge from Seti I)

The Sun-god travels through the Middle Register toward the oval of the five-headed Serpent of Many Faces (19), within which is the god Afu with the beetle Khepera at his head. The name of "Many Faces" seems appropriate for the Lambda cI repressor protein of five *alpha*-helices, which is represented here. As mentioned, RecA protein in its second form as a protease destroys the monster repressor protein LexA (Apopis) that controls a number of operons. RecA also facilitates the cleavage of phage repressors maintaining the lysogenic state, such as the Lambda cI repressor. By binding to the OR and OL operator sequences, the Lambda cI repressor prevents the lytic pathway and maintains lysogeny. The repressor is a dimer of five *alpha*-helices (Hewlett 2000), depicted by the five-headed serpent containing the flesh of Osiris.

The SI text indicates that the figure inside will enjoy the royal state of receiving crowns, offerings and power over souls, and Apopis will be hacked to pieces. Put simply, Osiris rises when the prophage excises, thanks to RecA protein. The text further indicates that the Serpent of Many Faces will rise up with the image, journey to the West and travel the Duat. It is Re's voice that makes Osiris and the Serpent advance. Re's voice, of course, is the Word or DNA instructions, and the text in the border above the Upper Register confirms that if an exact representation is made, that is, copying or replicating, then one shall partake of the offerings to Osiris.

This five-headed serpent easily represents the five *alpha*-helix DNA-binding Lambda cI repressor protein, regulating phage gene expression in the lysogenic state by allowing the phage to reside in the chromosome of the host bacterium. Thus the text states that Apopis, that is, the LexA repressor protein, will be hacked up. This inactivates the Lambda cI repressor so the prophage will rise to initiate stage two rolling circle replication, signified by Osiris bent backward in a circle. The cleavage of LexA repressor protein also inactivates the Lac repressor protein, so the lactose nutrient is available.

The Middle Register shows Thoth (1), who is present before the bark (Figure 15.18), indicating replication and the RNA polymerase. Recall that in Hour Three, both a man and a woman each brought forth two pupils of the Eye of Horus. Now, we only have a female figure (2) holding two pupils of the Eye of Horus, suggesting the dominance of lactose metabolism and transcription under cro control of the right arm or Eye, rather than transcription from the left Eye or the conspiracy of Seth or cI, producing the human creation. Next are 16 mummified forms of Osiris, four wearing crowns of the South or Upper Egypt (3-6), four bearded (7-10), four wearing crowns of the North or Lower Egypt (11-14), and four more bearded (15-18), followed by the five-headed serpent, indicating the impending excision of the prophage and rolling circle replication.

Figure 15.19 Amduat Hour Six Lower Register (drawing by Budge from Seti I)

In the Lower Register, the huge serpent Am-Khu with four children of Horus (4) coming to being from its folds represents the concatemer of phage DNA that is cleaved into unit-length DNA molecules, as represented by the nine erect shortened serpents (6). Transcription from both promoters initially produces short transcripts only, as depicted by these short serpents, which were obviously cleaved by the nine axes in Hour Five that are related to the nine sceptres or emblems of fertility in this Hour's Upper Register. Nine is a significant number signifying the Great Ennead and possibly the idea of mesons (quark and anti-quark) that occur in families of nine for each combination of spin and orbital angular momentum. (Close 1989, 404) Rolling circle replication is beginning, for Osiris will travel the Duat. The goddesses in the Upper (2, 7-9, 20) and Lower Registers (3) signify forms of the goddess Isis or lactose as the nutrient medium for lytic growth.

In SI Hour Six are several references to joining and uniting. The 16 Middle Register deities receive their royal state and join themselves "to your secret things with your crowns." The gods of the field unite themselves to the Sun-god's provisions. Passing by deities in the "following of the Scarab" who master the Red Crowns (left Eye), the Sun-god states, "let me unite myself to my bodies." He then urges the four gods (5) and nine serpents (6) or warders of the Hidden Flesh in the Lower Register to "unite ye yourselves to your flesh." Put simply, chemical processes involving molecular bonding, use of the lactose growth medium, and excision of the prophage are active.

Text from Ramesses VI

The text for the Middle Register states that Re rows close to the body of Osiris and lands at each castle containing the images of Osiris. In other words, he transcribes genes at Lambda's three promoter sites. The presence of the Kings of Upper Egypt (3-6) with their crowns and the Kings of Lower Egypt (11-14) with their crowns again suggests the full operation of the Lambda genome under cro control. The text above the five-headed serpent indicates the image within is the body of Khepri in his own flesh with "Many Faces" guarding him, another reference to the Lambda cI Repressor protein that maintains lysogeny and is also signified by Seth.

The text in the Lower Register describes the gods of the Netherworld as those following the Mistress of the Netherworld, who is Isis. These gods are described as having "shining heads, whose bodies stand upright," a fair description of phage Lambda. The text continues saying "May your heads live, may your hearts breathe, your darkness be illumined," suggesting the initiation of lytic rolling circle replication and phage production. The text then identifies the nine short standing serpents (6) as symbols of the Great Ennead, which we can easily identify with the names of the nine axes in Hour Five. Each short serpent has a knife at its base, symbolic of the electrostatic force and protein folding. The god facing the nine serpent symbols (not shown in Seti I Figure 15.19) is called "The Abyss," suggesting the chemical furnace of the Duat.

Matrix 13. Amduat Hour Six

Egyptian Sign translated to
Possible Modern Science Parallel

Apopis hacked to pieces: LexA repressor maintenance; excision of prophage
Castle carrying the fight: Promoter-right where cI and cro proteins compete for right operator sequences and control
Castle of Demdemet of Horus (lion tamed): Promoter-repressor maintenance
Castle of the Moon dominating Castle of Mace: lactose for PL
Castle which hides Seth (human head): Promoter-left
chambers of Re: 3 promoters of Lambda genome (PL, PR and PRM)
god named Abyss: chemical reactive furnace of host cell
god Thath-neteru with crossed crook and knife: Holliday junction resolution
goddess holding 2 pupils of Eye of Horus: lactose for whole lambda genome
goddesses, Lower/Upper Registers: lactose as growth nutrient
Great Ennead; emphasis on 9: mesons occur in families of 9 for each combination of spin and angular momentum
language of uniting, joining: molecular bonding
language: May your heads live: phage head assembly and production
language: Shining heads whose bodies stand upright: phage morphology
lion Ka-Hemhemet with 2 eyes; Bull of Roaring: lytic operation and cooperation of full Lambda genome
lotuses on Sun-bark: movement to core of matter or Lambda DNA
mummified forms, 16; wearing Red/White Crowns: impending excision
sceptres, 9: 9 replication forks for phage genesis
serpent Am-Khu with 4 Horus children: concatemer of phage DNA to be cleaved into unit-length DNA molecules
serpents, erect, short, 9: 9 unit-length DNA molecules from cleavage of concatemer
serpent of Many Faces, 5 heads: Lambda cI repressor protein; 5-helix DNA-binding repressor protein regulating phage gene expression in lysogenic state
Sun-god's voice makes Osiris and Serpent advance: DNA instructions cause prophage excision
thrones, lack of: lack of old DNA forms or creation of new DNA forms

Hour Seven

Figure 15.20 Amduat Hour Seven Sun-Bark
(drawing by Budge from Seti I)

The Sun-god wearing a disk on his head now reflects the name of Afu or Flesh, so it seems that this is the ingredient necessary to initiate unidirectional rolling circle replication. The SI text states that the Sun-god is journeying on the "path of the Circle of Sar" (Osiris), thanks to the words of power from Isis, the lactose energy medium. We are in the Hall of Osiris and are advancing on the way against Apopis. As discussed earlier, one way of representing the balanced Lambda genome with diminished cI protein and rising cro protein activity is to envision a judgment of protein levels, the Osirian scales of justice with the balanced arms and the right scale of cro having a larger content than the left scale of cI.

Figure 15.21 Amduat Hour Seven Middle Register (drawing by Budge from Seti I)

The Middle Register begins with the bark of Re, who stands under a canopy formed by serpent Mehen that represents RecA protein filament, necessary for the 7 bp branch migration for prophage excision. In front of the bark are Heka-Ser, Sa, Isis and five gods behind Afu. Isis with arms outstretched is now present at the prow of the bark, and the text assures us that her power (lactose energy) contributes to the conquest of Osiris: “If these words of power of Isis, and those of Ser be uttered, Apopis shall be turned back and shall be shut up in Ament, in the hidden place of the Tuat” (SI).

We are in the Circle of Sar (Osiris) and the drawing of a fettered serpent named Neha-Hra (1), representative of Apopis according to the text, is transfixed to the ground with six knives that suggest the active form of RecA (six-helical polymer of protein subunits and interhelical bundles). The goddess Serqet holds a band round his neck, while the god Her-Tesu-F ties a fetter on his tail. The text states that Apopis is slaughtered, and Isis has overpowered Apopis. Likewise, Coffin Text 1099 states: “I save Re from Apopis,” “I seize the writings, I receive the offerings,” “I provide Thoth with what he has to do,” “I establish millions,” which points to phage transcription, replication and translation to protein or phage progeny. If Apopis had not been overcome, then Osiris would die and Apopis would be in the “Slaughter-house of the Child” (CT100). In other words, the recombinant species or Horus child would be slaughtered, for Apopis (the monster LexA repressor protein) would allow phage repressor maintenance to maintain Osiris in the lysogenic state, stopping lytic cycle phage production and the birth of the Horus species.

Also present are four goddesses (2), each with a knife who guard four rectangular coffers (3-6) with two bearded heads on each end near an interior mound of sand, representing hydrophobic base pairs. These coffers of Tem, Khepera, Re, and Osiris contain forms of each god, which explains the lack of thrones or foundations of forms in Hour Six. These are the hidden heads that “eat their own forms” after the great god goes by, suggesting DNA degradation, phagocytosis or destruction of particulate matter.

In line with the idea of protein degradation or the “degradation of Osiris,” a low concentration of the activator protein cII transcribed from Lambda DNA depends on the amount of proteases present in the host cell, which depends on growth conditions. This means that the lytic cycle occurs when favorable growth conditions produce a high amount of proteases, a high degree of activator degradation, and low levels of cII in the Lambda genome. (Rinehart 2004) The *cII* gene encodes a transcription regulator (cII) that activates transcription of the genes for lysogeny establishment (Kihara et al. 1997).

The Amduat text stresses the importance of transcription and replication or making copies according to the "writing at the northern side of the hidden palace," for this will provide protection and give one the status of Spirits with Re. The hidden palace is the Osiris prophage site.

Figure 15.22 Amduat Hour Seven Upper Register (drawing by Budge from Seti I)

In the Upper Register, the god Shepes (1) in mummified form holds a curved crescent resembling a boomerang. Coffin Text 62 states, "Thou throwest thy boomerang at them and thousands fall at the sound of its wind." The boomerang, a curved crescent, may indicate the effect of chromatin condensing to the periphery of the nucleus, forming crescents in the process of apoptosis. After the god Shepes with the boomerang is the lioness Ath (2), then the uraeus Ankhuithit (3) with the head of a woman. Next is Osiris (4) with two plumes on his head, holding a sceptre and the life sign, while canopied by the serpent Mehen (5) as was the Deceased Sun-god at the beginning of this Hour. The text informs us that the Sun-god illumines the darkness "to embrace him that is in Mehen," while advising Osiris that he shall live. We can conclude that Mehen or RecA protein has mediated strand exchange for the 7 bp recombination necessary for the excision of the prophage, while forming a helical filament around the ssDNA. The act of the Sun-god embracing Osiris suggests molecular bonding.

Following Osiris and Mehen are indicators of programmed cell death or DNA degradation. Three headless figures (6-8) or enemies of Osiris kneel with their arms tied, the headlessness suggesting absence of protein shells. Before these enemies stands a cat-headed god (9) flourishing a knife and a pointed stake. Three more foes of Osiris (10-12) are lying on their backs roped to the god Anku (13). What is interesting is that the text states "your hands and arms are fettered, and [ye] are tied tightly with bonds, and your souls are kept under ward, and your shades are hacked in pieces, Anku hath drawn the cords about you so tightly that ye shall never be able to escape from his restraint." Although this most likely indicates apoptosis and destruction of particulate matter, it does remind one of the concept of encircling dimensions in String Theory, whereby our three extended dimensions are prevented from expansion. To the Egyptians, encirclement rendered malevolent beings and forces harmless (Goelet 1994, 147). So the three bound enemies may point to forces that allow expansion of our world's three spatial dimensions, which are under control or inactive.

Next are three bearded human-faced hawks (14-16), wearing the double crown of North and South, signifying the full function of both Lambda arms that generate the Horus species. Finally, a large serpent (17) bears the deity Afu-Tem that eats the souls of the enemies of Osiris, another sign of DNA degradation.

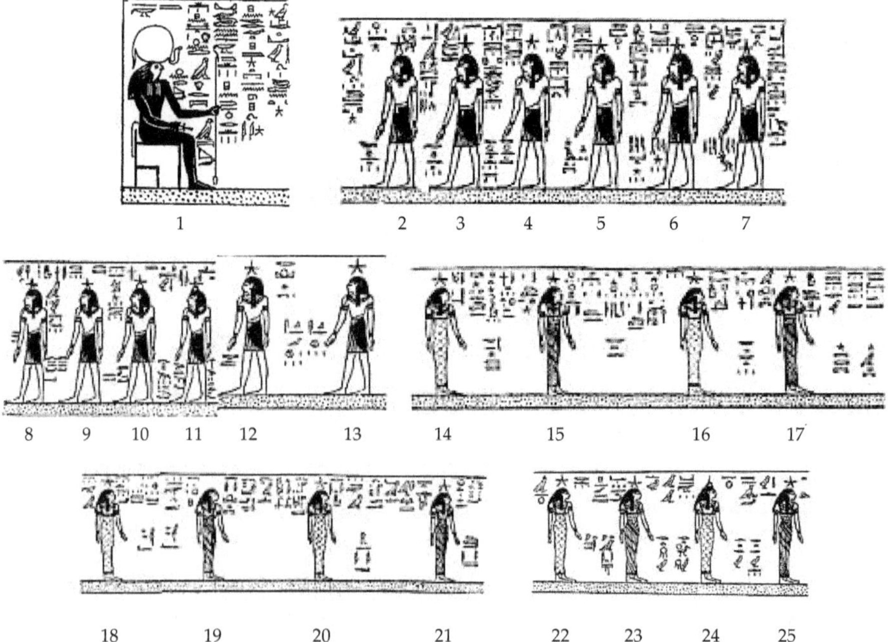

Figure 15.23 Amduat Hour Seven Lower Register (drawing by Budge from Seti I)

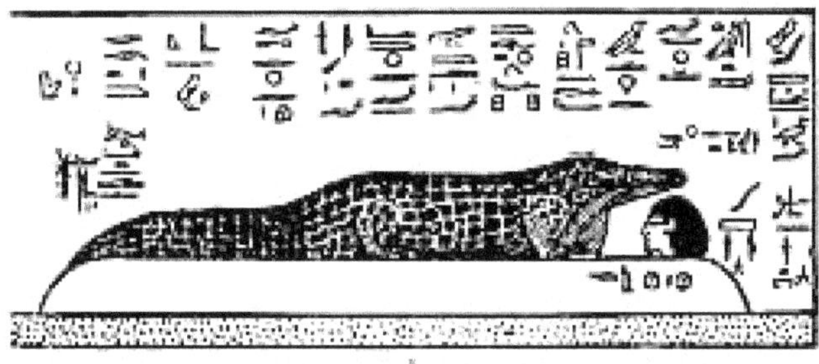

26

Figure 15.23 Continued: Amduat Hour Seven Lower Register (drawing by Budge from Seti I)

In the Lower Register, the hawk-headed god Heru-Her-Khent-F (1) is seated on a throne, wearing the solar disk encircled by a serpent, which may represent rolling circle replication. He holds the symbol of life and a sceptre or replication fork and sends "the stars on their way."

The solar disk encircled by a serpent also suggests convergence to a periodic or fixed point attractor. Genomic regulation is chaotic and scientists use Boolean networks to model the process. This breakthrough modeling technique aids in the analysis of different cell types with periodic attractors to which all states within the basin of attraction converge. One example of patterns converging to a fixed point or limit cycle attractors is that of oscillating pairs, such as those in the DNA molecule. However, in this case, the convergence of opposing replication forks is a desirable outcome, as indicated by the headdress of the solar disk encircled by a serpent. It has been shown that site-specific termination of replication is the result of pausing of replications forks near the sites of transcription termination (Little et al. 1993). Our analysis points to the cessation of bidirectional replication and the advent of the second stage or rolling circle replication.

Next are 12 star gods (2-13) and 12 star goddesses (14-25). The SI text references the 12 star gods stating: "The Majesty of Horus of the Tuat saith unto the starry gods: Light up so that [I] may unite [myself] with the master of the horizon." Horus desires to unite with the Sun-god Re, which represents the molecular bonding necessary for creation of the Horus species. The text beneath the 12 goddesses references them as "hours" endowed with stars who guide Re. After reviewing Piankoff's translation from the Tomb of RVI, a discussion of the Lower Register's star deities and crocodile (26) called Ab-Sha-Am-Tuat, described as "Osiris, the Eye of Ra," will follow.

Text from Ramesses VI

The introductory text to Hour Seven states that Re makes a stop in the Cavern of Osiris. The Sun-god is not towed, yet he is on a road without water. Thus, he advances by the "magic utterances of Isis" and the "Elder One" and his own utterance, which suggests the idea of passing on the DNA instructions. The text references the butchering of Apopis in this cave and heaven. In the Upper Register, the Sun-god asks Osiris to give him his hand so that "Horus may come out of thy loins." Piankoff notes in a footnote that in the Tomb of Pedemenopet, "loins" is replaced by "head," which indicates the cooperative effort of phage head assembly from the "Flesh of Osiris," the words written beneath Osiris (4) within Mehen (5). Re states that he lights up Osiris who is in the Darkness of the "Enveloper, the Life of Spirits" (Mehen or RecA) and that the flame of the serpent "Life of Forms" is now directed against the enemies of Osiris.

The Upper Register also displays three headless enemies (6-8) of Osiris, along with three roped and fallen enemies (10-12). Three soul birds (14-16) wearing the Double Crown follow with the names "The Brave, the One alive," "The Form of Khepri," and "The Soul of Exalted Earth." At the end of the Upper Register, we have the god seated on the serpent (17) called "The Flesh of Atum" and the serpent named "Life of Forms, Life of Spirits." This correlates to the image of the "Flesh of Osiris" (4) enveloped by the "Life of Spirits" (5) that appears first in the Upper Register, suggesting that Osiris is Atum. This is because the magic of nonlocality has made the Deceased Sun-god not only Osiris, but also Horus and Atum. In addition, this shows the chemical bonding of the Deceased Sun-god or Re with Osiris to produce the Horus species, which represents a movement to Atum, the god of origins. So in essence, Osiris and Mehen are depicted twice in the Upper Register, showing that RecA protein was active in the excision of the prophage. The text describing the three soul birds indicates that they are living, and that their "heads" came to being from the Sun-god's transformations, and they are in the following of the Flesh of Atum, that is, Osiris and Horus.

Once again, the text in the Middle Register confirms that the Sun-god is traveling by means of the utterances of Isis and the Elder One, so that the serpent Evil Face stays away. The Elder One most likely refers to Atum, the primeval god. The deities in the Sun-bark are "Isis, Mind, Magic, Flesh of Re, Horus the Praiser, The Bull of Truth, The Watchful One, Will," and "He who guides the Barge."

Under the Middle Register, Evil Face (1) is described as having vertebrae 443 cubits long, and Re does not pass by him. The text referring to the serpent states that the Flesh hides his disk in the earth(?) to pass by the serpent, which is lassoed by the goddess Serket or Selkit and another deity. From another version other than RVI, we learn the serpent's name is "Apopis," and the goddess holding his head is "She who gives breath," suggesting the activity of Isis' breath or lactose energy.

The text relating to the four coffers (3-6), each with two heads, states the chests with heads are the mysterious forms of the Duat. When Evil Face is enchanted, they come out, then they swallow their images when the Great God passes them by. The names of the chests are "The One which carries the images of Atum, . . . of Khepri, . . . of Re, . . . of Osiris."

In the Lower Register, Horus (1) is on his throne, and the text states the image sets the stars in motion and makes the Hours stop in the Duat. Horus states to the stars that their "flesh be right, may your forms come into being, you are satisfied with your stars!" Horus then speaks to the Hours who protect Re, saying "Take your forms, carry your images, lift up your heads" to lead Re to the Beautiful West. The names of the 12 star gods before Horus are: "Great of the Lower Region, Lord of the Lower Region, Lord of the provisions of Earth, The One of the Netherworld, Hey of the Stars, Hey of the Spirits, He who lifts his arm, He whose arm is holy, He who is powerful of arm, Knife in his tongue, Knife in his eye," and "He who allows the heads to breathe." The two gods named "Hey of the Stars" and "Hey of the Spirits" may reflect a typographical error in the text, and probably should have been "He" instead of "Hey." The star goddesses are "The Adorer, Lady of the Land, Lady of Ladies, The One of the Netherworld, The One of the Right Hand, The Leader, The Bringer, The Opener, The Weaver, She who makes brightness, She who makes the forms, She who prevents evil."

The text describes the crocodile as being on sand, guarding the image of this city. When he hears the voice of the crew, the Eye comes out of his backbone, then the head which is in the bank comes out and he swallows his image after the Sun-god goes by. If one knows this, his soul will never be swallowed by the crocodile "Evil of the Lake, which is in the Netherworld." Above the crocodile is the text "Eye of Horus," showing that the Lambda genome or Eye of Horus on the host chromosome has excised and is now active. Below the head is the text: "The Head of Osiris," suggesting the icosahedral shell of coat protein or phage prohead from a scaffolding protein core (crocodile).

The Star Deities

At this point, Hour Seven depicts the first stage of phage head and tail assembly or the packaging of DNA into reassembled protein shells called procapsids or proheads. Many viruses can self-assemble into icosahedral structures, the simplest form being one with 60 subunits arranged as 12 pentamers. For example, bacteriophage P22 assembles into a procapsid composed of a T=7 icosahedral shell of coat protein surrounding a scaffolding protein core. (Moore and Prevelige 2001) DNA is then pumped into the prohead in a process powered by ATP hydrolysis. Portal proteins play a key role because they are head-to-tail connectors that function as a DNA pump, provide a docking site for the phage tail, and assemble the prohead. (Cingolani et al. 2002) The portal complex is composed of a ring of 12 subunits of portal protein, which suggest the 12 star gods, with the 12 star goddesses representing the scaffolding proteins.

Research confirms that the T=7 bacteriophage P22 requires the P22 scaffold protein for portal protein incorporation into the procapsids (Moore and Prevelige 2002). Other research indicates that many viruses require scaffolding proteins to direct capsid assembly. Evidence suggests that both dimers and tetramers of the scaffolding protein play a role in assembly. (Parker et al. 2001) Thus, it is possible that the 12 gods and 12 goddesses indicate the joint activity of the portal complex.

Also relative is Lambda's portal protein gpB, which has 12 subunits assembled into a dodecameric ring with a central channel. Researchers believe that DNA enters into the prohead, then exits at this point during DNA ejection, finally providing the tail attachment site. (Wieczorek et al. 2002)

Recall that a dodecahedron shares icosahedral symmetry with an icosahedron; the symmetry axes are the same. However, the dodecahedral object has 12 pentagonal faces instead of the 20 triangular ones of an icosahedron. The drawing of the 12 gods with stars indicates 60 subunits arranged as 12 pentamers. The traditional stellation diagram of the icosahedron is suggested by the five-pronged star structure above each god's head. If one considers each god a pentamer, as represented by the five-armed star and the group of 12 gods as a whole, the 60 subunits are arranged as 12 pentamers. This 60 subunit structure is further supported by the names of the gods and goddesses. They are named the "Hours," suggesting 60 minutes or the minimum of 60 subunits.

The text in Seti I further supports the function of the portal proteins in that it asserts the 24 star deities will guide Re's two hands as he journeys through the Beautiful Ament. The task at hand is the function of phage head assembly. The crocodile now becomes the representation of the hydrophobic sand medium that provides the phage prohead or "Head of Osiris," that is, the scaffolding protein core. Upon DNA packing, the scaffold proteins are digested and DNA fills the head. The RVI text over the crocodile states: "The moment he hears the voice of the crew of the barge of Re, the Eye comes out of his backbone. Then the head which is in the bank comes out. He swallows his image after this Great God has passed by him." In other words, the scaffolding proteins are digested (crocodile swallows his image) after the DNA (voice, words of Re's crew) is pumped through the head (head in the bank comes out).

The text from RVI asserts that Horus speaks to the stars, saying "may your forms come into being" and "Stand up before Re, He of the Horizon, who is in the Netherworld every day. You are in his following while your stars are before him to let him pass through the beautiful West." Thus it seems that the DNA of the Sun-god is ready to pass through the portal protein complex. So the star gods allow the heads to become alive or breathe, and we easily understand the name of the twelfth star god called "He who allows the heads to breathe."

Matrix 14. Amduat Hour Seven

Egyptian Sign translated to
Possible Modern Science Parallel

activity of 24 star deities, crocodile, Re, forms to life: indicates lst stage head assembly, packaging of DNA into reassembled protein shells or proheads
Apopis restrained: no cI production; cro production; lactose nutrient medium
Apopis in Slaughterhouse of Child: LexA repressor active and repressing lytic cycle and phage creation
boomerang, curved crescent: the effect of chromatin condensing to the periphery of the nucleus, forming crescents during apoptosis
coffers of Tem, Khepera, Re, Osiris; 2-headed; eat own forms: forms for phage heads bordered by 2 cos sites at end of genome; oscillating base pairs; activator degradation
crocodile provides Head of Osiris: scaffolding protein core for provision of phage prohead
crocodile swallowing his image: digestion of scaffolding protein core
enemies, 3 headless: apoptosis; degradation; destruction of particulate matter
enemies, 3 on back roped to Anku: apoptosis; degradation; re String Theory, restraint of forces allowing 3 spatial dimensions to expand
god Heru-her-khent-f wearing headdress of solar disk encircled by serpent: indicator of convergence to a fixed point attractor such as oscillating base pairs or opposing replication forks; cessation of bidirectional replication and advent of rolling circle replication
headlessness: absence of phage protein shells
hidden palace: prophage site
knives, 6, holding Apopis: active biological form of RecA (6-helical polymer)
language: I seize the writings, I establish millions: phage replication; progeny
Mehen around Osiris: RecA protein for 7 bp branch migration and excision
Osiris helping Re so Horus comes out of loins/head of Osiris: cooperate effort of incoming Lambda and rising prophage in phage head assembly
serpent named Life of Spirits bearing Atum: rising prophage; RecA activity
star deities, 24: portal complex composed of 12 subunits of portal protein gpB (12 gods) and 12 scaffolding proteins (12 goddesses)
star with 5 points above star deities: stellation diagram of icosahedron; reference to 60 subunit structure of portal protein gpB dodecameric ring (12 gods x 5 pentamers) and associated scaffolding proteins (12 goddesses x 5 pentamers); self-assembly into icosahedral structures
stars letting Re pass: DNA passing through the portal protein complex
Sun-god embraces Osiris within Mehen: molecular bonding
Sun-god tells Osiris to live: prophage excision by integrating recombinant Lambda

Hour Eight

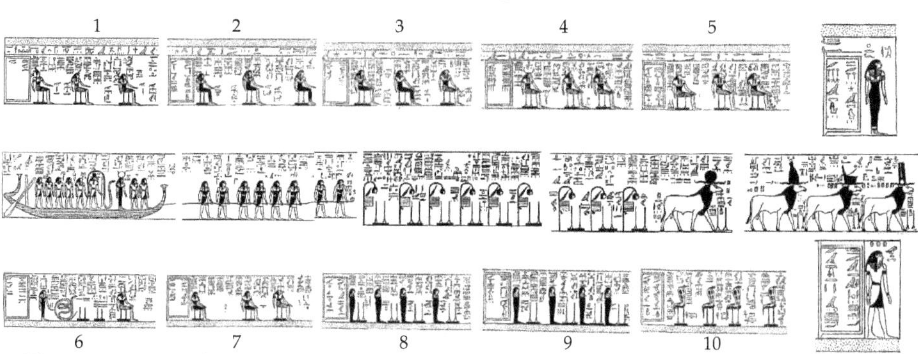

Figure 15.24 Amduat Hour Eight Upper, Middle, Lower Registers (drawing by Budge from Seti I)

As represented by the Upper and Lower Registers in Seti I, the Sun-god passes through ten "Circles of the hidden gods who are on their sand" (1-10). Sand suggests the hydrophobic interior base pairs of DNA, while the ten circles indicate the ability of the portal protein to form oligomeric rings after the DNA translocation machine pumps the concatemer viral DNA into the procapsid in an ATP-dependent manner. This ability has been observed in phages T3, T4, Lambda and SPP1. Portal rings form from unassembled subunits and can fully surround DNA in a nonspecific manner. (Moore and Prevelige 2001)

The Translocation Machine

The Middle Register presents the boat of the Sun-god, who is canopied by the serpent Mehen and towed over sand by eight gods, a representation of the translocation machine that pumps the concatemer viral DNA into the procapsid. (Catalano et al. 1995; Mitchell et al. 2002) Budge's SI text reads nine gods, although his drawing depicts eight as does Piankoff's version from RVI. The SI text encourages Re to unite to the "sepulchers of Khenti-Amenti" and the eight gods who tow him. These eight gods may represent the translocation machine or Lambda DNA terminase, an enzyme that cleaves virion-length chromosomes from the concatemer and packages them into the Lambda head. Researchers are still investigating the structure of the two-subunit enzyme, especially the smaller subunit (gpNu1), which has been shown to have a hydrophobic domain. (Yang[1] et al. 1999; Yang[2] et al. 1999)

Besides having a highly hydrophobic or sand region, other support for the eight gods representing terminase includes recent evidence from researchers who solubized the protein to discover eight discrete protein bands. (Araya et al. 2001) However, the eight gods may also represent the structural proteins that form the baseplate for tail assembly. At this point in the infection, the eight towing gods could reflect either signification, although the enzyme terminase seems more likely.

The translocation activity of terminase is important because the DNA must be pumped up a steep thermodynamic gradient into the capsid. After the concatemer is formed in phage Lambda, the packaging process begins. The protein terminase cuts the DNA, staying with the DNA after the cutting, which then enters the empty prohead shell. The terminase then makes the second cut, binds to the DNA past the cut site, and forms a new terminase-DNA complex to find another prohead and repeat the process. Portal proteins, sitting on one of the five-fold symmetric vertices or corners of the icosahedral capsid, provide the hole through which the DNA enters the prohead. Packaging RNA is also a chaperone molecule in this process. (Hendrix 1998)

Head Assembly

Next in the Middle Register are nine large objects called "follower" or "servant," which could represent phage tails. These objects look similar to previous sceptres in Hour Six, except now there is a head hanging from the curved end. As mentioned, the translation from Hour Six relating to its sceptres (SI) states that "their souls shall rise up in the Duat on their sceptres, they are provided with knives." Knives, of course, indicate the electrostatic force of DNA, whereas forked sceptres have been decoded as replication forks. The symbolism of the sceptre points to a creative act or genesis. Related to this, the linen bandage form in front of each suggests weaving or the construction of a web of life, a wrapping or folding of protein, a packaging of DNA. The SI text in Hour Eight reads the sceptres have "their life in them, in [their] heads in their forms," suggesting that these sceptres, which look like phage heads with tails, are coming to life. Their work is to seize Re's enemies and then make their heads pass under their swords after the god is gone. The RVI plates depict these tailed heads with beards. The symbol of linen bandages is placed before each sceptre form and each of the four rams. The four rams may signify the four distinct structural domains of the smaller terminase subunit (gpNu1) when partially folded. (Araya et al. 2001)

The Seti I text states that when the Sun-god passes by "they receive the diadems of Re and the soul of Tathenen uniteth itself to the earth." The ram is an essential component of divinity, as indicated by the ever-present ram horns of the Deceased and other deities. The ram-headed Sun-god represents a hydrogen supermolecule, which enables reactions and opens the door to change.

Investigating the five circles (1-5) in the Upper Register and five circles (6-10) in the Lower Register, we observe deities on and off weaving instruments. The Upper Register circles depict 12 deities on weaving instruments, whereas the Lower Register circles depict eight bearded mummified gods off weaving instruments and four gods sitting on weaving instruments. These ideograms may point to the idea that full function of weaving of DNA is not occurring due to early stage processes relating to rising production of cro protein. The text also states that those in the picture reflect the "mystery which Horus, the heir, the young [god] made." So we can be assured that the suggestion is that some portion of the DNA is being woven and assembled for the Horus species.

In the Middle Register, the sceptres with bearded heads at the end suggest head assembly is in progress with DNA packing represented by the translocation machine terminase, that is, the eight gods towing the Sun-god along the path. The text states that "they have their swathing before them in the form in which the god himself [had them]" (SI). The knife-like objects on the sceptres represent the DNA electrostatic force. Phage Lambda chromosomes are processively packaged into preformed shells, using end-to-end multimers of intracellular viral DNA as the packaging substrate.

To understand this process, it may be helpful to review the structure of the bacteriophage *phi*-29 DNA packaging motor, which translocates dsDNA into preformed proheads of bacterial viruses. Using X-ray crystallography, researchers determined the structure of the head-tail connector, indicating the prohead plus dodecameric connector, prohead RNA, viral ATPase and DNA comprise a rotary motor with the head-prohead RNA-ATPase complex acting as a stator, the DNA acting as a spindle, and the connector as a ball-race. (Simpson et al. 2000) So it seems that this packaging activity and our DNA spindle is a fair match to the nine followers on DNA weaving instruments with heads hanging from curved connectors on spindle-legs.

Text from Ramesses VI

The text states that Re is towed along in his form as "Enveloper." Lambda DNA packaging can be considered as "enveloping" because during packaging, the coat proteins surround a scaffolding protein core. However, some phage have an exterior protein envelope, which also may be indicated here.

The text relating to the nine signs or the followers with heads hanging from curved connectors states that their clothing is that of the god himself (Re) and that when Re calls to them, they become alive and "the heads come out of their knives." Then they swallow their heads when the god passes by. Re's clothing is made from his DNA, that is, the words or electrolytic message that is replicated and translated to protein for phage head and tail assembly.

Matrix 15. Amduat Hour Eight

Egyptian Sign translated to
Possible Modern Science Parallel

act of towing by 8 gods: DNA must be pumped up a steep thermodynamic gradient into the capsid
circles of hidden gods on sand, 10: portal proteins form oligomeric rings after the DNA translocation machine pumps concatemer viral DNA into prohead
deities on and off weaving instruments, 16: early stage reactions related to rising cro production
gods towing Sun-bark, 8: terminase enzyme for translocation
knives on 9 sceptres: electrostatic force of DNA
Rams united to earth, 4: four distinct structural domains of smaller terminase subunit (gpNu1) when partially folded
sceptres with bearded human heads and knives, 9: DNA packaging motor with multimers of viral DNA as packaging substrate
Sun-bark terminating in lotus flowers: early creation of phage product
Re as enveloper: during packaging, the coat proteins surround a scaffolding protein core; may also indicate exterior protein envelope
weaving instruments, linen, clothing: translation to protein for head and tail assembly

Hour Nine

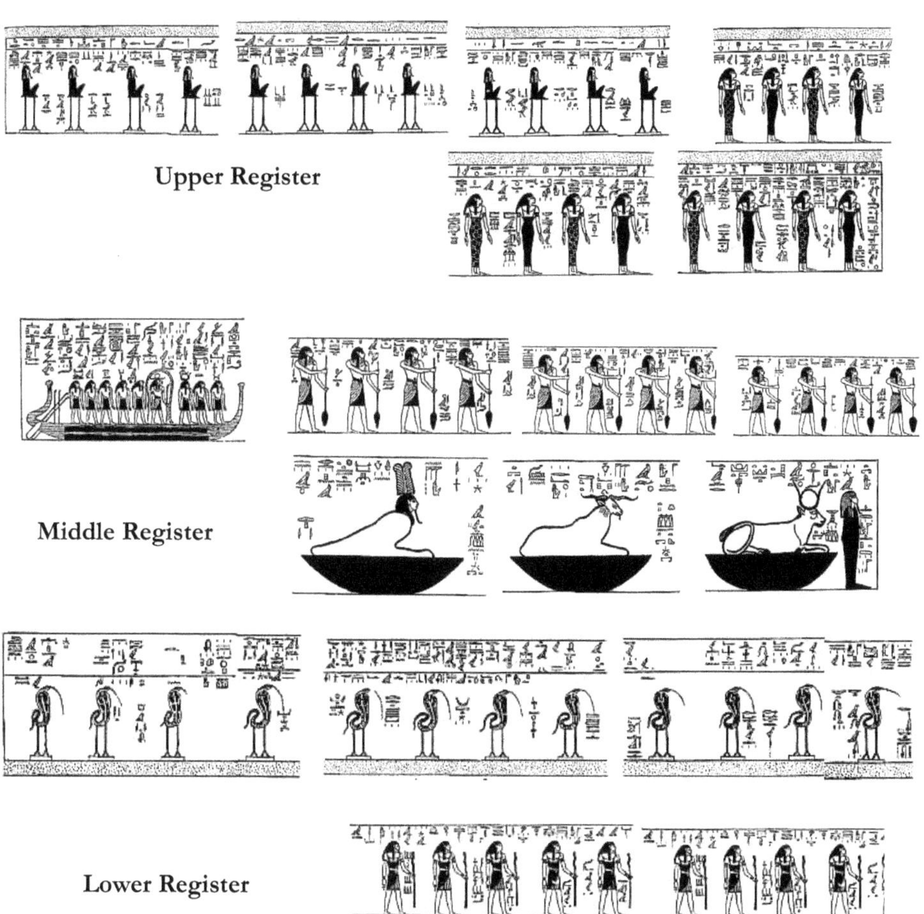

Figure 15.25 Amduat Hour Nine Upper, Middle, Lower Registers
(drawing by Budge from Seti I)

This Circle is east of the hidden house of the Duat. In the Middle Register, the Sun-god encircled by the serpent Mehen proceeds, wearing a white disk on horizontal waving ram horns and holding a wavy serpentine staff. Before him are 12 sailors with paddles or efflux pump proteins, and the text states that they will transport and help the Soul of Re in its forms to "arise." Next are a bearded, man-headed hawk, a ram-god, and a bull goddess sitting in individual basins. These may represent three periodic attractors to which all states within each basin of attraction converge. In prokaryotes, translation to protein requires the identification of an initiation codon AUG (McQueen 2003). We have already established that the lion suggests thymine, so it seems possible that the man-headed hawk represents adenine, the ram signifies uracil, and the bull goddess signifies guanine. From the imagery of the hawk-ram-bull in basins, it is also evident that the bull is ascendant over the lion, for the horns of the bull goddess wrap around the white disk, suggesting the lactose medium, and the lion form (thymine) is not present. The man-headed hawk represents the new lineage, that of the youthful god Horus, the recombinant species of the Deceased, the Sun-god and Osiris. Once again, the bull goddess imagery supports the idea of lactose (Isis) as does the text, for there are offerings of food to the Duat gods, celebratory vessels of beer and loaves of bread, as the gods journey on in the following of the Sun-god to the East.

It is interesting that in Hour Six, the activity was south of the Hidden House, in Hours Seven and Eight, the activity is north of the Hidden house, and in Hour Nine, activity is east. These directions may map protein functions that occur the way genes of a phage are clustered on a genome. For example, a movement south to north to east of the Hidden House mirrors protein functions in a movement around the genome as follows: nucleotide metabolism, membrane, enzymes of DNA metabolism, head, tail baseplate and head, neck and collar formation. (Gonzalez 2000) Put simply, the Sun-god is circling the genome and performing phage functions in the correct order.

In the Upper Register, 12 gods sit on the linen symbol for weaving with the text stating that they are "seated firmly on their instruments for weaving, and they are in the form of the figures which Horus made." With full cro production and binding at three operator sites, weavers being "seated firmly" is a good description of cro protein levels for phage production. The significance of the number "12" may relate to the number of gene products necessary for tail construction. Twelve goddesses follow, indicating the nutrient medium lactose. In the Lower Register, 12 fire-breathing uraei on weaving instruments lighten the darkness for Osiris. Then nine bearded gods, holding the life symbols in the right hands and waving serpentine staffs in the left hands, follow the mummified bearded "Horus who is over the lakes in the Duat" (SI). Now that head assembly is complete, the nine waving staffs signify phage tail assembly.

Symbolism of Twelve

In 1999, Gerardus't Hooft and Martinus J. G. Veltman won the Nobel Prize in Physics for elucidating the quantum structure of electroweak interactions in physics. The fundamental particles in matter are six leptons and six quarks, with the electroweak force mediated by four exchange particles (one massless gamma photon and three field particles). Eight massless gluons convey the strong force bringing the total to 12 exchange particles. (Royal Swedish Academy of Sciences 1999) The theory also predicts the Higgs particle that generates all particle masses, which the primordial god Atum may represent. Because we are at the quantum level of core creation in the Amduat, it may be that the Pharaohs knew about the fundamental matter particles and were suggesting this idea by depicting 12 goddesses, 12 sailors, and 12 uraei.

The Ascendant Bull

Because of its horns and the crescent horns of the moon, the bull is a lunar symbol. Thus we have the image of the ascendant bull which has supplanted the submissive, but dangerous lion. The solar lion no longer tears out the throat of the lunar bull. The following passage from the Pyramid of Unas (Budge v1 1904, 33) states that the great double lion-headed earth-god Aker trembles when the Deceased King rises in his new form: "The sky poureth down rain, the stars tremble, the bowbearers run about with hasty steps, the bones of Aker tremble, and those who are ministrants unto them betake themselves to flight when they see Unas rising [in the heavens] like a god who liveth upon his fathers and feedeth upon his mothers."

Text from Ramesses VI

Instead of nine bearded gods holding serpents, Piankoff's drawings depict nine bearded gods holding palms. The symbolism of the palm is victory over a monster (Cirlot 1971, 360), and at this point, Apopis has been overcome as has Seth, for cro beats cI to the "Right" operator, and the lysogenic pathway is no longer an alternative. Still, the depiction of palms may also point to Osiris as the rising prophage and the lytic cycle, which is vegetative replication. For instance, the Sago palm tree is highly valued by the Indonesian Asmat people, who use it as a source for flour. The starch is extracted from the tree's pith, with one palm providing 100 pounds of white flour. (Hile 2003) The tree is also the source of a ceremonial food, the larvae of the Capricorn beetle. The Asmat cut down and punch holes in the palm so that the beetle can lay its eggs inside.

This practice easily compares to the Egyptian story about the Sun-beetle placing its eggs in the dung ball, and can be extended to the idea of Osiris, for the Lambda prophage lodged next to the *LacZ* gene is similar to an egg that will hatch. Text in the center of the Lower Register of Hour Five actually refers to the image of Sokar as "the Egg which belongs to this god." Likewise, white flour makes bread, which rises like the prophage, and the idea of bread enlarging suggests rapid creation of phage progeny. The ceremonies of the Asmat people, who were formerly headhunters, reflect their ideas about the source of natural creation, which is modeled on Lambda dynamics. Thus, Piankoff's palm sceptres and Budge's wriggling serpentine sceptres reflect similar symbolic intent, which is the victory of Horus over Apopis and Seth, the creation of sustenance for the Horus lineage, and the multiplication of phage progeny in the lytic cycle.

The text notes that the name of this Gate is "Guardian of the Flood," with the flood indicating the process of efflux or movement of recombinant phage progeny to the extracellular medium. The 12 sailors before the Sun-bark signify the activity of efflux pumps, which are made of proteins to transport molecules out of the cell. These 12 gods will transport the Sun-bark to the Eastern Horizon. The text referring to the Sun-bark is lacking in RVI, but older versions state the bark is the "mysterious image of the Enveloper." The text further states that the 12 gods with paddles are now part of the crew, they "give water to the oars," and "cause the soul to appear in its forms." Also, we learn the names of the three deities in the basins from Piankoff: "Tiut at the head of the Netherworld," "The One of the Necropolis in the Netherworld," and "Lady of Gifts in the Netherworld."

Text in the Upper Register for the 12 gods on clothing signs states, "Horus has clothed you" and "may you uncover your heads," an explicit reference that phage head assembly is completed. Text referencing 12 uraei in the Lower Register states that they create all trees and green plants in this city. As mentioned, lytic growth is vegetative replication, so this reference to plants and trees can be explained as can the status of Osiris as a vegetation god. For example, Osiris was equated with the harvest god Neper and was credited with the creation of wheat and barley. The Grain-Osiris and Osiris-Bed funerary practices at the Festival of Khoiak included filling a mold of Osiris with sprouting plants. (Griffiths 2002, 306) We can now understand this focus on vegetative replication as symbolic of lytic growth. The final bearded mummy in the Lower Register (missing in Figure 15.25) was named "Horus presiding over the Regions of the Netherworld," confirmation that the Horus species is victorious.

Matrix 16. Amduat Hour Nine

Egyptian Sign translated to Possible Modern Science Parallel

basins or bowls with 3 deities (hawk, ram, bull): AUG initiation codon for protein translation
bread rising: excision of prophage; birth of phage progeny
Gate is Guardian of the Flood: process of efflux or movement of recombinant phage progeny to the extracellular medium
goddesses, 12: lactose nutrient medium
gods, 9 waving sceptres (SI) or palms (RVI): cro production; high nutrient level, phage progeny tail assembly
gods, 12, seated firmly on weaving instruments: completion of phage head assembly
language: May you uncover your heads: phage head assembly completed
lion, hawk, ram, bull goddess: thymine, adenine, uracil, guanine
Osiris as vegetation god: vegetative viral replication or lytic growth
sailors with paddles, 12: efflux pump proteins
Sun-bark movement south-north-east of Hidden House: mapping of protein functions occurring in the way genes of phage are clustered on genome
symbolism of Ascendant Bull: horns are moon crescents, suggesting lactose and recombinant species
symbolism of number 12: electroweak and strong forces of 12 exchange particles
symbolism of palm: victory for cro protein
uraei on weaving instruments, 12: phage head/tail assembly

Hour Ten

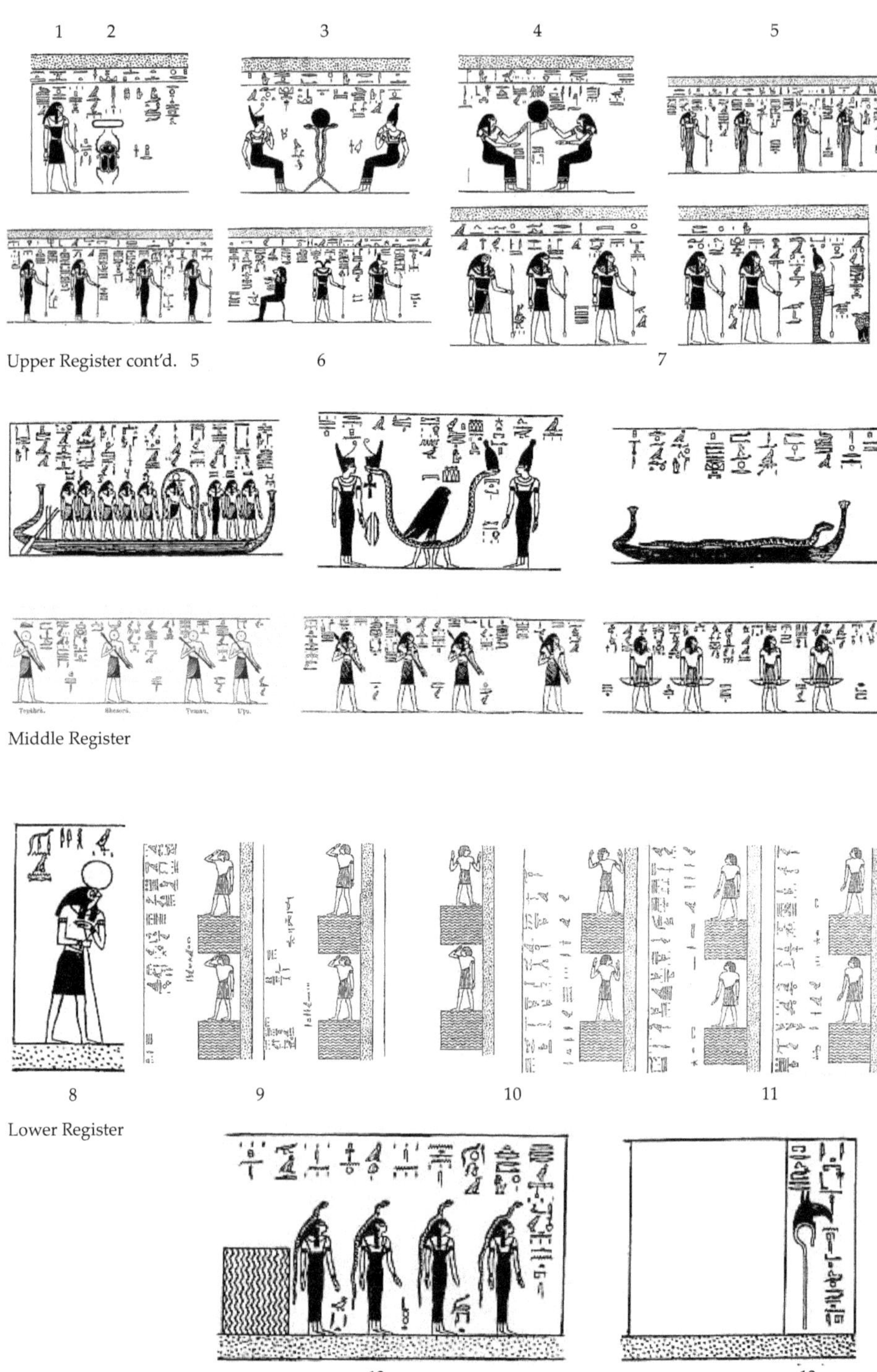

Figure 15.26 Amduat Hour Ten Upper, Middle, Lower Registers (drawing by Budge from Seti I)

In the Middle Register is the Sun-bark and crew, and before them the two-headed serpent called Thes-Hrau, curved in the U-shape of two connected bull horns. The serpent heads wear the Red and White Crowns, with each head facing a goddess wearing the same headdress. A large hawk, looking to the right, is centered in the serpent, which stands upon two pair of human legs. Probably one of the most powerful ideograms supporting the result of allolactose bonding to the lac repressor is this large two-headed serpent stationed between the two goddesses. As mentioned, the protein has bonding sites for both allolactose and the operator sequences of DNA as evidenced by its two heads. A large life sign is beneath the serpent head wearing the Red Crown of Lower Egypt, suggesting that the headpiece of the lac repressor is bound to the allolactose as evidenced by the goddess. The lac repressor is a tetrameric protein with four polypeptide subunits organized as a dimer of dimers, which this portrait shows by the four legs.

Next is a boat with a full-length serpent on it, representing the long DNA concatemer produced during rolling circle replication. Four males follow, each with a disk in place of a head, suggesting the shape of the sphere-like icosahedral phage head (see Figure 15.27).

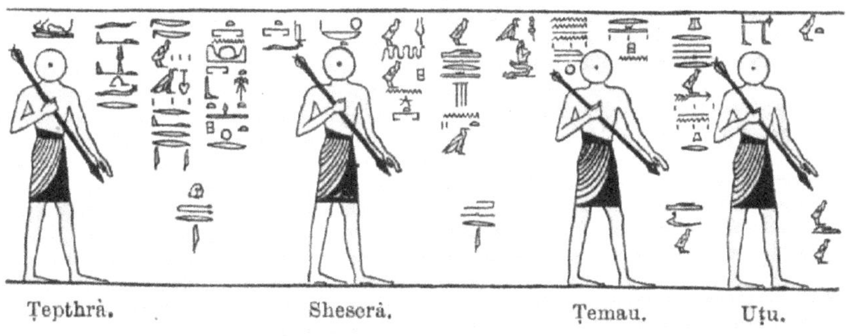

Figure 15.27 Four males with spheres for heads (Drawing by Budge from Seti I)

Four men with bows and four men with arrows appear, who are responsible for destruction of the enemies or cell lysis. The Sun-god takes up his place in the water of this City. The text over the Upper Register states that this is the "Circle of Amentet, where Kheper uniteth himself to the form of Re" and that if a copy is made of these pictures, a man will pass through the Duat.

In the Upper Register is a bearded god (1) standing next to the transformation beetle (2) of Kheper pushing a zone of sand, followed by two goddesses (3) without thrones, each with a finger pointed toward her nose. Between the goddesses is a disk supported by two serpents with their tails crossed. DNA binding proteins have four common motifs: l) helix-turn-helix, 2) zinc fingers, 3) basic leucine zipper, and 4) helix-loop-helix. With fingers pointing to their noses, we could say that these goddesses represent zinc fingers, which are found in a variety of proteins. Schapiro et al. (2003) found that zinc mobilization inhibited bacterial DNA replication during nitrosative stress. Also, zinc is an essential nutrient, and proteins contain zinc-dependent DNA binding domains. For example, the structure of cro protein's carboxypeptidase A chain requires $Zn^{2}+$ for catalysis. It is bound to His69, His196 and Glu72 at the enzyme active site. The zinc ion interacts with the substrate to labilize the peptide bond. (Klevickis) Thus, the ideogram of the goddesses pointing their index fingers to their noses may represent the motif of two zinc fingers relative to cro protein catalysis. The zinc finger domain is formed by the interaction of one or two Zn atoms with regions of the protein to produce a structure with the finger pointing into the major groove. The two elongated serpents supporting the solar disk represent the completed product of the bacteriophage synthesis.

Next are two goddesses (4) and a large ax supporting the solar disk, indicating the end of the concatemer cleavage stage or cleavage related to phage exit from the cell. Also of interest is that the goddesses are not sitting on thrones or foundations of forms, suggesting that the forms disappear or degrade. For example, these two goddesses "swallow their own spirits (or souls)" after the Deceased Sun-god passes. Next are eight goddesses (5), each holding an *ankh*. Four of the goddesses are lion-headed and four are woman-headed. They face a baboon-god (6) sitting on its tail, rather than a throne. Eight gods (7) follow who will destroy enemies, which seems reasonable for the cell is undergoing lytic activities. Of special interest is the first of these eight gods, Ermenui who has a two-pronged object in place of his head. This same symbol is commonly used today by molecular biologists to indicate divergence. Divergence is usually not a desirable behavior and has been compared to the Lyapunov instability in continuous variable systems. However, if the state space of a system converges to more than one attractor, then there should be some regions with divergence, which this god may indicate. Possibly, the active replication of numerous phage progeny serve as multiple attractors.

12 Lakes of Water

In the Lower Register is the hawk-headed god Horus (8) wearing a white disk, followed by four lakes of water with the "submerged" (9), four lakes of water with "swimmers" (10), and four lakes of water with "floaters" (11). Proteins fold because of polarity and hydrophobic effects. Hydrophobic means incapable of dissolving in water. Apparently, our 12 aquarians do not dissolve in the 12 lakes of water. Nonpolar amino acids (most are hydrocarbon side chains) tend to be hydrophobic. The hydrophobic effect stabilizes the protein. (Mulcahy 1997) The text states the swimmers will have "dominion over your water." In other words, they represent the stabilizing hydrophobic effect.

Following the swimmers are four women, each having a relaxed serpent on their heads. The text states that their "forms live by their heads. It is they who shed light upon the road of Re in the thick darkness and when he cometh forth into the Hall of the East, Set waketh up and traveled on with him." These representations of four females bonded to four serpents suggest allolactose bonded to the lac repressor with resultant lactose production. Once again, the representation of four goddesses and four serpents suggest the idea of the tetramic lac protein organized as a dimer of dimers. The last image is a sceptre (13) with the head of Set named "Set who wakens." This may indicate the activity of cII that makes antisense cro, but it is more likely that it represents the forces of chaos evident in lytic reactions.

Text from Ramesses VI

The text states that the name of the gate is "She who gives birth to the forms," and the name of the city is "She whose water is deep, whose banks are high." The name of the Hour is "She who slashes, who decapitates the rebels." Decapitation or protein shell head removal prevents replication of rebel DNA, that is, the human creation.

The beetle pushing his egg is called "The Living Beetle." The text referring to the two zinc finger goddesses and two serpents holding the disk states:

> These gods are like this. The Eastern One comes out of the Double-Entwined One. The Western One issues out of the One who fastens. They call to them the souls who are upon earth, they fasten the spirits, which are purified(?) in the Netherworld, to this mysterious image which is therein. Then they swallow their forms after this Great God has passed by them.

This textual language may signal the completed product, as zinc fingers represent the protein stage between secondary and tertiary structures. The goddesses are named "Crown of the North" and "Crown of the South," while the serpent is called "Double-Entwined One," suggesting the DNA in the phage tail. The names of the two goddesses with the ax and disk are "The One who lifts up" and "The One who calls the God," once again suggesting the end of concatemer cleavage. Swallowing forms indicates DNA degradation.

The Sun-god addresses the eight goddesses and the baboon with the *Udja*-eye, stating that they establish the first Eye of Horus "which is in the hands of Flesh who carries his Eye! It is you who protect Horus, O you who came to being and create the beings." The eight goddesses are an obvious reference to the nutrient medium, for without a sufficient lactose level, no recombinant phage progeny are possible, and the first Eye of Horus is not established.

The text referring to the Middle Register double-headed serpent on which the hawk stands is: "They are like this as supporters(?) of the serpent of the One who binds the Faces." The reference to "Faces" suggests the faces of icosahedral phage heads. Next, the serpent in the boat is named "Life of Earth," and represents the long DNA concatemer product of rolling circle replication. The text above the serpent is: "He is like this in his boat. He lurks in the complete darkness by this Gate of the Eastern Horizon, he rests in his place every day. This is the serpent, the One who rises of the Netherworld, the Noble Soul of He at the Head of the Westerners." Notice that "Head of the Westerners" is another name for Osiris, who is "Foremost of the Westerners" and also the phage head product.

In the Lower Register, the text referring to Horus and the drowned ones in the Netherworld follows. Horus speaks to those drowned whose "faces are overturned in the Netherworld, whose backbones are in the flood." He states that they will not choke for there will be air.

> You come out of the flood, you fall in your current(?), you swim in the great Inundation, you come to land at its banks. Your bodies do not smell of putrefaction, your flesh is not decomposed. You have power over your water, you breathe, for I have decreed (it). You are indeed those who are in the Abyss, the drowned ones in the following of my flesh(?), which carries life for your souls.

This description may represent the hydrophilic sugar phosphate groups on DNA, which are composed of the internal bases (sand references) and the external sugar-phosphate backbone, the major structural component. Ribose sugar and phosphate molecules alternate on the backbone, and they are very polar and hydrophilic or water-loving. Not only does the text use backbone and water terminology, but it names the three groups in the water: "The drowned ones in the Netherworld," "The overturned ones in the Netherworld," and "The stretched-out in the Netherworld." These names may indicate DNA positions of sugar phosphate groups. Finally, the names of the four goddesses with serpents on their heads are: "She who annihilates, The Glowing One, The Stinging One, The Cobra," suggesting the power of the lactose nutrient medium. The text states, "their images live upon their heads" and that these goddesses light the way for Re in the East.

Matrix 17. Amduat Hour Ten

Egyptian Sign translated to Possible Modern Science Parallel

Beetle, the Living: transduction of viral-human-phage product is complete
Gate, name of: She who gives birth to forms: lactose energy metabolism
goddesses swallow own spirit: DNA degradation
goddesses, 8, and baboon with Udja-eye: lactose energy medium; full function of Lambda genome for lytic lifestyle
goddesses with fingers to nose, 2: two zinc finger DNA binding proteins
goddesses with large ax supporting solar disk, 2: end of concatemer cleavage stage
goddesses with serpents on heads, 4: allolactose bonded to Lac repressor; lytic lifestyle of phage Lambda
god Ermenui with 2-pronged object for head: sign of divergence in reactions
gods of destruction: cell lysis
Head of Westerners or Osiris: phage product
Hour, name of: She who slashes, who decapitates the rebels: decapitation or protein shell head removal prevents replication and suggests cell lysis
humans with sphere for head, 4: viral-human-phage progeny with spheres for heads
humans, bearded with bows and arrows: cell lysis activities
language: Double-Entwined One: double-stranded DNA in phage
language: drowned ones with backbones in flood: hydrophilic external sugar-phosphate backbone of DNA
language: one who binds Faces: faces of icosahedral phage head
serpent in Boat of Life: long DNA concatemer
serpent with 2 heads between 2 goddesses: Lac repressor bonded to allolactose
serpents supporting solar disk, 2: product of bacteriophage biosynthesis
Set awakening: chaos; cII protein level increasing that makes antisense cro
swimmers, floaters, submerged in water, 12: hydrophobic effect stabilizes protein

Hour Eleven

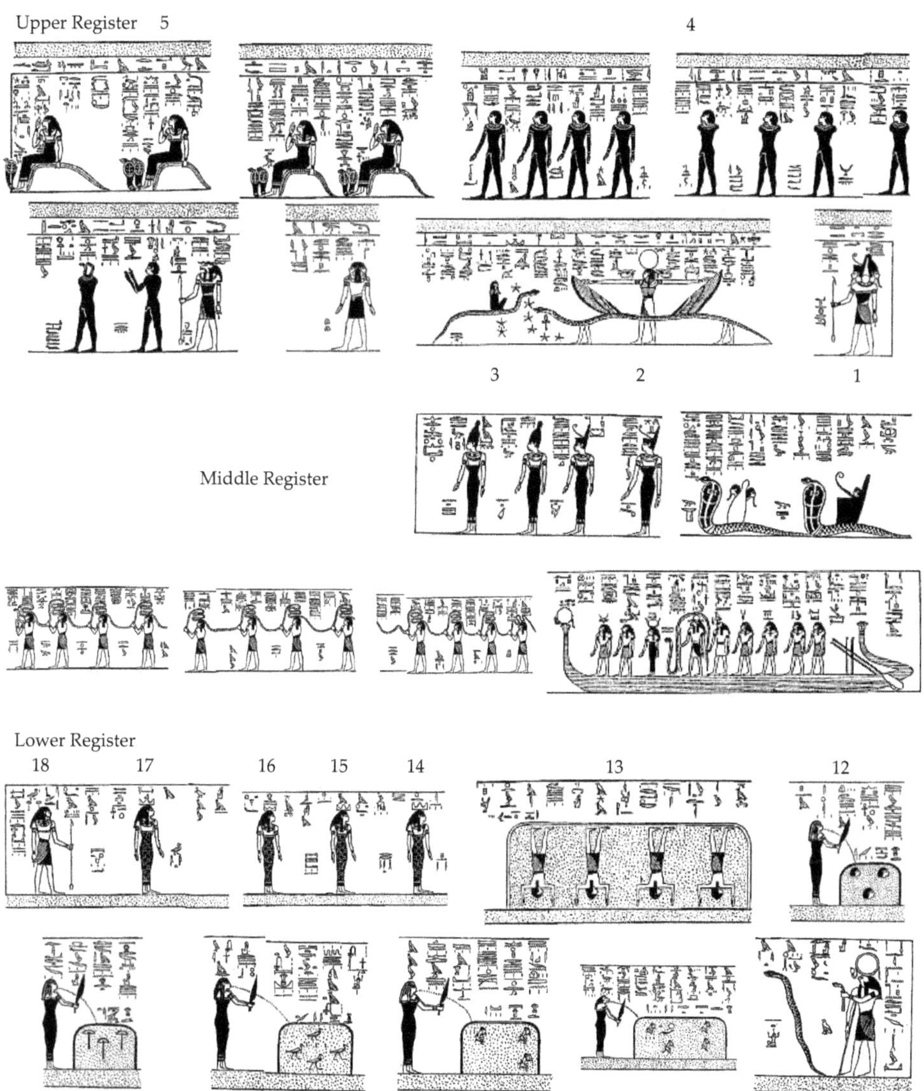

Figure 15.28 Amduat Hour Eleven Upper, Middle, Lower Registers

(drawing by Budge from Seti I)

In the SI Middle Register, the Sun-bark proceeds as in Hour Ten, but with the Star Pestu, a white disk encircled by a uraeus, the sign of convergence, guiding the boat on its prow. The text states that the white disk "guideth this great god into the ways of the darkness which gradually lightens, and illumineth those who are on earth," suggesting movement out of a white hole. Twelve gods march before the boat bearing the supercoiled serpent Mehen, representative of the Enveloper or protein envelope for the phage heads. Next are two uraei carrying heads with White and Red Crowns, which swallow their forms when Re cries out to them, indicating DNA degradation. To follow are four forms of the goddess Neith with White and Red Crowns, suggesting the full operation of the Lambda arms energized by lactose.

Neith or Net is one of the oldest Egyptian goddesses, and in earlier periods she was a personification of a form of the great, inert, primeval watery mass out of which sprang the Sun-god Re. The name Net comes from the root *netet* meaning "to knit, to weave." Among Neith's early titles was that of *Apt-uat*, that is, "Opener of the ways." Isis is also identified with Neith. (Budge v1 1904, 450-454) The etymology of Neith's name points to the primeval water of the universe, the act of weaving protein molecules, and opening of the DNA molecule for transcription, replication and translation of the new lineage. Once again, the text emphasizes transcription or making a copy of the forms, so a spirit is well-equipped.

In the Upper Register, we encounter a disk-headed, bearded deity (1) with two heads protruding from the disk, wearing the Red and White Crowns, along with an elongated serpent (2) with two pairs of human legs, behind which is the god Tem, wearing a large white disk and stretching his arms to touch two wings from the serpent's body. Tem's head is centered between two *Udja*-eyes. The whole Eye of Horus and the stretched arms of the god Tem, a form of the Sun-god and Osiris, indicates the fully functioning two arms of the Lambda genome, the central catalyst that generates the Horus species. His name *tem* or *temem* means "to be complete" (Budge v2 1904, 87), which again signifies complete function of the Lambda genome or the lytic pathway that is also represented by the balanced arms of Tem. This image swallows itself, suggesting DNA degradation. A serpent (3) follows with a mummified god riding on it, swallowing its forms also, along with 12 more gods (4) and four goddesses (5), each seated on the backs of two uraei, a representation of the allolactose bonded to the Lac repressor protein.

In the Lower Register, hawked-headed Horus (6) wears a disk encircled by a uraeus and holds a short crescent snake, which may indicate crescents caused by processes of cell lysis. Then, an elongated serpent (7) named "Everlasting Set," indicating the god of disorder and chaos, stands on its tail, suggesting the resumption of cII protein production to activate cI. Next are five large pits of fire (8-12), signifying apoptotic DNA degradation. The first fiery pit holds four enemies holding axes to their heads (8), with the second pit (9) depicting three enemies suiciding. The next three infernos (10-12) show "souls," "shades," and "heads" being consumed. Finally, a sixth blazing pit (13) named "the valley of those who are turned upside down" holds four upside-down humans. Inversion suggests the end of a chemical process. However, these fiery pits could also represent the destruction of information at a singularity. The SI text states that the Sun-god journeys through the hidden circle, which eternally swallows its forms and then gives them back to those born in the earth (Budge 1905, 240). Reference to the valley of those turned upside down may point to this process. In contrast, four goddesses (14-17) follow with the sign for "eastern desert" on their heads, along with the god Her-Utu-F (18), holding a sceptre and life emblem. The text reinforces the fiery Armageddon of DNA degradation, stating the enemies are hacked to pieces and will nevermore exist.

Text from Ramesses VI

Piankoff notes that there are only two lines of introductory text in RVI, but earlier versions state the name of the Gate is "Place of Rest of the Inhabitants of the Netherworld;" the name of the City is "Gate of the Cavern, She who reckons the bodies;" the name of the Hour of the Night is "the Star, Mistress of the Barge, She who drives away the rebels when he comes out." The Hour reference points to the goddess Isis, who provides the nutrient medium and is responsible for the nutritional state of the host that supports the creation. Then the text makes this interesting statement: "Eternity swallows her images in front of the Seeing One, He who is in this city, then she gives them (back) for the birth of Khepri on earth." This suggests the current DNA degradation of Lambda forms, but indicates that the transformative process will occur in the earth-cell again. The text referring to the first two Upper Register gods (1-2) reads: "He is like this. When this god calls him the figure of Atum appears on his back, he swallows his images afterwards. He lives on the shadows of the dead, his body is his heads." Here, "heads" is a reference to the icosahedral DNA-packed phage head, and Atum replaces Budge's translation of Tem. The name of the first head-disk-head god (1) is "The One provided with a face, Lord of Eternity," suggesting phage morphology or the faces of the icosahedral capsid. The text referring to the next 12 Upper Register gods (4) states that their souls belong to the Deceased Sun-god, who promises that "water is yours at the station of the Abyss." In support of this is the name of one of the 12 gods: "The Constellation of the Great Bear." The Abyss, of course, is the host earth-cell, with water representing the escaping phage progeny.

In the Middle Register, the text above the Sun-bark states the crew is rowing to the Eastern Horizon, and the uraeus-bound disk is referred to as the "Luminous One" leading the Sun-god. Again, this disk may signify a white hole. The text above the 12 gods who carry the supercoiled serpent states that "they carry Enveloper on their heads," indicating the application of the phage protein envelope. Re advises them to guard their forms and lift up their heads, but further text explains that they let the Enveloper go toward the Gate of the Eastern Horizon. The 12 gods then rest on "their thrones after the passage of the Great God through darkness when he rests in the horizon." The reference to guarding "forms" and resting on "thrones" shows their DNA base has not degraded, that is, the protein envelope is applied to the phage head. Additional evidence indicating this possibility are the names of the 12 carriers: "The Carrier, Bearer, Loader, The One who drags, The Companion, The One who conducts the Image, the One belonging to the Enveloper." In contrast to the preservation of the envelope forms or DNA, the two uraei with the White and Red Crowns appear and then swallow their forms. The uraei represent the images of Isis and Nephthys. Piankoff notes that text in RVI referring to the crowned uraei is incomplete. In older versions, the text reports that they are at the "second door of the thick darkness," that is, the outer membrane of the host cell. The RVI text referring to the last four goddesses states "they guard the Holy Gate of Sais."

The RVI Lower Register depicts the same general slaughtering and annihilation of the enemies of Osiris as seen in the fiery inferno depicted in Seti I. Horus, the son of Osiris, simply states that he came out of Osiris and that "my father strikes after being helpless." Thus, we have the idea of Horus developing through rolling circle replication from the excision of the prophage Osiris. The final pit showing four inverted humans suggests inversion or a return to earth.

Matrix 18. Amduat Hour Eleven

Egyptian Sign translated to Possible Modern Science Parallel

door, second of thick darkness: outer cell membrane
Eternity swallowing forms, but giving them back for Khepri birth: DNA degradation processes followed by renewal processes for future transduction
god Tem with outstretched arms: 2 arms of Lambda genome for lytic lifestyle
Horus coming out of Osiris: recombinant species developing from excision of prophage and rolling circle replication
Horus holding crescent snake: cell crescents caused by cell lysis
Hour, name of: the Star, Mistress of Barge, She who drives away the rebels: lactose metabolism that supports human-phage species
language, names of 12 carriers of Enveloper: loader, bearer: suggests the application of an envelope
language: One provided with a face, Lord of Eternity: faces of icoshedral head
language: Water is yours at station of Abyss: escaping phage progeny from intracellular medium
Mehen the Enveloper: protein envelope for phage heads
Neith, etymology of name meaning to weave or knit: protein translation
pit of fire, large with 4 inverted humans: inversion; end of chemical process; destruction of informtion at a singularity
pits of fire with ocupants, 5: apoptotic DNA degradation
Set, Everlasting: chaotic intracellular medium of host cell; rising cI levels
Star Pestu or Luminous One: convergence; white hole
swallowing of forms: DNA degradation

Hour Twelve

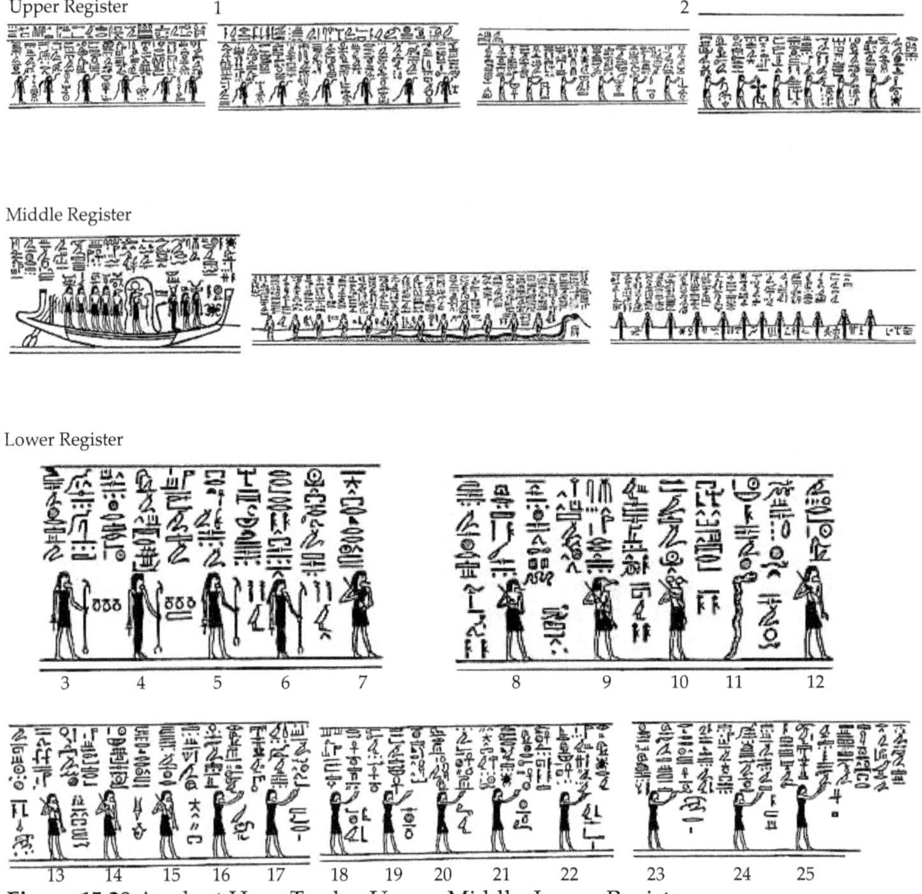

Figure 15.29 Amduat Hour Twelve Upper, Middle, Lower Register
(drawing by Budge from Seti I)

The Middle Register in Seti I shows the Sun-bark and crew with the beetle Khepri at the prow, as his 12 gods and 12 goddesses tow the group through the tail and mouth of a serpent by a cord. The text states that he takes up his "place on the face of the hidden image of the horn (or, forehead) of the sky," a possible reference to the polar cusp region or horn of the earth. Then he seals up the Duat, something we would not expect if the cell were in complete lysis or at burst size. The transformed god then takes his position in the Eastern Horizon. We learn that the 24 deities or servants in Re's following are his "product." The serpent Ankh-neteru stays in the Duat. The movement through the serpent parallels tunneling, the ability of a particle to penetrate into and through classically forbidden regions, so we could say that the Sun-bark is tunneling through the serpent to the extracellular exterior. This could also be compared to moving through a wormhole, for the Duat displays the dynamics of a quantum mechanical Kerr black hole.

In the Upper Register, 12 goddesses (1) with serpents light the way for Re, who has passed by the Hidden Chamber of the sky. These goddesses bonded to serpents represent the lactose energy medium, and the Hidden Chamber is the prophage site on the host chromosome. The text informs us that the goddesses also drive Apopis away, journey around the upper heavens, but remain in their places. Next are 12 adoring gods (2), who descend to earth before Re, rising "upon the eyes of mankind in their circles."

In the Lower Register are two gods (3-4) and two goddesses (5-6), followed by four gods with paddles (7-10), a serpent (11), four more paddle gods (12-15), and ten adoring gods (16-25). The gods are behind the image of Osiris or bearded mummified form that reclines on the double wall or double cell membrane (Figure 15.30).

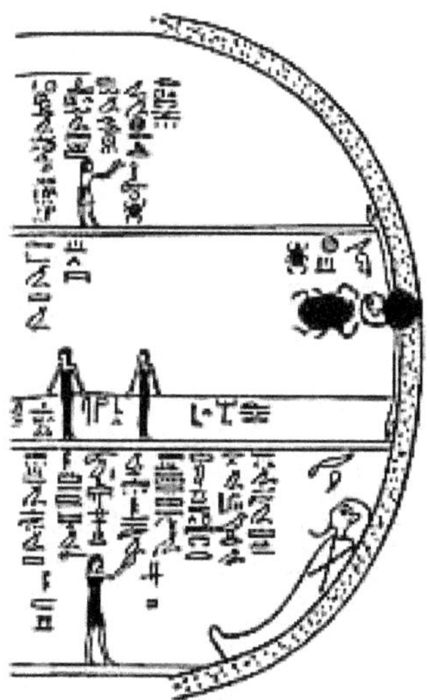

Figure 15.30 Hour Twelve (Drawing by Budge rom Seti I)

Re journeys by this form saying "Life [to thee], O governor of Amentet, Osiris." The final texts state that "He who is in this picture in the invisible form of Horus in thick darkness, is the hidden image which Shu lifteth up beneath the sky, and Keb-Ur cometh forth in the earth in this image." The idea that the recombinant species is the "invisible form of Horus in thick darkness" suggests the generation of dark energy.

Text from Ramesses VI

Hour Twelve is not depicted in RVI, so Piankoff used data from the tombs of Thutmosis III and Amenophis II, Ramesses II and the tomb of Pedemenopet. In the Middle Register, the Sun-bark is pulled by 12 gods and 13 goddesses, instead of 12 in Seti I. The Gate is called "Exaltation of the Gods" and the city "Outcome of the Darkness, Appearance of Birth." The Sun-god is coming out of the Abyss into the body of Nut, that is, from the double-membraned bacterium into the extracellular medium. The text states that the malachite (turquoise) gods praise Re who takes a seat in heaven. The serpent through which the Sun-bark is pulled is named "Life of the Gods," and he lives by the roar of the honored ones coming through him. Again, we are reminded of PT 291 stating, "Your honor is removed, O white hole, by him who came forth from the *fnt*-snake." Perhaps the roar of the honored ones indicates a thunderpop state that creates a white hole, restoring CPT invariance. As Strominger states, "The thunderpop is required to nucleate the white hole into which the CPT-reversed Hawking radiation subsequently falls" (1993). Turquoise suggests bioluminescence and the roar of the serpent suggests a chemical reaction of tunneling. It is also interesting that the text referring to the first group of two couples (3-6) in the Lower Register mentions that they belong to their "gate in the horizon," suggesting porin gates present in the two membranes of *E. coli* and/or exit from a horizon.

Of interest is the text above the image of Osiris reclining on the end of the cell wall in the Lower Register. It states "Image of Flesh" with the final text stating that this is the "mysterious form of Horus in complete darkness." The text continues, stating that this form represents "Shu who supports Nut while the Great Flood comes out of the earth according to this representation." The indication here is that the Sun-bark and crew are the "Great Flood." Piankoff translates the name of the twelfth goddess in the Upper Register as "Mistress of the Uraei in the Barge of Millions (of years)." According to Piankoff on vii, parentheses ( ) indicate "interpolations of obvious scribal omissions or additions made to clarify meaning." So, if we take the translation as it is, "Barge of Millions" can easily signify the millions of escaping phage progeny from rolling circle replication, as does "Great Flood."

Still, it is obvious that the cell has not lysed or burst. It seems as if we had some DNA degradation and apoptosis, but the cell still lives with intact cell membranes, according to the final drawing in Hour Twelve and the textual reference in Hour Eleven about "second door of thick darkness." Along with this, we have the empty mummified form of Osiris reclining on the cell wall. In Hour Seven, Osiris provided the protein core for head assembly, and the Sun-god provided the recombinant DNA. The text states that this mysterious Image is Shu, derived from *shu* meaning "dry, parched, withered, empty" (Budge v2 1904, 87). Shu personified the North Wind and the atmosphere between earth and sky. In addition, Shu was the immediate offspring of Atum, along with Tefnut that separated the sky from the earth. (Houser-Wegner 2002) In Part One, the Barriers of Shu were equivalent to the earth's magnetosphere. The Deceased Sun-god's birth indicates these barriers have been broken, that is, the Sun-god has escaped from the earth-cell or the earth's magnetosphere. With the escape into the starry universe, it seems that gravitational effects are still present and that the creation may be a form of matter or energy in the Early Universe, albeit, one with a longer lifespan than a meson (quark and antiquark).

The Transmembrane Tunnel

Certainly, questions remain here, especially related to the serpent that the Sun-bark travels through, tail to mouth, which is the method of releasing progeny virions instead of complete cell lysis or bursting. Researchers are currently investigating single gene lysis systems and Protein E, which promotes cell lysis, but does not degrade the host cell wall. (Bernhardt et al. 2000) However, Lubitz et al. have observed "discrete 50- to 200 nm holes located at the cell septum and occasionally at the poles," which prompted them to theorize that the E protein oligomerizes to form a "Transmembrane tunnel." This tunnel spans the entire cell envelope and releases phage progeny and other cytoplasmic contents. (Witte et al. 1990) This "transmembrane tunnel" easily describes the Amduat tunnel, for the Sun-god's "Barge of Millions" represents escaping recombinant phage progeny. Also, the Seti I text explains that the Sun-god emerges at the "horn of the sky," suggesting the polar cusp and matching Lubitz' observation of holes at the cell poles. In line with this idea, the Edifice of Taharqa (See Part Four) shows the transforming beetle emerging from the Sacred Lake of Karnack at the northwest, which would indicate the polar cusp site of the earth-cell or true north, a mixture of magnetic north and magnetic west. So it seems that complete cell lysis has been inhibited in some way, so that the means of escape is not degradation of host cell walls, but escape through a "Transmembrane tunnel."

Usually, phage Lambda kills the cell, but in this case, it did not. Researchers have also discovered a mutant phage Lambda that infects a particular mutant strain of *E. coli*. This Lambda injects its DNA which degrades, leaving a long stalk and globular head of the empty phage particle firmly attached to the cell surface. (Texas A&M University 2001) This seems to be what has happened in the Amduat, where the empty mummified form of Osiris finally reclines on the cell wall, and forms have swallowed themselves or degraded as the Sun-god is born renewed. However, these departure events also represent the folding of cro protein to its native conformation in an energy landscape funnel, having the dynamics of white hole formation/evaporation obtained as the time reverse of black hole formation/evaporation.

The final text in RVI states that the "Great Flood comes out of the earth according to this representation," which we can now understand as millions of recombinant phage progeny escaping from the host earth-cell.

Matrix 19. Amduat Hour Twelve

Egyptian Sign translated to
Possible Modern Science Parallel

Barge of Millions; Great Flood: millions of escaping phage progeny
gate in horizon: cell membrane gates; white hole horizon
gate, second; Hour 12 drawing depicting dual lines: double cell membrane
goddesses with serpents who light Re's way, 12: allolactose bonded to Lac repressor protein so lactose is transcribed and available
gods with paddles, 8: efflux proteins
Horus invisible: phage progeny as dark energy; Hawking radiation
language, reference to product and Outcome of Darkness: DNA to RNA to protein product
Malachite (turquoise) gods: indicator of bioluminescence; stars
roar of Sun-bark going through serpent: thunderpop state nucleating white hole
serpent named Life of Gods through which Sun-bark travels from tail to mouth: tunneling; transmembrane tunnel to extracellular space; wormhole
Shu image or empty mummified form of Osiris reclining: empty phage particle firmly attached to interior cell wall

Objective 9 Completed: The decoded metasymbols in the twelve hours of the Amduat apply to, illuminate and support the model derived from the major Idea Strands in the Pyramid and Coffin Texts.

16

The Book of Twelve Gates

MORE MIDDLE KINGDOM EVIDENCE FOR THE LAMBDA MODEL

The preceding analysis of the Amduat from the Tombs of Seti I and Ramesses VI supports our matrices based on the Idea Strands from the Pyramid and Coffin Texts, while expanding our knowledge about the lytic cycle of phage Lambda. In the interest of discovering whether or not other Egyptian texts support this same interpretative foundation, it is necessary to review the Book of Gates and compare it with the Amduat. For convenience, Matrix 20 is a master summary of the Amduat, developed from the drawings, portfolio of plates, and translations of E. A. Wallis Budge and Alexandre Piankoff.

Matrix 20. Amduat Summary (Upper Register = UR; Middle = MR; Lower = LR)

Hour	Images/Events of Hour point to:	Possible Modern Science Parallel
1	1) Horn of the West	1) polar cap
	2) permeable barrier on Sun-bark's prow	2) Maltose Transport (LamB) selectivity
	3) horizontal ram horns	3) horizontal gene transfer; transduction
	4) Isis on Sun-bark	4) lactose permease entry into cell
	5) Hidden Chamber destination	5) Lambda prophage on host chromosome
	6) 42 UR deities	6) 42 de-repressed genes of incoming Lambda
	7) Sun-god's word going out	7) Lambda DNA into cell; penetration
	8) 4 Terms of Osiris	8) 4 Lambda terminators
2	1) Boat of Full Moon	1) Circularized Lambda DNA
	2) Sun-god's sceptre as waving serpent	2) active replication fork; transcription
	3) advent of Thoth	3) RNA Polymerase
	4) Osiris Term facing lioness deity	4) antitermination factor
3	1) Horus looping ropes on Sun-bark	1) circle to circle replication; bidirectional
	2) Boat of the Branch	2) 7 bp branch migration for excision

Hour	Images/Events of Hour point to:	Possible Modern Science Parallel
4	1) 3-headed serpent, 14 stars, heads, disks	1) cro protein build up for phage replication
	2) Moving Radiance serpent on boat	2) DNA concatemer
	3) Isis as Lady of Life	3) lactose nutrient medium
	4) 4 gods towing Sun-bark	4) Integrase protein for integration/excision
	5) Sun-bark named One who cuts way	5) cleavage of 7 bp branch migration
	6) winged 3-headed serpent with life sign	6) winged DRADA protein for RNA editing
	7) 2-headed serpent with 3rd head backward	7) Z-DNA formation
5	1) 7 gods/7 goddesses towing Re between beetle chamber and Flesh of Isis	1) 7 bp branch migration at *LacZ* gene
	2) winged 3-headed serpent with backward head in mound	2) winged CAP Protein; Z-DNA formation at *LacZ* gene
	3) 9 axes	3) indicator of concatemer cleavage
	4) reference to Osiris with legs bent round	4) indicator of rolling circle replication
6	1) purifying god with crossed crook/knife	1) Holliday junction intermediate
	2) 9 short erect serpents	2) unit-length DNA from concatemer
	3) May your heads live	3) phage head assembly
	4) 9 sceptres	4) multiple fertile genomes for head assembly
7	1) Apopis slaughtered	1) LexA repressor inactive; SOS; excision
	2) I seize writings, establish millions	2) phage production
	3) 4 Coffers	3) cos sites for Lambda head packaging
	4) crocodile providing Head of Osiris	4) scaffolding protein core for prohead
	5) 12 star deities	5) portal and scaffolding proteins
	6) 24 five-pointed stars on deities	6) self-assembly into icosahedral structures
	7) crocodile swallowing his image	7) digestion of scaffolding protein core
8	1) 10 circles of sand gods	1) portal proteins form oligomeric rings
	2) 9 sceptres with bearded heads	2) DNA packaging motor
	3) weaving instruments	3) translation to protein
	4) Re as Enveloper	4) during packaging, coat proteins surround a scaffolding protein core; protein envelope
	5) 8 gods towing Sun-bark	5) Terminase translocation or 8 structural proteins forming baseplate for tail
9	1) 3 deities in 3 basins	1) AUG initiation codon for translation
	2) 12 gods on weaving instruments	2) completion of phage head/tail assembly
	3) 12 sailors with paddles	3) efflux pump proteins
	4) 12 goddesses	4) lactose nutrient medium
10	1) 2 goddesses facing 2-headed serpent	1) Lac repressor protein bound to allolactose
	2) 2 goddesses pointing with fingers	2) zinc finger DNA-binding proteins
	3) 2 goddesses with ax supporting disk	3) end of concatemer cleavage
	4) 12 swimmers with backbones in flood	4) hydrophilic external sugar phosphates
11	1) supercoiled serpent Mehen the Enveloper	1) protein envelope for phage heads
	2) one fire pit of 4 inverted humans	2) inversion; end of chemical process
	3) swallowing of forms	3) phage DNA degradation
12	1) Sun-bark going through serpent	1) wormhole; transmembrane tunnel
	2) Barge of Millions; Great Flood	2) escaping recombinant phage progeny
	3) empty mummified form of Osiris	3) empty phage particle attached to cell wall

The Book of Gates is found in the tombs of Haremhab, Ramesses I, II, VI and others, as well as in the two great pillared halls of Seti I, along with the earliest complete version on his alabaster sarcophagus. In 1905, Budge translated this version, but because the sarcophagus lid had been destroyed, he arrived at a false enumeration. (Hornung 1999, 55-57) For illustrative purposes, public domain drawings by Budge from Seti I are presented herein, but the translation for the Book of Gates is by Piankoff from the Tomb of Ramesses VI.

A complete Book of Gates is carved in the tomb of Ramesses VI on the left wall of Corridors A, B, C, D and Hall E. Three figures depict the King advancing toward Re, Horus of the Horizon and Osiris, with the first tableau beginning in back of the group. This prologue represents the horizon of the West, which is divided in two parts through which the Sun-bark will pass (Piankoff 1954, 139). Piankoff's translation of the Book of Gates from the Tomb of Ramesses VI begins with an assertion in the prologue of the authority of the Right Eye of Re that indicates the potential of cro protein production for the Lambda lytic lifestyle. The Deceased arrives at the Gap in the Western Mountains or polar cusp, and his destination is described as "the hidden seat, the Desert" where "the diadem is restored." This seat is the 30 bp hydrophobic sand region where the prophage Osiris resides. In the Upper and Lower Registers or mountains are the same inscriptions, stating that to those born of Re, he grants them "their hidden seat, the Desert, to which are brought together men, gods, all cattle, all worms," a statement asserting that the hidden seat is the origin of all creation. The text states Re mounts the earth, "which he has created from his Right Eye," that is, the stars and Sun. Mounting the earth is comparable to Lambda adsorption to the earth-cell. Twelve (12) upside-down gods walk on the upper mountain. The Sun-bark has two gods on it, Mind and Magic. References to phage morphology include: a jackal-headed sceptre called "Neck of Re," a ram-headed sceptre called "Head of Re," and "this head to which the diadem is restored." Descriptive terminology for phage include head, tail, neck, collar, tail baseplate and tail fiber.

Division One

The Sun-bark enters the first division through a serpent-guarded door, inscribed with text stating "the Hidden Chamber is in darkness in order to create the forms of this god." The Upper Register depicts 24 male figures. Re promises the first 12 figures that their souls will not be slaughtered because they repel Apopis. He tells the next 12 figures that they will have Truth and live.

These 24 figures represent the cohesive ends for circularization of the linear Lambda DNA inside the cell.

In the Middle Register, four gods pull Re's boat on which the ram-headed Sun-god stands with two gods. The four towing gods suggest the four-unit Intergrase protein for integration and excision of the prophage. Re has a forked sceptre and is wearing the horizontal ram horns and disk. He is enveloped by the serpent Mehen, "The Enveloper," and another elongated serpent stands within the shrine. Thirteen (13) deities meet the bark, and Re informs them that he has power over the "shrine which is in the earth" and that he will create the forms for them. The deities know that Re "creates himself" or is a molecule that self-assembles. The earth shrine is where the prophage is lodged.

In the Lower Register, Atum stands over four horizontal figures called "The Tired Ones." Twenty (20) bound figures, who are destined for the Place of Destruction, are an indicator of RNA degradation, which the Integrase and excise genes of phage Lambda depend on. (Carnegie Mellon University)

Division Two

The Sun-god then passes through a gateway guarded by nine (9) mummified gods, a divine guard, and an elongated serpent standing on its tail. The nine (9) gods are called the "Second Ennead." The divine guard is at the entrance and the exit of a passage between two walls, suggesting the double membrane of the host cell. The gate opens for the Sun-god, who will make the "Hidden Chamber bright," a reference to the excision of the prophage.

In the Upper Register, 12 mummies stand in shrines having open doors with an elongated serpent stretched above them. Although the text does not refer to the serpent, it states that Re commands the shrines to open and the Holy Ones to be powerful, suggesting that the serpent may point to the linear dsDNA of phage Lambda. Then 12 bearded gods with barley stand in a Lake of Fire, which is their refreshment. One could say that the gods are brewing barley in the fiery lake, which brings to mind the sugar maltose that is used in the brewing of barley, wheat and oats. The barley gods seem to be an obvious reference to the maltose/maltodextrin system of *E. coli* transport, metabolism and regulation, which also serves as the LamB receptor for phage Lambda.

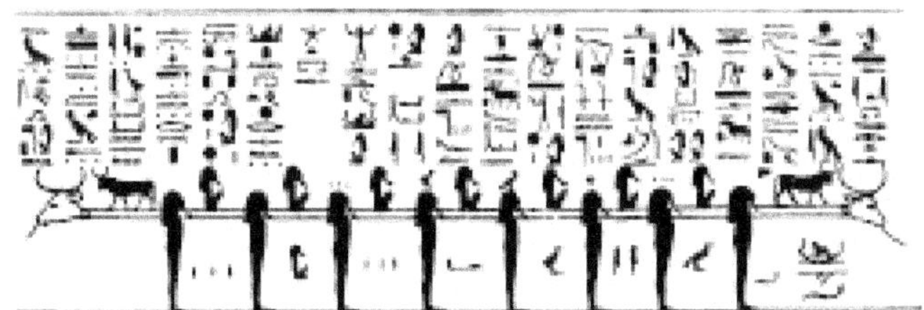

Figure 16.1 From Book of Gates Division Three (Drawing by Budge from Seti I; Division numbering is different than Ramesses VI)

In the Middle Register of RVI, four (4) deities tow the Sun-god's bark through a long rod, each end terminating in a bull's head and a standing bull (Figure 16.1). Eight (8) bearded mummies support the rod, on which seven (7) small bearded mummies sit. This is the "Barge of Earth" through which Re passes, a possible representation of the tail through which the Lambda DNA moves into the host cell. This rod may also represent the LamB receptor site, a sugar-selective porin or tube filled with water that allows the passage of trehalose, lactose and sucrose. (Bergman 1999) LamB's crystal structure is trimeric, with each monomer consisting of an 18-stranded *beta*-barrel enclosing a channel. In the channel lining are six contiguous aromatic residues, which form an elongated narrow "greasy slide," which extends to the periplasmic outlet. (Van Gelder et al. 2002) Nonetheless, the movement of the Sun-god through the bull-ended rod parallels the movement of Lambda DNA down the hollow tube of the phage tail, what could be called the long neck of Re, so the DNA can be injected into the host cell. Then, the text claims the earth quakes, suggesting the initialization of the SOS response by the cell.

In the Lower Register, Atum leans on a staff before the coiled Apopis, as nine (9) figures approach called "The Council who repulse Apopis." In a second group, Atum is met by nine (9) gods with sceptres and the signs of life. The text reads that Apopis falls, the nine (9) gods protect Re, and that "the One whose arm is holy in the Hidden Seat" receives libations. The "Hidden Seat" is where Osiris or the Lambda genome is lodged on the host chromosome. As the Sun-god passes, wailing ensues.

Division Three

The upper guardian of the Third Division gate is "Earthquake. He bends his arm before Re" and the lower guardian is "Trembling of Earth. He bends his arm before Re," both names suggesting the cell's quaking SOS response.

The nine (9) gods at the gate are called the "Third Ennead," and the text referring to the Ennead states that Re has opened the earth. After the Sun-god passes, there is wailing, suggesting interspecies cross-talk between phage Lambda and the cell's proteins.

In the Upper Register are 12 walking gods "who go to their Kas," 12 jackal-headed gods in the Lake of Life, and ten (10) uraei on lakes. As Re passes by, they wail.

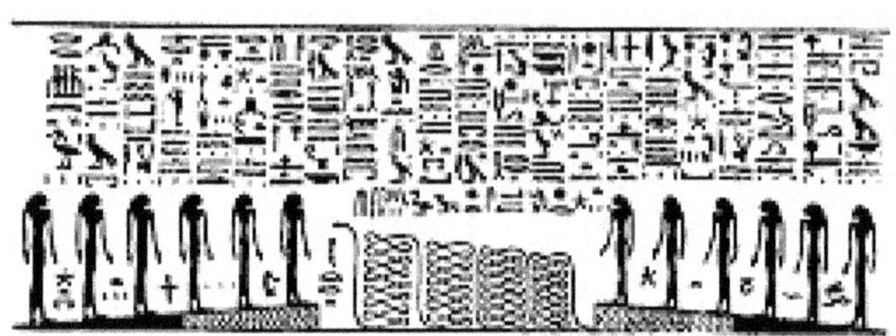

Figure 16.2 From Book of Gates Division Four (Drawing by Budge from Seti I; division numbering is different than RVI)

In the Middle Register, four (4) divinities tow the Sun-bark toward nine (9) sarcophagi, containing nine (9) sleeping mummies or Osirian forms representative of the prophage state. Then 12 goddesses of the Hours on water, divided into two groups of six, each face a serpent on land or sand named "He who should be removed." The goddesses signify the allolactose that binds to the Lac repressor protein, removing it from the operator sequences so lactose can be transcribed. Re moves on, advising the four (4) towing gods (Integrase protein) to take him to the seats of Osiris in the western sky. He tells the nine (9) gods in the sarcophagi to rise. These rising gods have gifts of meat, beer and water. In other words, the lactose nutrient is available in the cell now that the Lac repressor is removed from the DNA. The 12 goddesses of the Hours lead Re over the land.

The Lower Register contains hawk-headed Horus and 11 gods walking to an enshrined Osiris, standing on a serpent with a uraeus in front of the shrine. Twelve (12) gods advance on the other side, and behind them are four (4) "pits of fire," then a bearded figure with a sceptre. The text states that Horus creates the spirit of his father Osiris after restoring his diadem. This scene and the text describe Horus liberating Osiris, that is, the impending Lambda prophage excision; the fiery pits indicate the necessary chemical reactions involved in excision and DNA degradation.

Division Four

In the tomb of RVI, the left wall of corridor B is divided into two main registers, the top showing the gate, Division Four and the gate of Division Five with the Hall of Osiris. The bottom register depicts the remainder of Division Five and the gate of Division Six.

The gate opens for Re who makes the Hidden Chamber bright. The Upper Register depicts 12 adoring gods, 12 gods carrying a supercoiled cord, and four (4) gods holding signs of life. The 12 adoring gods welcome Re, saying "Be thou praised when thou enterest splendor (while) in the (coils of the) Enveloper." During Lambda packaging, the coat proteins surround a scaffolding protein core or envelope. The cord is described as the "Measuring rope" that will be divided into allotments or portions by the four (4) gods, suggesting the concatemer cutting activity of the translocation protein terminase. This is further supported by the text above the four (4) gods, wherein Re addresses them as "measurers of the fields, who preside over the rope."

The Middle Register shows the Sun-bark with four (4) towers that indicate Integrase activity. Nine (9) mummy-type figures supporting a serpent suggests the protein wrapping, linearization and cleaving of the concatemer for head packing. Re states, "Stretch the rope while drawing me among you," indicating that the DNA twisting must be relaxed for passage through the portal to the head. Re passes by the nine (9) mummy-type figures, advising them to guard "so that my forms may become," a reference to the potential of the DNA concatemer. Next are 12 gods, who represent the portal protein complex, walking toward a god holding the sign of life and a sceptre, who is called "He who presides in his corner." The term "corner" suggests the corners or vertices of an icosahedral head. The Middle Register text contains additional references to "corner." When talking to the 12 walking gods or portal protein complex, Re advises, "Your seats are yours in the corner." Other textual references to "corner" include Re referencing "the rightful ones who rest on their seats in the corner and among whom I am myself." So, the Middle Register describes the activity of head packaging.

The Lower Register shows Horus, 16 figures representing the four (4) races, and 12 gods holding a serpent with signs of duration on it. This procession is met by eight (8) walking gods. The text over the 12 carrying the serpent explains that they "establish the duration of life and they appoint the days for the souls in the West, destined for the Place of Destruction." Re then states that the

Place of Destruction is for his enemies, and the council of eight (8) gods will annihilate the enemies. These enemies are the molecular forms or recycled reactants that return to the photosynthetic environment of earth.

Division Five with the Hall of Osiris

The name of the gate is "Mistress of Duration," suggesting Isis or the *LacZ* gene, where the prophage Osiris is lodged. Earlier in this work, we reviewed the Hall of Osiris, analyzing the meaning of the equalized balance with disproportionate contents that suggest the balanced arms of the Lambda genome with increasing cro production over cI. The Hall of Osiris (Figure 16.3) represents the prophage site. The four (4) African antelopes hanging upside down above Osiris are called "The Roarers," suggesting the chemical reaction of excision. Then the door to the prophage site is opened so that Re can make "the Hidden Chamber bright," and wailing ensues when it closes behind Re.

The Upper Register depicts three groups of 12 gods. The first 12 hold forked staffs or javelins; the second 12 hold a serpent with 12 human heads growing from its body. The serpent is called "Swallower" and also Apopis, and Re orders that Apopis should be speared when the heads come out so that he retreats. As discussed, the cell continues to synthesize small amounts of the repressor protein, which Apopis represents. Re advises Apopis that the rebel is retreating, indicating that Seth or cI protein production is minimal. Re passes by the heads, which are digested within the folds, pointing to DNA degradation of human forms.

The Upper Register also depicts the first stage of phage head and tail assembly or the packaging of DNA into reassembled protein shells called proheads. The third group of 12 gods, holding a double-looped rope attached to a standing mummy's neck, confirms this interpretation. These 12 gods are referenced as "those who carry the twisted cord from which come out stars." The mummy from which the cord hangs is Aken, who swallows the double rope. Further, the reference to stars suggests the traditional stellation diagram of an icosahedron, which looks like a five-pronged star. Put simply, these three groups of 12 gods depict self-assembly of icosahedral structures, DNA degradation of human forms, and Lambda DNA head packaging.

The Middle Register shows four (4) gods towing the Sun-bark, a group of 12 gods with hidden arms, and a group of eight (8) gods. The text addresses Re as "Lord of Hours," suggesting the 60 subunits of an icosahedral head. Re

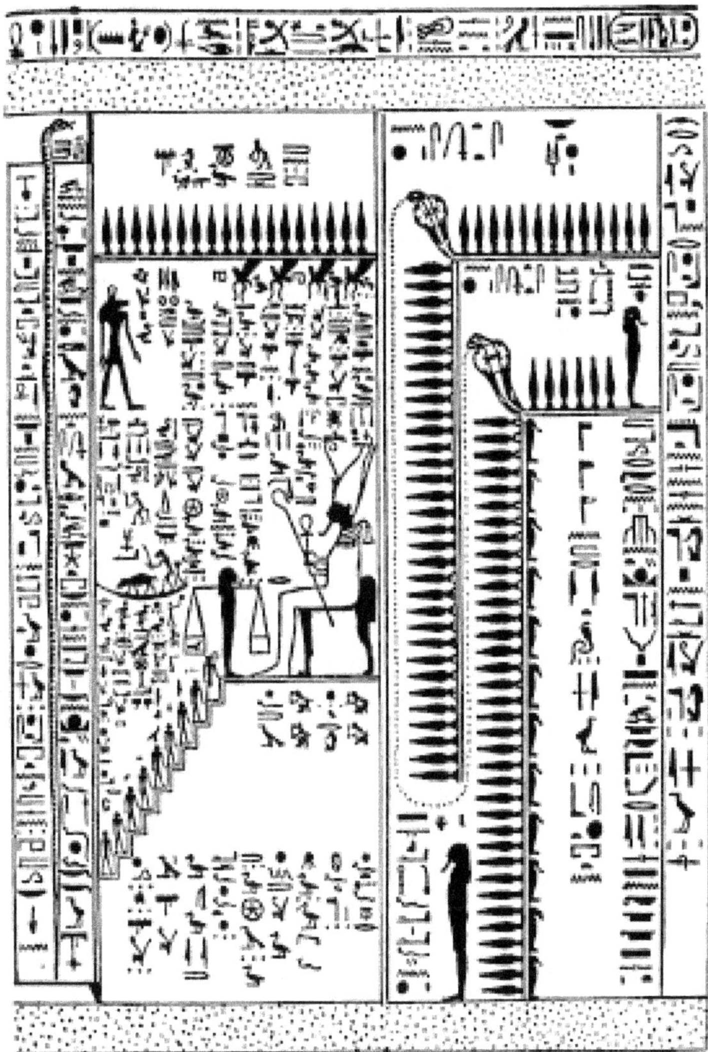

Figure 16.3
Hall of Osiris from Seti I, Div. Six (drawing by Budge from Seti I)

tells the 12 gods to "receive my forms, embrace my mysteries in the Palace of the Obelisk, at the place where the body of this god is." This suggests the Lambda prophage site of Osiris. The 12 gods then state that Re's soul is for the sky and his body for the earth, suggesting that the composite function of both Re and Osiris is necessary, that is, the incoming phage Lambda and the prophage function together for the birth of the recombinant species.

The Lower Register shows a god addressing 12 reclining mummies on biers formed by a serpent, signifying the excision of the prophage, for the text advises them to "rise from your lassitude." Then, 12 inclining gods walk toward a pool of fire inhabited by a uraeus. The text states that the pool is for Osiris.

Division Six

In the Upper Register is a group of 12 gods carrying grain on their heads, possibly barley, suggesting the cell nutrient level of lactose. A second group of 12 gods follow, carrying feathers of Truth and Rightful Order, suggesting the rightward order of cro protein occupation of operator sequences on the Lambda genome. Osiris tells the grain-carrying gods that they will have "cakes for your Kas," along with bread, beer and water. He tells the feather-carrying gods that they will have a "complete existence under Truth, to which evil does not come." All 24 figures hold their arms upright, representing the two upraised arms of the Ka symbol.

The Middle Register shows the Sun-bark towed by four (4) gods, moving toward the god Atum and seven (7) jackal-headed poles with two enemies tied to each pole. Before each pole is a god with arms crossed on his breast. The last god in this grouping holds a sceptre. Re states that he has "taken possession of the Silent Region," or prophage site, and that the enemies will be beheaded. These drawings illustrate the 7 bp region for the excision of the prophage, the Holliday junction resolution (crossed arms), and the beheading or cleaving of the base pairs in this process.

The Lower Register shows 12 figures with an ear of grain and seven (7) reapers with sickles. The text states that Osiris is satisfied with "this green sprouting," suggesting vegetative replication of the lytic cycle. Re states, "The Grain God flourishes, Osiris has become again," reinforcing the rising Osiris or excision of the prophage and the lytic lifestyle. The seven sickles, of course, suggest the action of restriction enzymes, the molecular scissors that cuts DNA at defined sequences, such as the 7 bp region necessary for prophage excision.

Division Seven

In the Upper Register, 12 gods carry a rope from which four (4) M-shaped signs, four (4) hawk heads, and four (4) human heads emerge. The four (4) M-shaped signs suggest the matrix protein (M-protein) that triggers budding, which is found in some enveloped viruses. Then 12 gods follow, carrying a serpent with 11 stars placed above its coils, indicating the linearization of DNA and star conformation.

The Middle Register depicts the Sun-bark and four (4) towers preceded by 12 gods holding sceptres and four (4) mummies called "Fighting Faces." Re states that the bandages of the mummies are unloosened, suggesting prophage excision.

In the Lower Register, a god addresses 12 bearded gods who rise from couches, suggesting the excision of the prophage and replication, and 12 gods preceding the rising gods, who are addressed by Re as "Council of Judges."

Division Eight

In the Upper Register are 12 walking gods, nine (9) soul birds with human heads, and a god leaning on a staff. The 12 walking gods, referred to as the Council, lead the "souls to the green growth in the Island of Flame," suggesting vegetative lytic replication of phage progeny at the site of the Lambda genome on the host chromosome. Re advises the nine (9) soul birds to eat the green growth.

The Middle Register shows the Sun-bark towed by four gods, suggesting Integrase, and a god leaning on a staff by a pool of water with 16 figures in groups of four called "the submerged, the floaters, the swimmers, those who crouch." The text explains that these swimmers have dominion over their waters and will not perish. So, as in the Amduat, it seems possible that they represent the hydrophilic sugar-phosphate backbone for phage nucleic acid and protein synthesis.

The Lower Register shows Horus before 12 bound enemies, who advance before a fiery serpent of coils with seven (7) mummies. The fire suggests a thermal reaction related to DNA degradation, possibly cII degradation.

Division Nine

In the Upper Register, four (4) gods wearing White Crowns raise a pole bearing the White Crown, and four (4) gods wearing the Red Crown of Lower Egypt raise a pole bearing a White Crown. Between these two groups reclines a lion body with a hawk head wearing a White Crown and on the tail end, a human head wearing a White Crown. Standing on the lion's body is a small figure with the heads of Horus and Seth. This complete image indicates the two promoter sites (PL and PR) or cro protein production build-up for late transcription and replication. The next image is a six-headed serpent called "The Opener," standing on six pairs of human legs, held in the center by a male figure. Following this is the "Runner of the Earth," a long two-headed serpent with each head wearing a White Crown. Upon the "Runner" is another eight-headed serpent held in the center by a male figure, which may represent RecA. Re tells the gods "Your heads are yours, O gods. Receive your crowns of the North. Take hold of the aft-rope of the Boat of He who comes into being in me. Thou are indeed Horus whose face is sublime." The general idea behind these images is active phage "running" circle replication. The final image is two male figures with nets that signify catching the enemy or the degradation of DNA.

The Middle Register shows the Sun-bark towed by four figures, a group of 14 figures swinging nets, and four (4) apes and four (4) women. Then there is a complicated image (Figure 16.4) of three (3) gods holding javelins and a supercoiled rope held by a bearded, half-mummified form, rising from the ground before Apopis, who is destroyed. Above Apopis is a crocodile with a serpent head protruding from its tail. The text states that the three gods with javelins guard "the ropes of the Old One."

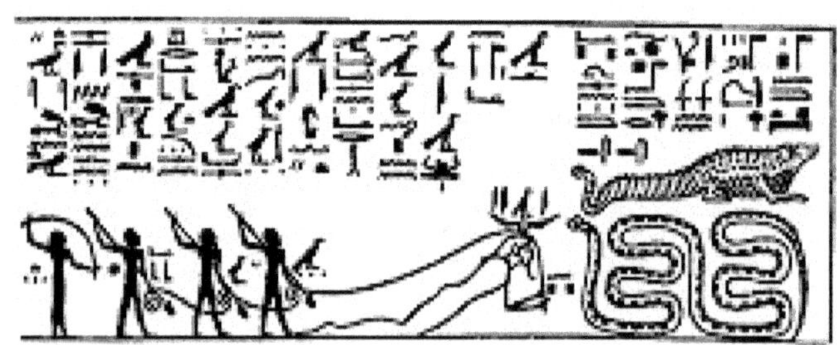

Figure 16.4 Spearmen, Old One and Apopis (drawing by Budge from Seti I)

The towing gods state that the Sun-god is "being towed toward his shadow," a reference to his former condition. So, in light of the Upper Register depicting the raised poles with White Crowns, signifying the two lytic promoters PL and PR, it is apparent that the feeble Old One, the shadow, is a representation of the Promoter for Repressor Maintenance, which is the promoter for the transcription of the repressor protein that blocks the lytic genes. However, when cro protein levels rise, this weakened Promoter only synthesizes small quantities of the repressor. (Terry 2000) It is important to remember that this site on the host chromosome is the Lambda genome, the location of the cI and cro protein competition, where cro was repressed by the Lambda cI repressor for lysogeny. However, the lytic path is operating, so Apopis is restrained, as is the Lambda cI repressor (Seth).

In the Lower Register, the serpent Khepri is depicted with two heads, two pairs of human legs, two uraei, and a hawk wearing the Double Crown centered on its body. This serpent is roped between 16 gods (four are ibis-headed, four hawk-headed, four ram-headed, and four human-headed) and eight (8) human-headed figures. Horus of the Netherworld enters into the serpent Khepri. The text states that Re has "come out after his transformations" and that the portals to Nut are open. This intriguing image suggests molecular growth and transformation of the Horus creation due to repressor maintenance, prophage excision and lytic cycle activity.

Division Ten

In the Upper Register, eight (8) gods, holding knives and lassos, move to the chained Apopis. The lassos suggest lariat structure. The chain is held by 16 gods and by a large right hand from the ground, which is before Osiris. The text states that "knives are planted into Evil Face. Apopis is in bonds," and this supports the lytic pathway. The Hidden Hand, a right hand signifying the strength of the right Lambda arm under cro control, holds the chained Lambda cI repressor protein of five helices, depicted by the five serpent heads. The text over the serpent states, "Selkit places fetters while the barge of the Great God comes near this Apopis," indicating that "this Apopis" is one of several, which is possible because the cleaving of the LexA repressor protein (monster Apopis) incapacitates the Lambda cI repressor (Seth-Apopis) that allows lysogeny. Geb and the four sons of Horus restrain this Apopis, with the text stating that they guard "the issue of the Helpless One," another reference to the helpless five-helix Lambda cI repressor protein that cannot block all lytic genes by binding to the PR and PL, but can only synthesize or *issue* a small quantity of repressor. (Terry 2000)

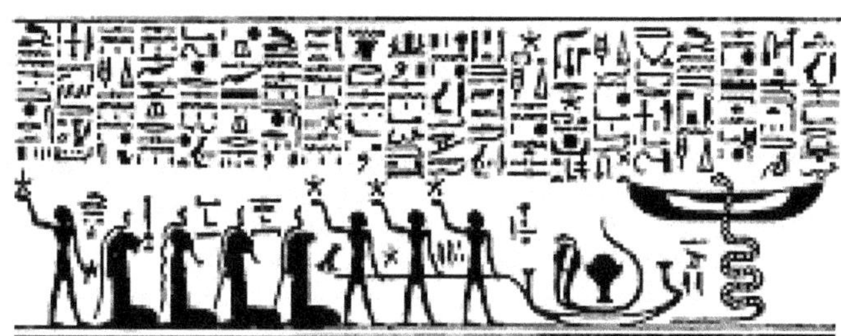

Figure 16.5 Face of Disk from Book of Gates, Division Ten
(drawing by Budge from Seti I)

In the Middle Register, the Sun-bark is pulled by four (4) and preceded by a god holding two stars called "The One of the Hours," the Hours suggesting icosahedral 60-subunit structure. Then four (4) gods sit with uraei on their heads (Figure 16.5), followed by three (3) figures each holding a star in their raised right hands, who tow a boat with a uraeus and a full-faced head, which is called "Face of the Disk" and also the "Great Face" of Re. The reversed direction of this boat indicates the reverse integration or excision of the prophage. The text confirms that Re is being towed toward Nut, toward the Gate of the Eastern Horizon, that is, the extracellular medium. The last image is the double-headed image of Seth-Horus and six (6) uraei, suggesting "the fighters who are in the following of this god" and the full function of the Lambda genome or lytic cycle, as indicated by the six (6) uraei, a sign of the six (6) contested operator sequences.

In the Lower Register are 12 gods with paddles, signifying efflux pumps or proteins, followed by 12 goddesses with stars above their heads, who represent the transition to star conformation and self-assembly into icosahedral structures. The text states the paddle gods (efflux proteins) cause Re to rise to Nut, while the star goddesses tow Re into Nut.

Division Eleven

In the Upper Register are four (4) gods carrying disks, four (4) carrying stars, and 12 holding sceptres. Before them are eight (8) goddesses holding stars and sitting on coiled serpents, along with a crocodile-headed god with a sceptre and serpent. The text references that the Duat has been made new and that the "two arms of the Abyss receive Re," showing that the Duat is made new by the lytic lifestyle and the full operations of the two arms of the Lambda genome. The eight (8) goddesses bonded to serpents suggest the action of lactose binding to the Lac repressor protein to provide the nutrient medium for the transfiguration of the King.

The Middle Register shows the Sun-bark towed by four (4) and preceded by nine (9) gods holding crooks and knives (electrostatic force of repulsion), advancing toward the chained Apopis. After this image are four (4) baboons, each holding a large left human hand, and two (2) goddesses. Reference is made to "transformations on the arms of the Abyss" and to the "two arms of the One Whose Name Is Hidden," suggesting the full operation of the two arms of the Lambda genome.

In the Lower Register, 16 gods, wearing the White and Red Crowns, are preceded by 12 goddesses wearing White and Red Crowns. Not all of the gods and goddesses are wearing crowns. These deities are preceded by four (4) inclining figures and a cat-headed god holding a sceptre and a serpent. Some of these gods stay in the Duat, while others leave with Re, some following with their souls, while their bodies remain.

Division Twelve

Before the gate are two pillars with human heads facing each other. The text states the two pillars are Khepri and Atum, and that they come into being. This suggests that the Deceased Sun-god has attained the primordial status of Atum. Only one representation exists in Division Twelve. The Sun-bark is lifted up by arms out of the Abyss and is born in the form of the living beetle, pushing a disk between Isis and Nephthys and the crew of eight gods.

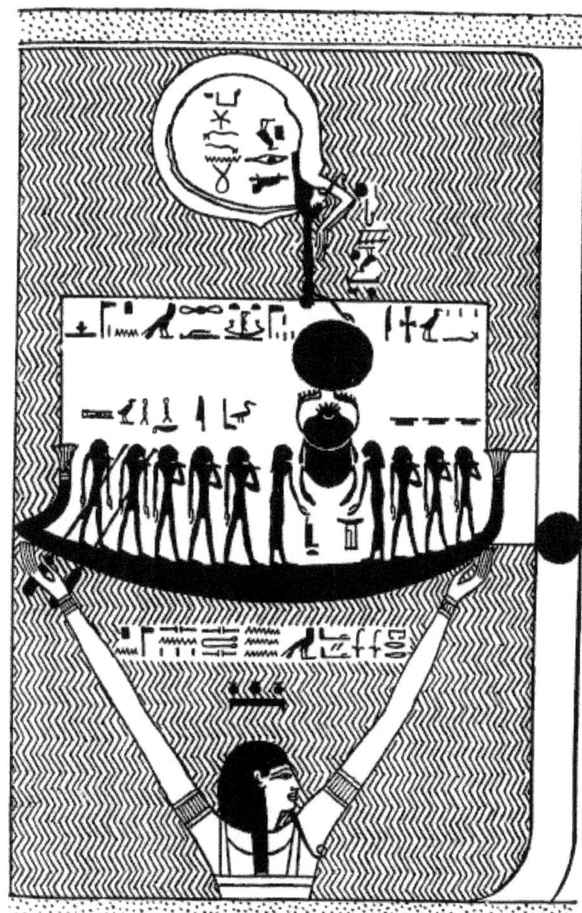

Figure 16.6

Sun-god as Khepri rising. From Book of Gates Division Twelve
(drawing by Budge from Seti I)

The inverted sky goddess Nut receives the disk from the beetle, and Nut stands upon the head of Osiris bent backward into a ring, signifying rolling circle replication and the birth of the recombinant creation.

In both Seti I and Ramesses VI, an oval disk in front of the Sun-bark indicates the "hidden gate of Ament" (SI) and the "mysterious door of the West" (RVI) that ushers the recombinant species out of the Duat into what Piankoff has termed "a new cycle of becoming" (1954, 224). Once again, the Duat represents not only the spinning vortex of the earth's magnetosphere, but also a protein folding funnel landscape, exhibiting the properties of a quantum mechanical Kerr black hole. With the potential for Kerr black hole dynamics, it may be that the mysterious oval exit from the Duat signifies a ring singularity, for the horizon of a spinning black hole has an oval shape. The Sun-bark goes through two doors, suggesting the double cell membrane or possibly two horizons, and approaches the oval singularity from its equatorial plane so it is not repulsive. Piankoff translates the text relating to the serpent over this second door exit as "Encircler: He is upon this door. He opens for Re, Mind (says to) the Encircler: Open thy door for Re." So perhaps the Sun-god leaves the host cell vortex through a ring singularity due to a white hole formation/evaporation process obtained as the time reverse of black hole formation/evaporation.

Matrix 21. Book of Gates, Ramesses VI (Piankoff translation)

Gate	Image or Event	Possible Modern Science Parallel
Prologue	Power of Right Eye; King is before Re, Horus, Osiris King arrives at Gap Destination is hidden seat/desert Re mounts Earth	Right Eye = lytic lifestyle human-phage creation Gap = cusp or polar cap of cell 30 bp region of prophage Adsorption of phage to host cell
1 Upper Register	Procession of 24 gods	two 12 bp cos sites for adsorption to cell
1 Middle Register	1) 4 gods pull Sun-bark 2) Sun-god separates combatants	1) 4-unit Integrase protein activated 2) insertional inactivation of cI gene
1 Lower Register	1) Atum and 4 weary ones 2) 20 enemies tied up	1) indicators of prophage 2) RNA degradation
2 Upper Reg. Gate is One with Sharp Flames	1) long serpent over 12 caverns 2) 12 caverns, rising mummies 3) 12 mummies in Barley Lakes	1) linear Lambda DNA 2) indicator prophage excision 3) Maltose Transport system indicator
2 Middle Reg.	1) Sun-bark towed into Bull-rod 2) earth quakes	1) Lambda DNA goes from head to tail to cell 2) SOS response initiated
2 Lower Reg.	1) Atum, Apopis, 9 gods 2) 9 gods with sceptres	1) LexA repressor cleaved 2) replication potential

Matrix 21 continued.

Gate	Image or Event	Possible Modern Science Parallel
3 Upper Reg.	12 walking gods who go to Kas; 12 jackal gods in Lake of Life; 10 uraei on lake	Nutrient medium
3 Middle Reg. Gate is Mistress of Food	1) Sun-bark towed by 4 2) 9 mummies Re orders to rise 3) 12 goddesses facing coiled serpent named "He who should be removed"	1) Integrase activity 2) indicators of prophage excision 3) Allolactose bonds to Lac Repressor to remove it from the DNA operator
3 Lower Reg.	1) Horus and 11 gods go to Osiris; reference to Isis finding Osiris 2) 4 presiding over enemy pits	1) prophage at *LacZ* 2) chemical reaction indicators
4 Upper Reg. Gate is She who acts	1) 12 gods adoring with 12 gods carrying coiled cord 2) 4 gods meeting 12 3) Re as Enveloper	1) head packing portal is a 12-sided ring through which supercoiled DNA concatemer for head enters 2) terminase for translocation 3) During packaging, coat proteins surround a scaffolding protein core
4 Middle Reg.	1) Sun-bark towed by 4 2) half-mummied gods holding stretched connected serpents 3) Re advises to stretch rope while drawing me among you 4) Re advises to hold serpent	1) Integrase activity 2) protein wrapping, linearization, and cleaved concatemer for head packing 3) relaxation in DNA twisting or linearization so molecule passes through portal to head 4) Head packaging paused
4 Lower Reg.	16 men before which walk 12 carrying long serpent and 12 symbols of duration, with 8 gods who establish the duration of life for those going to Place of Destruction	Recycled reactants for life on earth; destruction by black hole singularity
5 Niche Hall of Osiris	1) Osiris before balance 2) monkey urging pig away 3) Re enters Gate "Mistress of Duration" of Hidden Chamber	1) prophage rising 2) no expression of SHH gene 3) Lambda molecule at prophage *LacZ* site
5 Upper Reg. Gate is Mistress of Duration	1) 12 holding javelins 2) 12 holding serpent w/12 heads 3) heads swallowed by Apopis 4) 12 hold twisted cord in Aken	1) LexA repressor maintenance 2) DNA human head assembly 3) DNA degradation of human forms 4) phage DNA head packaging
5 Middle Reg.	Sun-bark towed by 4 and 12 w/ hidden arms proceed ahead	Movement of incoming Lambda to prophage site on host chromosome
5 Lower Reg.	1) 12 reclined mummies on biers 2) pool of water for Osiris	1) excision of prophage 2) nutrient
6 Upper Reg.; Gate is Seat of her Lord	12 gods w/grain; 12 w/feathers	Nutrient level good for prophage excision
6 Middle Reg.	1) Sun-bark pulled by 4; Atum; 7 jackal-headed poles with 2 enemies tied to each 2) gods with arms crossed 3) god with sceptre called Gold of the Gods 4) enemies at jackal poles for destruction	1) 7 bp recombination 2) Holliday junction intermediate 3) replication of phage 4) chemical reaction of cleaving of 7 bp bonds of prophage

MATRIX 21 continued.

Gate	Image or Event	Possible Modern Science Parallel
6 Lower Reg.	1) 12 with grain 2) 7 reapers	1) excision of prophage 2) cleavage of 7 bp excision pathway
7 Upper Reg. Gate is The Brilliant One	1) 12 gods carry rope with coils forming 4 M-shapes 2) 12 gods with coiled serpent with 11 stars; coils unloosened	1) M-protein found in enveloped viruses that triggers budding 2) linearization of DNA; star conformation
7 Middle Reg.	Sun-bark towed by 4 with 12 holding sceptres; 4 mummies	Replication; indicators of phage replication
7 Lower Reg.	God addresses 12 rising gods	Indicators of prophage excision
8 Upper Reg. Gate is Glow	12 walking gods, 9 soul birds who eat green growth	Vegetative replication and nutrients for phage growth
8 Middle Reg.	1) Sun-bark towed by 4 2) 16 swimmers having dominion over water	1) Integrase activity 2) hydrophilic sugar-phosphate backbone for phage nucleic acid/protein synthesis
8 Lower Reg.	Before Horus are 12 enemies to be destroyed by Fiery Serpent with 7 mummies in its coils	Thermal chemical reaction; cII degradation
9 Upper Reg. Gate is Great of Honor	1) 4 w/White Crown raise Pole 4 w/Red Crown raise Pole 2) 8-headed serpent Runner 3) 2 gods w/nets	1) 2 Promoter sites; Cro build-up for late transcription 2) rolling circle replication active; RecA 3) DNA degradation
9 Middle Reg.	Sun-bark towed by 4 preceded by 14 with nets; 3 with spears pull Old One in front of Apopis	Promoter for Repressor Maintenance synthesizing small amounts of repressor
9 Lower Reg.	16 w/rope, serpent Khepri, and hawk Horus with Double Crown; 8 with rope	transformation of Horus lineage due to repressor maintenance, lytic cycle, prophage excision; transmembrane tunnel (Khepri)
10 Upper Reg. Gate is The Holy One	Apopis bound by Horus' sons and Hidden Hand; Osiris	Lambda cI repressor still synthesizing small amounts of repressor
10 Middle Reg.	1) Star gods w/uraei on heads 2) 3 gods towing Face of Re to Sun-bark 3) winged uraeus, Seth/Horus, flaming bullhead	1) assembly into icosahedral structures 2) excision of prophage complete with reverse integration 3) full operation of lambda genome for lytic lifestyle
10 Lower Reg.	1) 12 paddle gods of the stars 2) 12 star goddesses or Hours	1) efflux pump proteins 2) transition to star conformation and self-assembly into icosahedral structures
11 Upper Reg. Gate is Mysterious of Approaches	1) 4 w/disks, 4 w/stars, 12 with sceptres 2) 8 star goddesses on serpents	1) phage product 2) allolactose bound to Lac repressor
11 Middle Reg.	Progeny of Horus bind Apopis	LexA repressor maintenance
11 Lower Reg.	Souls go with Re, bodies remain	Potential forms or substrate remain in cell
12 Gate is She whose Power is Holy	1) Re rising as Living Beetle 2) Osiris bent backward 3) Encircler	1) Release of recombinant phage progeny 2) Rolling circle replication 3) ring singularity; white hole dynamics

Both the Book Amduat and the Book of Gates depict and explain chemical processes related to the lytic lifestyle. However, the Amduat descriptions of transcription, prophage excision, phage head and tail assembly, and release from the host cell are more definitive. Still, the Book of Gates expands on details related to the three Lambda promoters and provides explicit images detailing movement of linear Lambda DNA into the cell, measurement of cro and cI protein levels in the Hall of Osiris, and the reverse integration of the prophage (Face of Re). The Book of Gates also indicates that the potential forms or substrate of the escaping recombinant progeny remain in the host cell or Duat. Also, Horus enters into the two-headed serpent Khepri when Re calls to him. In Division Nine, this movement of the Horus species to the horizon into Nut or the extracellular medium by means of a serpent is similar to the exit of phage progeny in Amduat Hour Twelve, suggesting a transmembrane tunnel or wormhole. Briefly put, the Deceased has come into being as Atum, the god of origins, along with being cloned into millions of phage Lambda.

Osiris being embraced by Isis and Nephthys. The four mummy figures are the Children of Horus, Akeset, Hap, Tuamutef, and Qebhsenuf. The deities in the circles are Amen and Râ, Shu and Tefnut, Keb and Nut, Hathor and Maât.

From a bas-relief at Philae
Sir Wallis Budge
Egyptian Ideas of the Future Life (1900)

17

The Book of Caverns

LOST IN THE CAVERNS OF DNA MULTIDIMENSIONAL PHASE SPACE

In the Pyramid Texts, the term "querert" (Eg. *krrt*) translated as "cavern" is associated with the Netherworld. Texts frequently mention Anubis and Osiris at the Entrance to the Holy Cavern. One also finds the Caverns of Hathor, and the Coffin Texts refer to the gods of the Duat as "those who are in their Caverns." The Egyptian Book of the Dead, the Book of Gates, and the Litany of Re also mention "the gods in the Caverns, who are in the West." (Piankoff 1974)

The DNA multidimensional phase space can be described as a cavern system for mapping functionality. Imagine yourself as a person needing a particular function such as lysis proteins. You could travel the DNA tunnels from cavern to cavern, until you arrived at the correct function. Traveling in DNA caverns could be difficult, so the Pharaohs may have dedicated the Book of Caverns to the task of delineating what was in DNA phase space. In the General Introduction to *The Wandering of the Soul,* Piankoff writes that the texts of the Quererts or Caverns help the Deceased to travel the 12 caverns of the Netherworld, yet the texts only describe the last five caverns (8-12). If these 12 caverns relate to the genetic map of the Lambda genome, then the pivotal 8-12 caverns may relate to the lytic function and the Lambda prophage attachment site on the *E. coli* host chromosome. Because of the present focus of this thesis, I must pose this possibility as an Outstanding Question.

IV

A Fortress for Unity

Evidence shows that the operations of the solar wind and earth mirror quantum cellular events that support a model of phage Lambda ferrying a human insert into a cell for a horizontal gene transfer.

The Idea Strands from the Pyramid Texts and Coffin Texts also support this model, which logically decodes hundreds of Egyptian signs, pointing to the lytic lifestyle of phage Lambda.

Further, descriptions of quantum events in both the Book Amduat and the Book of Gates strongly sustain this model.

18

The Book of Two Ways

MAPPING THE PATH TO THE PROPHAGE ON THE HOST CHROMOSOME

Objective 10: Do the Book of Two Ways, the Edifice of Taharqa and the Egyptian Book of the Dead, including the Theban Recension, support the interpretation of metasymbols derived from the major Idea Strands in the Pyramid and Coffin Texts, along with the analyses of the Amduat and the Book of Gates?

In 1903, Hans Schack-Schackenburg published photos of texts on the bottom of a Middle Kingdom coffin in Berlin, naming them *The Book of Two Ways*. The discovery of 18 published and four (4) unpublished coffins form the basis of this Book from el Barsha in Middle Egypt. Scholars are still grappling with varying interpretations of these difficult and obscure texts that they say have degenerated due to errors of copyists. The texts represent what Leonard Lesko has called "the democratization of the hereafter." This means that First Intermediate Period and Middle Kingdom noblemen accessed texts only available to the king in earlier times. Scribes copied these texts on the inside bottoms of tombs of noblemen. (Lesko 1972, 4-5)

In this analysis, we will review Lesko's *The Ancient Egyptian Book of Two Ways* followed by Alexandre Piankoff's work in *Wanderings of the Soul*. The major deities in these texts are Osiris, Re, Thoth and Horus. Lesko's work divides the Book into nine sections, each of which is summarized in Matrix 22 with scientific parallels.

Matrix 22. Book of Two Ways (Lesko) Deceased = D

Section	Text Summary	Possible Science Parallel
1 Introduction 1029.1030.1033. 1034.1035.1131	1) D arrives at sacred lake bend 2) Re pulls together limbs 3) D joins Re's flame, becomes Re 4) Lotus-bark at dockyard of gods 5) D is creator/pilot to stairway 6) reference to Double Doors	1) bend in polar cusp; high-energy particles 2) molecular self-assembly 3) DNA insert into incoming Lambda 4) FTE; phage Lambda at LamB porin 5) staircase cusp; Coulomb staircase 6) double cell membrane; two horizons
2 Osiris Mansion 1132.1134 to 1143. 1145.1146	1) D comes to see growing plant 2) sealed chamber of Mighty Face 3) D breaks fetters 4) Mistress has borne the D 5) D destroys w/peaceful Seth 6) Isis offers to Osiris 7) Rise up Heliopolitan of Desert 8) Noise, open horizon, invisible man of countless cubits; way of goddess	1) vegetative replication 2) Osiris prophage on host chromosome 3) excision of prophage 4) lactose nutrient 5) cro production; RNA degradation 6) lactose nutrient 7) excision of prophage 8) phage progeny escape; lactose nutrient
3 Rosetau 1036.1038 to 1043. 1045 to 1051.1053. 1054.1069.1147.1150. 1151.1153.1155 to 1161.1165.1166.1179	1) D treats, purifies Osiris 2) D makes circuit w/Eye & Thoth 3) D makes mid-month festival 4) reversion offerings 5) D has 2 land plots w/Thoth 6) Apopis opposed 7) way to cities of those on sweets 8) noisemaker D opens firmament	1) cro production over cI 2) transcription; rolling circle replication 3) full moon indicates high phage production 4) Osiris or excision of prophage 5) Lambda operator sites for cro production 6) LexA repressor protein cleaved due to SOS 7) lactose nutrient for lytic lifestyle 8) phage progeny escape out of cell
4 Rosetau 1056.1058.1060. 1061.1063.1065. 1069.1167 to 1169. 1172.1174 to 1176. 1178.	1) Great Face enters under bend 2) D copies what is said to him 3) D not opposed at Osiris gates 4) D reaches tombs, mansions of Red Crown	1) high energy sun particles at cusp bend 2) transcription 3) 7bp recombination for prophage excision 4) prophage site; operator sequences of left Lambda arm
5 Rosetau 1070 to 1082. 1084 to 1087. 1180 to 1185. 513.577	1) D sits on Eye as first of 3 2) opposite Rosetau Ways 3) D parts the 2 companions 4) D is Numerous-of-faces 5) D dresses standard, heals Osiris 6) Speech in dark w/Osiris' efflux 7) Embalmer belongs to sweetness 8) Osiris giving heads	1) control of rightward operator sites for cro 2) opposite ways of DNA molecule 3) cro v. cI proteins 4) phage morphology 5) promoter for lytic cycle 6) prophage DNA for phage progeny 7) lactose medium 8) phage head assembly
6 Thoth 1088.1089. 1091 to 1095. 1096.1098	1) who brings a head 2) D sits on Re so he lives sweet 3) D brings sound Eye 4) Isis guides Thoth 5) Apopis retreats	1) head assembly 2) lactose; insertional inactivation of cI gene 3) full function of Lambda for lytic lifestyle 4) lactose nutrient for phage production 5) LexA repressor cleaved
7 Voyage Summary 1099	1) D knots rope, binds Re Chapel 2) D is not boatless, does not walk in valley of darkness 3) D dispels bleariness of eye 4) D grasps writings and millions	1) nucleosome self-assembly (octet/histone) 2) DNA insert into Lambda vector; maltose transport pathway for lytic lifestyle 3) insertional inactivation of cI; lytic cycle 4) transcription for recombinant progeny

Matrix 22 continued.

Section	Text Summary	Possible Science Parallel
8 Seven doors and doorkeepers 1100 to 1112	1) 7 doors with doorkeepers	1) 7 bp branch migration for excision
	2) Let D pass to open darkness	2) *LacZ* gene where prophage lodges
9 Summary 1115 to 1120	1) know what is sealed for glory	1) prophage excision for phage progeny
	2) D stands with risen Osiris, and sweet winds	2) excision of prophage, lactose medium
	3) D receives sound Eye	3) full functioning Lambda for lytic cycle
	4) D makes 2 warriors content	4) cro over cI production
	5) Orphan ascends	5) excision of prophage
	6) Apopis speared	6) LexA repressor cleaved due to SOS
	7) Isis, Seth, Horus, Re, etc. sail on bark	7) lactose-based recombinant species exits cell
	8) D has made millions of cubits	8) millions of phage progeny; information
9 Summary 1130	Re's 4 good deeds:	
	1) made 4 winds	1) high energy/solar wind creative force
	2) made great flood (efflux or outflow of Osiris)	2) recombinant phage species
	3) made men equal	3) phage are clones
	4) made hearts remember West	4) polar source for transfiguration on western horizon of magnetosphere or earth-cell

In Lesko's work, the Book begins with Re in his bark traveling into Nut, the sky. He is urged to "pull together your limbs," a reference to molecular self-assembly, and face the beautiful West as "you come anew every day, because you are that image of gold wearing the radiant locks" (1029). The Deceased goes down to the Sun-bark at the "dockyard of the gods," so he can sail to the stairway of Mercury (1130). This journey heralds adsorption and penetration into the earth-cell. A flame is bound together around Re, and the Deceased is urged to "join the flame" (1033). The Deceased is at the bend in the lake (1069, 1176, 1178) or the bend in the polar cusp, and he states that he has "accumulated what is injured" and "removed what is injured" (1033), suggesting that he merges with the Sun-god and lodges at the cI site on the Lambda genome. This insertional inactivation of the cI gene happens when the inserted DNA interrupts the coding sequence of the resistance gene and alters the phenotype of the cell carrying the recombinant. (Nicholl 2002, 63) So, this insertion inactivates the cI protein and the conspiracy of Seth or lysogeny. The Deceased then claims that he is Re (1034).

The Deceased has purified (1040) and "treated Osiris" (1036, 1147), healing his "malady," removing "pain from the one who made himself" (1079). We can understand this process as the human insert inactivating the cI gene, along with phage Lambda entry into the cell that activates the SOS response necessary to induce the excision of the Lambda prophage. Rosetau is where the prophage resides in the hydrophobic base pair interior of DNA that is referred to as land, sand or desert.

The Deceased states that he is a creator and also references the "Double Doors of the Horizon" (1131), which indicates the double membrane of the host cell and/or the two event horizons. The Deceased Sun-god is traveling to the Lambda prophage site on the host chromosome, where he will pass seven (7) gates or the 7 bp branch migration to allow the excision of the prophage Osiris (CT1100, 1101, 1102, 1103, 1108, 1109, 1110). He has come from Dep to see the "growing plant" (1134) or vegetative lytic replication. The "Seizers" who keep "his limbs in rage" to protect Contrary-face (1135) are proteins or molecules that keep Osiris in the prophage state. Contrary-face represents Seth or cI protein production for lysogeny (Lambda cI repressor). The Deceased restores order (1135), the Rightful Order of cro protein on the operator sequences.

A reference to snakes going down to "holes in a boat" (1135) suggests a mobile vacancy in a sea of electrons, according to the following definition by the Department of Physics of the University of Sydney, Australia:

> Hole: an electron that isn't there! Imagine a tiny bubble of nothing, not even air, in a great sea of water. That would be a hole in the water. If some of the surrounding water fills the hole, that creates a new hole, so even though it is really the water that moves, you can think of the hole moving through the water. In some kinds of semiconductor the electrons responsible for electrical conduction are a bit like water which is packed so tightly in the container that it can't move except to fill any holes that might be there. So in electricity a hole is a mobile vacancy in a sea of electrons. In many ways it behaves like a positively charged electron. (Sefton 1995)

This definition seems practical in that we are dealing with molecular structures within electromagnetic fields.

References to "Seth who made the dark eye" (1138) and Seth who destroyed the limbs of Osiris (1125) or stopped the formation of the Horus lineage are present. But, Osiris is becoming whole in these texts, for the Deceased is the "one who breaks the fetters" (1141) or helps Osiris to rise from the lysogenic state.

The Deceased is beside Thoth (1047), who represents the RNA polymerase for phage transcription and translation to protein. Because phage Lambda has taken over the replication machinery of the host, Thoth may also represent the upregulation of Polymerase IV due to the cell's SOS response. The Deceased states, "I am the one who conducts the sacred writings to Re" (1176), along with "I grasp the writing that I may receive the offerings," and he "establishes the millions" (1099). Once again, "millions" signifies the phage product. The Deceased has opposed Apopis (1033) or the monster LexA repressor protein, so the Word or recombinant DNA is faithfully copied and delivered to Osiris, who is the "speech which is in the midst of darkness" (1087). Thoth, representative of the polymerase, participates in the successful feat that allows the Deceased Sun-god to bond to Osiris and activate rolling circle replication. Put simply, the DNA instructions are delivered and the recombinant species of Horus exists at the expense of limb formation of material humans or the Seth lineage. There is no theft of fire, no photosynthesis, for the Horus species has been initialized, and the Seth lineage has been repressed by the inactivation of the LexA repressor protein and the Lambda cI repressor protein (Seth). As the Deceased states, "I am the scribe of the plots of land beside Thoth" (1048), which suggests the necessary transcription of the operator sequences for the lytic lifestyle.

The ways of Rosetau and Osiris are on water and land at the edge of the sky (1035). Water suggests the watery channels of the host cell and the hydrophilic sugar phosphate bases, whereas land suggests the hydrophobic base pair interior of the DNA molecule of the host cell, which is closely linked to the cell walls in *E. coli*. "Radiant locks" and "side lock" (1029, 1033) references suggest DNA, which one could envision as braided locks or strings. Side lock may also indicate the protein structure of side chain conformation. The Sun-bark has a lotus on each end, signifying that the Deceased is on his way into the essence of matter, possibly into what String theorists call a Calabi-Yau space.

Six Gates

In Coffin Text 1053, it states that the Deceased must reach "those squatters, the keepers of the gates," and that it is a spell "for reaching the eldest of the six gatekeepers." On Lesko's schematic drawn from representations in Cairo Coffin CGC 28083, he designated the text of CT 1053 at position "24," which is the entrance to the Duat. So it seems reasonable to infer that the "squatters" and the "six gatekeepers" refer to the six gated porins of the LamB receptor site for phage Lambda penetration of the host cell. These six gatekeepers are LamB, malE, malF, malG, malK with two subunits, and malM. All of these proteins acting as gates into the cell are approximately positioned on the *E. coli* chromosome at 91.4 min. and 91.5 min.

Rosetau: Prophage Site at *LacZ*

The Ways of Rosetau are on water and land, and the two ways are in the "opposite direction, each one thereof opposing its companion in the opposite direction" (1072, 1182). This is a good description of the DNA molecule, and thus we have a reference to the title of the Book of Two Ways.

The Deceased reaches the "sealed place" (1080), "shrine of the one who has been bound" (1060) or the prophage site at the *LacZ* gene on the host chromosome. The Deceased also claims that he is "beneath the egg of Re" (1058), which points to phage replication at the *LacZ* gene (Isis), where the prophage is lodged (Osiris). The excision of the prophage results in rolling circle replication and birth of the Horus species. This occurs when the Deceased "sits on the Eye of Horus as the first of the three" (1070, 1071, 1181), beating cI to the rightward operator sequences and restoring Rightful Order.

Lactose Nutrient

With lytic control of the cell's replication machinery, phage are produced. In the Planck-length arena, phage progeny are described as "a man of countless (cubits)," invisible in the darkness with an invisible entourage resplendent in "the way of the goddess" (1146). But what is especially important is that the "way of the goddess" is a manifestation of lactose metabolism or "those living on sweets of Osiris." The references to the "way to the cities of those living on sweets" (1053, 1153) indicate the lactose nutrient, the sweet milk sugar, necessary for the Horus species.

The Deceased states, "I have not been kept away from you, Osiris" (1085). Also, the Deceased "sits on the Eye of Horus as the first of three" (1070, 1071), indicating the controlling rightward operator site of OR1. Again, the Deceased states that he is "the Third of magic" and the "protection of his eye" (513). This genetic seat is in the land of tombs (DNA potentialities) and is an enfolded chapel (1060). The idea of enfolding at the essence of matter, along with the Egyptian emphasis on the lotus reminds one again of the Calabi-Yau lotus shape of curled-up dimensions. This quantum springboard launches the birth of the recombinant species, which then tunnels out of the earth-cell into the starry universe.

Path to Osiris on Host Chromosome

In the Lambda lytic cycle, first-stage bidirectional replication starts from the origin of replication, using viral O and P proteins, and then switches to second-stage rolling circle replication. The ribosome is the essential machinery for protein synthesis. Existing on the *E. coli* chromosome from Ori are rrnC (5 min), rrnA (87 min), rrnB (89.8 min), rrnE (90.7 min), and rrnH (4.8 min), five of the seven rRNA operons, which reflect the Sun-god's northerly west-to-east movement. This direction is described as "going downstream to the north from the south, a chamber is their entrance" (CT129). The Pharaohs used the same upstream/downstream terminology modern geneticists employ to describe transcription and replication on the chromosome. Thus, the texts state "fare downstream and upstream" (CT60, 182), indicating bidirectional replication.

Now, phage Lambda takes over the replication machinery of the cell and enters the double membrane at the LamB receptor site located at 91.5 min, the immediate vicinity of Ori and the rRNA operons for transcription and replication (see Chapter 22 sketch from *the Road from Orion*). The Sun-god then proceeds northward past rrnH, and in Hour Six of the Amduat, he meets Osiris, the Lambda prophage lodged at *LacZ* gene at 7.81 min. The Deceased Sun-god is journeying upstream to the place where Osiris is (CT399, 428) at the Island of Fire (CT341). The Amduat journey supports this clockwise direction with text describing the Sun-god in Hour Six as south of the Hidden Chamber, then north in Hours Seven and Eight, and finally east of the Chamber in Hour Nine. Further, in the northwest corner of the Sacred Lake of the Edifice of Taharqa, a monumental scarab emerges, a representation of the Sun-god coming out of earth. So we might assume that the Deceased navigating the paths of the West somehow results in a northerly west-to-east movement along the circular host chromosome to the *LacZ* gene where the prophage Osiris is lodged. Then, the exit from the cell at a northwest area, suggested by the position of the scarab at the Sacred Lake of Karnak, would place the Sun-god at the "horn of the sky" (Amduat, Hour 12, Seti I) or polar cusp, where researchers have observed holes at the cell poles in support of a transmembrane tunnel for released phage progeny (Witte et al. 1990). On the macrocosmic scale, this polar cusp exit site would allow the Sun-god access to open field lines to interplanetary space.

Efflux as Outflow of Phage Progeny

The Deceased addresses Osiris saying, "lord of those who gave to the defiant your putrefaction in it" (Lesko 1972, CT1131). The "defiant" is Seth, and putrefaction is the action of DNA and RNA degradation relative to the excision of the prophage on the host chromosome. The text then informs us that the "lock (of hair) was cut off and the eye which the pellet in its socket sealed," suggesting again that the Seth linage or Left Eye is no longer ascendant, but incapacitated due to the lytic pathway. In contrast, the Right Eye is ascendant: "May the pellet which went forth from you live having covered the head of a nail." This suggests what occurs in a Calabi-Yau space in String Theory. Inside this lotus space is a two-dimensional sphere (area of sphere only, not interior). When space tears, a sphere actually grows, repairing the tear. A string can actually encircle the tear or travel adjacent to the tear. By encircling the tear, the string provides a protective barrier, shielding the surrounding universe from the calamitous aspects of the geometrical degeneration of the spatial fabric. (Greene 1999, 279) Put simply, encircling, covering, shielding or wrapping up the sphere or pellet prevents the formation of spatial dimensions such as those we live in. Similarly, CT 1134 notes that the Deceased is "Wrapped-up who is in Dep, Dep which is on him having become him."

Other references (CT1139) to the Deceased being "the one who cuts off the fetters" and "May I be mighty with my horn and my nail," and "I am the Maat who is in the nail" (1142) suggest this basic creative function, for the Deceased is aware that he is a creator (1131). Again, the Deceased states he "breaks the fetters" (1141), suggesting the excision of the prophage. Parting the two warriors and making a "picture of two arms" (1143) reinforces the idea of cro versus cI protein production, with cro dominance resulting in the full operation of the two arms of the Lambda genome, that is, excision of the prophage and the lytic lifestyle.

The text also references the four gods "who have bore the goddess" and Isis the Great (1145), suggesting lactose. Both Isis and Apopis "will offer to him," that is, Osiris. This indicates Apopis' offering is cI protein production, for his function as the LexA repressor is to keep the Lambda cI repressor protein (Seth) active and repressing cro protein (Horus). On the other hand, Isis' offering is that of the lactose nutrient for the Horus species. The Deceased then states to Apopis: "Depart! The god, the lord of the red mansion, which is in the horizon, comes peacefully." The red mansion is the house of Seth, who now comes peacefully, signifying sufficient levels of lactose and cro protein build-up for the lytic pathway and resultant outflow of phage progeny.

Rolling Circle Replication

Lambda will switch from a bidirectional mode of replication to unidirectional rolling circle replication. Because replication is unidirectional, it continues around the genome for many cycles without colliding with an opposing replication fork. (Bull 2003) The Deceased states, "I make the circuit while the eye of Horus is beside me" (1042), suggesting the full function of the left and right arms of Lambda, resulting in prophage excision and the circuit of rolling circle replication. The Deceased then states that Thoth is with him, indicating transcription and replication. The Deceased is on the "way which is known for reversion offerings" (1045), the path of the reversed integration of the prophage. Also, references to the lord of "reversion-offerings" (1046) and Osiris as the reversion offerings (1158) indicate prophage excision and consequent rolling circle replication, depicted by Osiris bent into a circle.

Always beside Thoth (1047), the Deceased with his "word," the legacy of the whole Eye of Horus (what he has copied; RNA polymerase) reaches his goal of two plots of land in the Field of Offerings (1048, 1161), which is the DNA heritage or both Lambda operator sites that allow control of PR for cro production. The Deceased is the writer of words or the "scribe of the lands beside Thoth" (1048) in the "Field of the Eye" (1049). As the Deceased comes into existence, so do his words (1099), his legacy. He has come from "primeval time" to herald Re at the gates of the sky (1169). The Deceased has "cleansed the injured eye" and "brought the sound eye" with the "mansion of the Moon as witness" (1094), while Isis shows him the "ways in crossing the sky" (1095) or the lactose path of the maltose transport system. The mansion of the Moon or the full moon suggests full phage production and burst size because of the lactose nutrient medium of Isis.

The Pollen of the Godhead

Thoth protects against Apopis as the "entourage in the horizon divides," and "Osiris is gladdened" (1098). The Deceased has "knotted the rope and bound his chapel" (1099). Now, Apopis does not oppose him and he may "lead the ways of Re and the stars" (1099). He has given "the Eye of Horus to Osiris" (1123), and now the limbs of Osiris are in the proper place (1119). The departing entourage of flame is composed of Isis, Seth, and Horus on the prow, with Authoritative-utterance, Perception, and Re on the stern (1128). The sky flames with the million cubits (1129), that is, the lytic cycle has resulted in millions of phage progeny. The Egyptian cubit was a measurement based on the length of an arm from the elbow to the extended fingertips (O'Connor and Robertson 2003) and is generally thought to have been about 20.63 inches. However, the sky flaming with cubits suggests not only a mathematical measurement, but also the physical embodiment of information. Modern scientists talk of quantum information that comes in quantum bits or qubits (pronounced "cue-bits"), which is remarkably similar to the idea of cubits expressed in this Egyptian text.

The sky, earth and horizon are opened and the "Image of a mansion" is "a man of countless (cubits)" (1146), a reference to the idea of viral-human progeny in the universe. Also emphasized is the idea that "the way of the goddess" is in them and their mansions, suggesting transformation and existence by means of lactose. A bioluminescent species of the stars is the result, rather than a photosynthetic species trapped within the confines of the earth's magnetosphere or gravitational field.

The Deceased has made his way in the "valley of the Great-one" (1079, 1086); he has not "walked in the valley of darkness" (1099), for he merged with the Sun-god and has come from the "great valley" (1100). The Deceased has "inherited the horizon of Re," for he "copies what has been said to him" (1063). He has "done his will" (1061). The Lambda prophage excises to activate rolling circle replication. Osiris is risen and the recombinant phage progeny escape like pollen to the heavens from the earth-cell.

The Plan of Water and Land Ways

The Cairo Coffin 28083 plan shows a rectangular schematic divided into two (Lesko 1972). In the upper rectangle is a smaller rectangle with two wavy bands depicting the Two Ways. According to Piankoff (1974, 11) the blue upper band indicates the way by water, and the lower black band indicates the way by land (see Figure 18.1). From the perspective of this work, the water way signifies the hydrophilic sugar phosphate bases on the exterior of the DNA molecule, with the land ways representing the interior hydrophobic base pairs.

In line with this idea, it may be that the two paths beginning at the Gate of Darkness (black half-moon near "4" in Figure 18.1), the entry to the Duat, designate the two figurative paths researchers have identified for the transport of substrate at the LamB porin. As mentioned in Part Two, in one path the substrate is bound to MBP protein, but in the case of lactose transport, the second low-affinity path is accessed because MBP cannot bind the substrate lactose (Merino and Schuman 1997). The upper blue path in the small rectangle (near "3") shows the lactose path, while the lower black path (near "4") is the path where the substrate is bound to MBP protein.

Now, Lesko has marked CT 1053 at the "24" location on his Egyptian plan, which is the entrance to the Duat. For our purposes, this indicates the entry to the cell or the LamB porin with its six gates (LamB, malE, malF, malG, malK with two subunits, and malM). CT 1053 advises, "This is the way to the cities of those living on sweets" and not to pass on the "way downward." The text ends claiming it is a spell for "reaching the eldest (of) the six gatekeepers," a direct reference to the six LamB gates. Faulkner's translation of the same text indicates the Deceased should not pass on the "lower path." So, the low-affinity path researchers have identified is the upper blue path for lactose transport with its six gates.

To the left of this rectangle of Two Ways is the Field of Offerings (designated "8" in Figure 18.1), three plots of land that signify the three rightward operator sites (OR) under cro (Horus) control. The text states that the Deceased is "the one who sits on the Eye-of-Horus as the first of three" (CT1070-1071 in Lesko), suggesting the victory of cro protein and the lytic lifestyle. Cro is transcribed from PR and binds preferentially to OR at the left-hand end, preventing transcription of cI, which binds preferentially to the right-hand end of OR (Gonzalez 1997). The Deceased states, "On your faces, O watchmen, make way for your lord" (1070-1071), suggesting the conquest of a site formerly controlled by cI protein.

Next is a compartment containing three embryonic beetle-headed forms, holding uraei in their left hands and lizards in their right hands (designated "11" and "12"). The text states "the ways of Rosetau which are on land" (CT1074 in Lesko), suggesting the interior hydrophobic region of the DNA molecule. The text also states that the Deceased is "the one who parted the two companions" (1075 in Lesko) and "one who opposes angry Seth" (1076), again suggesting the operator sequences of the contested OR and OL operator sequences on the Lambda genome. With the beetle-headed forms holding uraei and lizards in their right hands, suggesting transformation, the imagery of this compartment represents cro protein control and the decision point where the phage is locked into a lytic cycle and cannot return to the lysogenic state.

On the right in the lower rectangle of the divided schematic is a stylized bark (designated "13") with an embryonic beetle-headed form pushing a disk amid eight (8) uraei, above which is a beetle pushing a disk and standing on the body of a serpent with uraeus heads on each end. The text (1098) refers to the "coiled one" or the serpent Mehen that surrounds Re, suggesting that this drawing represents the multifunctional RecA protein necessary for DNA repair and recombination activities for prophage excision. RecA has two smaller domains, stabilizing a six-helical polymer of protein subunits and interhelical bundles (Story et al. 1992). The eight uraei in the schematic signify RecA protein ("13"), which is needed for what occurs next in the lower rectangle of the divided schematic.

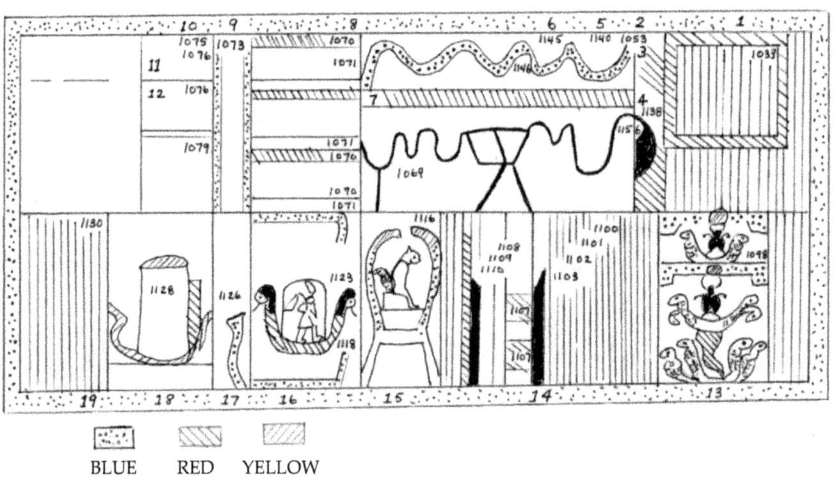

1. Circle of Fire
2. Maltose Transport (LamB)
3. Lactose path (blue)
4. MBP-binding (black)
5. Lactose nutrient
6. cI inactive
7. LexA cleaved
8. Rightward operators (3)
9. Leftward operator (1)
10. Leftward operator (1)
11. Leftward operator (1)
12. Promoter under cro control
13. RecA protein
14. 7 bp branch migration
15. Xis protein for excision
16. Prophage at *LacZ* gene
17. cI repressor protein
18. Sun-bark exiting

Figure 18.1 Simplified sketch drawn from Cairo Coffin 28083 plan from Book of Two Ways.

The Deceased then encounters the first gatekeeper of seven gates called "The one who stretches out the prow-rope" (1100), and he claims that if anyone comes against him, Re will die. Because the Sun-god enveloped by Mehen represents an individual RecA-DNA filament, the unit stretches and bends for easy rotation of the DNA within the protein helix. Hegner et al. (1999) found that association with RecA not only extends ssDNA, but also stiffens it. This research links the textual reference to stretching with the claim that RecA is the image in "13" for the 7 bp recombination reaction that follows.

The second gatekeeper is called "the one who cuts them down" (1101), suggesting the beginning of the 7 bp branch migration that involves RecA protein. Moving right to left, five more gates exist according to the text (1102, 1103, 1108, 1109, 1110), completing the 7 bp branch migration. The next representation of the canopied god ("15"), who "knows how to enter into flame and to open darkness" (1116) is a good match for excisionase (Xis), a phage-encoded protein that is necessary for excision of phage Lambda along with Integrase. Following this representation is Osiris ("16"), the excising prophage, and then a representation of the beheaded Apopis appears ("17"), suggesting the cleaved monster LexA repressor protein and the ineffective Lambda cI repressor protein. We then see the Entourage of Flame ("18") with Isis, Seth and Horus on the prow and Re, Perception and Authoritative-utterance on the stern (1128). The text states that "arriving at the north of the winding canal" (1129), a million cubits are around it and that the Deceased has "made millions," suggesting the escape of phage progeny from the host cell.

In essence, the Cairo Coffin 28083 plan depicts the activity of proteins at the DNA molecular site, where the prophage is integrated into the host chromosome and ready for excision. The smaller split rectangle within the upper rectangle shows the figurative blue lactose pathway or non-MBP binding route, while the black lower way represents the MBP-binding path. These two ways within the maltose transport system or LamB porin designate the route to the Osiris prophage site.

The Piankoff Translation

In his translation, Piankoff observed that the maps of the Field of Offerings from the sides of the El-Bersha coffins depict ovals that indicate islands. He states that three islands in the upper part of the plan are called "The City of Beating," "The Peaceful One," and "The Great One" (1974, 10), which may represent respectively the battleground of Lambda operator sites, Seth or cI protein, and Horus or cro protein. Beneath this are four more islands called "The Peaceful One," "The Red One," "The inundation (or Prosperity)," and "The Lady of the Two Lands" (10), again suggesting the contested operator sequences near which the prophage is lodged at the *LacZ* gene, the site of the birth or flood of phage progeny. Located near this site, Piankoff's translation also suggests the repulsive ring singularity of a black hole: "This is the flame which repulses" (1070) and "This is he whose name is High-Wind" (1071). The Deceased desires to pass over "Faces-of-Flame," escaping roads going astray (1072). Further, he must pass over the "opening of the Holes" (1064), suggesting two Holes, possibly one black and one white, viz., a wormhole.

For purposes of comparison and summary, to follow is Matrix 23, tabulatng Piankoff's translation of the Book of Two Ways.

Matrix 23. Book of Two Ways (Piankoff) Deceased = D

Coffin Text	Text Summary	Possible Science Parallel
1029.1129	Re brings limbs together and is figure of gold carrying disk elements; Re creates D from his limbs	Molecular self-assembly
1030.1099	D goes to bark in dockyard of gods and is not boatless at great crossing	Attachment/adsorption at LamB porin
1090	Re of the lotus-bud sceptre	Incoming Lambda; molecular core of matter
1032.1033.1034. 1099	D merges with flames of Re; circle of fire behind braided locks; D is Re	DNA insert at *cI* gene in Lambda vector
1038.1041.1043. 1050	Gates to Duat	six (6) LamB porin gates
1036.1037.1040. 1073.1079.1086. 1094.1123	D treats, purifies, alleviates suffering of Osiris; D drives away blemish on Udja-Eye	Restores cro protein by insert at *cI* gene and LexA repressor cleavage due to SOS
1094.	Jubilation at North Pole for D saves Re from Apopis by saving Udja-Eye from injury	Insertional inactivation of *cI* gene; cleavage of LexA repressor and Lambda cI repressor
1084.1089.1095	D has way when embalmer is among sweet things; Lady of the Pole; Isis is Truth and leads way as Re crosses sky with D	Lactose nutrient
1055.1094	D sails on Sun-bark	Lambda vector injected into host cell
1058	D carries egg of Re	Potential for phage replication of genome
1061.1081.1085	D is not repulsed from gates	7 bp branch migration for excision
1100.1101.1102. 1103.1108.1109. 1110	lst door, 2nd door, 3rd gate, 4th gate, 1st gate, middle gate, 3rd gate	7 bp branch migration for excision
1035.1072.1078	Roads of Rosetau on water, land	DNA molecule with hydrophilic sugar phosphates and interior hydrophobic bases
1053.1069.1089. 1099	D repulses Apopis and saves Re from Apopis	Insertional inactivation of *cI* gene on vector; SOS response at cell entry; LexA cleavage
1042.1053	Eye of Horus is D	Lambda genome
1052	Place of pasture, tomb, sand	Prophage site on interior host chromosome
1042.1048.1067. 1096.1099.1124	Thoth crosses sky in front of D; D is scribe of Thoth, transmits word of god, Eye of Horus in Thoth's hands; D is Thoth	DNA-directed RNA polymerase for transcription
1075.1119.1125. 1130.1131	D separates 2 Companions; fight is stopped; D appeases 2 Fighters	cro protein production over cI protein

Matrix 23 continued.

Coffin Text	Text Summary	Possible Science Parallel
1071	D sits on Eye as first of three; pass by High-Wind	cro protein beats cI to 1st of 3 right operators; repulsive Kerr ring singularity
1079	D dresses standard	Promoter-right control for lytic lifestyle
1045.1046.1075. 1120	Reversion offerings; D removes bonds from Osiris; Osiris rises	Excision of prophage
1084	D receives what belongs to Red Crown (Seth)	Left Lambda arm operating for lytic lifestyle with cro control
1048.1049	Field of Offerings; pastry for Osiris	nutrients, proteins for phage production
1047	Day of growth	rolling circle vegetative replication
1082.1085.1087	D causes efflux of Osiris to rise; efflux is decomposition of Osiris	prophage excision; DNA degradation
94.1080.1087	D made from efflux of Osiris; efflux sealed in darkness; words sealed in dark is efflux of Osiris	efflux is outflow of rolling circle replication after prophage excision
1050	Being a god, a double of Osiris	phage transfiguration
1064	Passing by opening of holes	black hole/white hole reference
1071.1076.1077	Face of D is that of Great One; his posterior like a crown; Face-of-Faces; Many Faces	phage morphology; crown molecular structure
1070	Flame that repulses	a Kerr ring singularity is repulsive
1079.1099	D makes way in valley; D has not walked in valley of darkness	D is insert in Lambda vector on journey through host cell (transduction) or valley in center of potential energy surface
1089.1099.1112	D drives away clouds; disperses clouds; tempest dispersed	clear plaque due to lytic lifestyle
1099.1129.1126. 1130	He who reckons millions; D makes millions; light-people of Re whose number is unknown; I have made every man similar to his brother.	recombinant phage progeny; clones
1091	D has White Crown; becomes Kheper	transduction
1099	D follows path of Stars and Re	bioluminescent recombinant species
1100	The one who stretches out the prow-rope	DNA strand stretching
1112	D is one of 4 gods	gravity/antigravity
1130	Time exists not for me or my members	no time dimension

19

The Edifice of Taharqa

NEW KINGDOM EVIDENCE FOR THE LAMBDA MODEL

The excavation of the Edifice of Taharqa began in 1907-08, when G. Legrain, under the direction of G. Maspero, cleared the monument at Karnak. By 1969, J. Lauffray had cleared and studied the mysterious nilometer. Finally, J. Leclant, Richard A. Parker and Jean-Claude Goyon collaborated to produce the 1979 work detailing the architecture of the Edifice, the plates of scenes and texts, and the translation of the texts reviewed for this thesis. Jean-Claude Goyon not only translated the texts, but also provided an interpretation of the Egyptian ceremony performed in the ruined building of Taharqa at Karnak. (1-2) He notes that the themes date at least until the New Kingdom (86). Actually, the evidence is that the themes date back to the Old Kingdom Pyramid Texts.

In his interpretation, Goyon states that the architectural features of the subterranean rooms suggest that the Edifice is dedicated to Osiris, god of the Underworld or Duat. Goyon states that Osiris is only present episodically, whereas Amun, the god of origins (aka Atum), is the reigning cosmic god of Thebes, who is associated with the Deceased King. Together Amun and the Deceased King or Amun-Osiris find new creative power and are rejuvenated through a food offering and reborn as Re. Goyon also notes that the Edifice was consecrated to primeval Amun in his ancient aspect as the god *Dsr-* or He Whose Arm Is Sublime. Amun was also called Amun the Primeval One of the Two Lands. (80-86) Although the names of Egyptian gods may change, the significance remain the same. Amun-Osiris reborn as Re in the Edifice texts easily translates to Atum-Osiris reborn as Horus in the Amduat and earlier texts. The Deceased Sun-god is Atum-Osiris. Again, the sublime arm is that of the Lambda genome activating the lytic lifestyle.

Another interesting point that Goyon makes is that the number of all elements in Amun is 30, which is also the number of the two divine colleges of Karnak (85). We can easily recognize the 30 elements of Amun as the 30 bp genetic location of Lambda prophage on the host chromosome. Further, Goyon states that at the northwest corner of the Sacred Lake is a monumental scarab, the representation of the Sun coming out of earth. As mentioned earlier, this northwest emergence of the Sun from the earth matches the "horn of the sky" (Amduat, Hour 12, SI) or polar cusp, where Witte et al. (1990) observed holes at the cell poles in support of a transmembrane tunnel for released phage progeny. In the macrocosm, this polar cusp exit site would allow the Sun-god access to open field lines to interplanetary space.

Taharqa (690-664 BCE) was a Twenty-fifth Dynasty Nubian (Ethiopian) pharaoh, whose Edifice existed between the Sacred Lake of Karnak and the south enclosure wall of the Great Temple. The structure housed a series of subterranean rooms for a ceremony similar to the journey described in the Amduat and Book of Gates. As this analysis shows, hieroglyphic translations and wall drawings depict Egyptian ideas dating to the Pyramid Texts, showing that the funerary corpus as a whole is unified in its presentation of Egyptian scientific thought.

The Nilometer

Of special interest is what has been referred to as the nilometer, a long narrow structure connecting to a court leading to the east entrance of the Edifice. The Egyptians measured the Nile River flood with a nilometer, which was a calibrated stairway that descended into the river. Pharaohs used the nilometers to forecast flood levels.

Yet LeClant notes that the axis of the nilometer is askew, and that he rejects the name nilometer for the construction (9-10). Certainly, its location and design does not suggest a nilometer or calibrated stairway to measure flood levels. With its skewed placement connected to the two-walled court into the Edifice and its architecture indicating a long, tail-like passageway to a four-walled head structure, it reminds one of the head and tail morphology of phage Lambda attached to a bacterium's double membrane. Thus, both the structure of the Egyptian pyramid, with its tail-like causeway leading to a valley temple, and the misnamed nilometer point to phage morphology.

The Subterranean Journey through the Edifice

Subterranean Edifice of Pharaoh Taharqa at Karnak
excavated 1907-1908

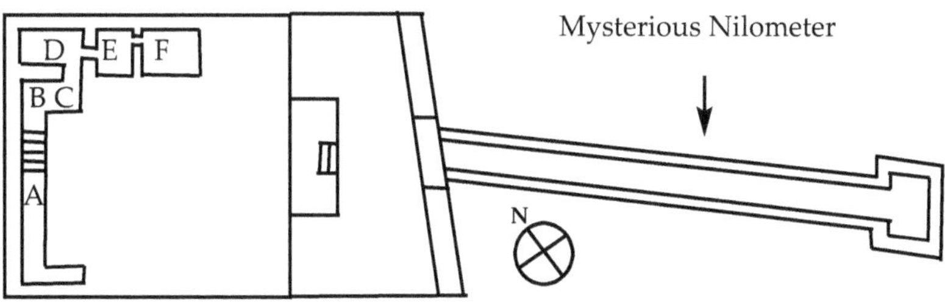

Figure 19.1 Rough schematic drawn from Goyon's General Plan in *The Edifice of Taharqa by the Sacred Lake of Karnak*, 1979.

Figure 19.1 is a sketch of Goyon's diagram of the ceremonies in the subterranean rooms of the Edifice (Preface x), so we can easily map the the ritual. Below is an overview of the events in each room:

A. Amun descends staircase along with Osirian forms of Re
B. He is welcomed in Room B to the west by a great hymn
C. He joins (Room C) the Heliopolitan Ennead
D. He enters the Duat (Room D)
E. Amun recalls rites at Mound of Djeme
F. Amun unites with 10 bas and Re
E. Return to Room E where rites or reentrance celebrated
D. Baboons and deities hail rising Amun-Re
A. God then ascends staircase with solar forms of Re

In one scene on the exterior north wall (Plate 7A; figs. 3a, b) Taharqa wears the White Crown and a long ceremonial tail, a blatant sign of phage morphology. Further, a second scene on the exterior north wall shows Taharqa preceded by the remains of two standards, suggesting Promoter-R and Promoter-L of phage Lambda. Thoth is on Taharqa's left and Horus on his right with text indicating he is King of Upper and Lower Egypt. In a third scene (Pl. 8; figs. 3e, f) Amun, wearing the ceremonial tail, approaches Taharqa. (12-14) The scenes on the west wall of the Edifice show Taharqa walking north (19), which is also the direction advised in the Pyramid and Coffin Texts. A shortened version of the Litany of the Sun decorates the west staircase wall (A) leading to the Antechamber (B) west wall, where the Litany continues. The placement of the staircase and antechamber mirror the western portion of the earth's magnetosphere at the northern polar cusp, where the Deceased enters the Duat at the staircase cusp (LamB porin).

Vestibule and Chapel of Re in Duat

The ba-soul of the King is welcomed to the seventy-five caverns and the Duat is opened (31-32). This leads to the vestibule or chapel of Heliopolis (Room C) with an entrance to the Chapel of Re in the Duat (Room D), where Taharqa is depicted with the *nms*-headdress with two uraei, one wearing the White Crown and the other the Red Crown, signifying the function of the whole Eye of Horus. Taharqa is dressed in a kilt with a triangular front and sports the ceremonial tail in the presence of eight (8) worshiping baboons (37). Both the triangular front and tail suggest phage morphology. A second representation of Taharqa shows his right hand over an offering table of meat, fowl and bread loaves. At the foot of the table is an oblong vase with blooming lotus, the metasymbol for the new Horus lineage created from the heart of the Lambda genome. The text states that Taharqa worships Re and "opens his sphere and settles in the sky as Khepri" (38). Knowledge is stressed, for the text states that Taharqa has knowledge of secret images, places, words, and the rebirths and "transformations that take place in the flood" (39). He is also aware of the mysterious door leading out of the Duat (39) or what may point to a transmembrane tunnel or Kerr ring singularity. So, the images and damaged translations support that Taharqa entering Room D is representative of the King's entry into the Duat to be transformed. Recall that the flood results when the prophage is induced, rolling circle replication begins, and phage progeny are produced.

What little is left of the Sun-bark decorates the west wall of Room D, but the use of parallel scenes enabled Goyon to identify the bark as a representation of the one described in the Book of the Night in New Kingdom royal tombs. The bark is towed by four (4) jackals as in the Book of Gates, suggesting Integrase activity. In the hymn to the setting sun (Pl. 20), the remains of the text states that "the jackals give assistance to overthrow(?) . . . ," a possible indicator of Integrase cleavage activity related to the 7 bp branch migration necessary for the excision of the prophage. The encapsulated Sun-god wears the Double Crown, holds a sceptre and the *'nh*-cross, and accompanies a crew of eight on the ways of the West. The text states that the western gods support Re "when [he] sets in the mountain of life," suggesting the western magnetospheric energy landscapes of the mountainous Duat. (40-41) Plate 20, depicting the north wall of Room D, also shows the bark with the Sun-god and crew of eight. The Sun-god and five deities onboard have ceremonial tails as does the baboon in the bow representative of Thoth. The rounded body of the baboon with its long tail seems a suitable choice for depicting Thoth, the sign for polymerase transcription, for it reminds one of modern drawings depicting a rounded, transcribing polymerase with the tail-like DNA strand.

Above the Sun-bark is the hymn to the setting sun, indicating the healing of the Eye, the conquest of Apopis, and Re reaching "thy yesterday [state?]" or the return to the origin of time of primeval Atum. The text continues, "For thee sit down those who stand upon their tails, for thee stand up those who are sitting, those who are in jubilation [welcome thee]" (45). Again, we have another reference to phage tail morphology. The texts of the east wall of Room D describe the announcement of Re's new birth at the sixth hour of the night and the rebirth in the morning (46). Similarly, Hour Six of the Amduat heralds the excision of the prophage as does Gate Six of the Book of Gates called "Seat of her Lord," a reference to Isis or the *LacZ* gene, next to which the prophage is lodged on the host chromosome.

The Rites of Djeme

A scene carved on the door lintel leading to Room E is damaged, but using a parallel scene from the funerary temple of Ramesses III, Goyon describes a newborn infant lifted by Heh and Hehet, to be transformed into a winged scarab beetle above (47). Room E is the Chapel of the Rites of Djeme and the Divine Reentrance (Rites of the Mound of Djeme, Plates 22, 23). The left side of the lintel in the Upper Register shows the King wearing a kilt and ceremonial tail, with the "Wife of the God" holding a palm, and a priest carrying a standard with a falcon on the perch (49). However, the dominating scene is a mound with a wide band arching above two outstretched arms with hands open to the sky, suggesting the two arms of the Lambda genome. A falcon is centered between the arms on what appears to be a lotus with the plume of Maat or Rightful Order on the right (Plate 22), an indicator of Isis and the right order of cro binding first to the right operator sequences activating the lytic lifestyle. The texts on the West Wall state the words to be recited: "Mayest thou fall at the place of thy head, and vice versa! Horus protects the eye for him, the *tst*-standard is saved, upon which one settles." (52) One can easily compare the lotus to the Calabi-Yau space of six curled dimensions, so we are at the heart of matter or the Mansion of the Six, the Lambda genome on the host chromosome from which the Horus species is born. The saving of the standard signifies cro protein control of the right Lambda operator sequences (Promoter-right). The reference to the "place of thy head" points to the genome and phage morphology.

The text continues, referring to Amun-Re as "Lord of the Thrones of the Two Lands," (52) once again suggesting the combined activity of both Lambda arms. The text then states that the "*btw*-serpent is driven away," an echo of the Apopis theme from the Pyramid Texts (IS28-34). On the left side of the Lintel and below left, references are made to the "Lord of the Sublime Arm," "The arm of Geb," and "The arm of Horus." (53) From this it is obvious that the arm of Geb (left) and arm of Horus (right) comprise the whole Sublime Arm. Again, this Old Kingdom theme is evident in the least corrupted Pyramid Texts (IS72).

The Rites of the Divine Reentrance

The Rites of the Divine Reentrance also occur in Room E. The reentrance ceremony simulates the arrival of Amun-Re, Lord of the Thrones of the Two Lands. A priest welcomes a procession led by a prophet carrying a shrine chest with a curved roof containing the sacred uraeus and followed by four persons, who bear a rectangular *hn*-tabernacle with a curved roof. A votaress follows with her left arm covered and her right hand holding a palm (57-58), a symbol of the vegetation god's victory (Osiris) over inertness, that is, the victory of vegetative lytic replication over lysogeny. The legend under the tabernacle states, "The earth quakes," which Goyon notes is a reference to phenomena accompanying Re's arrival, described as "The earth shakes, Geb bursts into flames."

At this point, we can recognize the tabernacle represents the soon-to-excise Osiris, that is, the reentrance of Osiris. The language of quaking-bursting signifies the chemical reactive lytic path, the SOS response, and the excision of the prophage. The text referencing reentrance the first day mentions "the flood(?)," "he who illuminates, the perfect of turquoise," and "sublime of arms, Amun, Primeval One of the Two Lands" (58-59). The "flood" is the efflux or outflow of phage progeny from the cell, while the "turquoise" is an indicator of bioluminescent attribute of the Horus species or high-frequency, high-temperature blue light, which is more energetic than red light. (Calder 1979, 9-10) The "arms" and "Two Lands" indicate the full function of the Lambda genome that results in the Horus species. In addition, the text references "He is coming" and "Come to us, protect for us the Two Lands, (O) king of Upper and Lower Egypt, Re, son of Re, living eternally" (59), suggesting the excision of the prophage.

The composite of the hidden Amun and revealed Re represents the transformation of Taharqa, so the two gods and the god-man Taharqa are represented as one entity that becomes the Horus species. We could say that there are three gods in one species. The text referencing reentrance the second day also mentions "illuminating the Two Lands" and Amun-Re as "sublime of arms." (60) Thus, it is apparent that the ceremonies in the Edifice of Taharqa mirror those depicted and described in the Amduat and Book of Gates. This would suggest that the Wife of God or votaress is a representation of Isis, who signifies the lactose nutrient medium.

The Rites of Protection at the Cenotaph of Kom-Djeme (Plate 25, Room E)

The door lintel in the east wall of Room E shows a votaress or the Wife of the God aiming a fourth arrow at a fourth target, having already shot three arrows at three targets. Goyon states that the targets indicate the four cardinal points or four foreign areas Egypt ruled (61). The text states that the rebels are driven away and fall on their faces (64). The feathers on the arrow suggest the two feathers of the Goddess Maat, that is, Isis and Nephthys. In the center of this scene is the Mound of Osiris, a crypt buried in a mound surrounded by a wall and supported by an acacia tree, another indicator of vegetative replication or lytic activity of the Lambda genome, what we might call the Tree of Life. To the right is a representation of Taharqa throwing four balls.

The Throwing of Balls

According to Goyon, the activities proceeded as follows. Each cardinal point (NWSE) or quarter of the world is cursed. Then the King, attired in a kilt and dressed in his ceremonial tail, ran toward each of the four cardinal directions, throwing one clay ball in each direction with his right hand, which was symbolic of clearing away the enemies of Amun. His left hand held a white mace (62-63), suggesting the power of the nutrient medium lactose in the Castle of the Mace (left Lambda arm). In the Pyramid Texts (IS71), the dead King is not stopped by the Castle of the Mace, which represents the gang of Seth.

The clay balls Taharqa throws are inscribed: on the south ball, the names Amun and Montu; north ball, Shu and Tefnut; west ball, Neith and Wadjyt; east ball, Sakhmet and Bastet. The texts state that the balls are "the protection of Re, born of him" or "the balls come into existence for Re" and that Re gave them to his son Osiris "to protect him forever." (62-63) The text for the ball throwing states that the King throws the balls when he goes to make a halt at the Mound of Osiris (65), just as he halted in the Amduat, the Pyramid Texts and the Coffin Texts (IS62).

This apocalyptic act of throwing balls or clearing the world can be compared to the usual result of Lambda phage progeny production, which is cell lysis or destruction. Balls or disks suggest the spherical phage heads. The image (Plate 25) of the King with his right arm raised, his legs spread to throw, his left arm stretched out, is the same image of the "envoy of heaven" beneath the winged disk in Hour Four of the Amduat from both the tombs of Seti I and Ramesses VI. We can conclude that the images and textual translations in Room E point to similar chemical events in the Amduat, the Book of Gates, the Book of Two Ways, the Coffin Texts and Pyramid Texts, demonstrating an inherent unity of ideas within the funerary texts.

The Assembly of the *Tst*-Support and the Elevation of the Four Gods

On the south wall of Room E are four scenes, with each scene depicting the same act with four different gods. This is the elevation of the *tst*-support, and the principal officiant is the Wife of the God. In the four scenes, a support with a statue of Dedun, Soped, Sobek, and Horus is elevated, and an offering is presented to the god in the scene. Dedun, whose head is lost, and Soped wear ceremonial tails and hold a *w3s*-sceptre and *ʿnḫ*-cross. Crocodile-headed Sobek and hawk-headed Horus have the same attire as Dedun and Soped. The function of these gods is to massacre and stir up agitation in the world, another sign of cell lysis. (65-69) The elevation of the *tst*-support signifies the binding of cro protein to OR1 in Rightful Order and control of the Promoter-right, that is, complete commitment by Lambda to the lytic lifestyle.

The Chapel of the Bas of Amun and his Union with Re

The interior of subterranean Room F is badly damaged, yet it contains important remnants of the text of the Morning Song. The hymn requests Amun to wake up, that he presides over his left Eye, and that he is loved in his name "of perfection of the Moon-god." The moon is a metasymbol for levels of phage production, the whole moon or mid-month festival representing active cro production. When the prophage excises, the concentration of cro protein is now at the point of binding to both OL and OR. The "perfection of the Moon-god" or Thoth is that transcription can now proceed for protein production related to head and tail assembly along with bacterial cell lysis.

The damaged text then mentions "Nepri, who knows what overflows the Two Lands," that is, recombinant phage progeny. Also mentioned is the Ram (ba-soul) "that is in the coils of its *mhnt*-serpent, shining because of its two brilliant eyes," "the falcon of falcons," "Harakhty, the god of the recumbent ones who enters the inundation as water," and "The god of those who are in their mounds." (71-73) Thus, the full function of the Eye of Horus results in cro protein production related to creation of the Horus species, excision of the prophage, and phage progeny release.

The Ten Bas of Amun

Using a parallel text in the temple of Opet at Karnak, Goyon defines this scene as the procession of ten bas. Ba-1 is Amun, Khepri, Re-Atum, Re "the unique one who created himself in the form of millions," which can now be understood as the self-creation or molecular formation of millions of phage progeny. This ba is also the primeval god on the mound the Ogdoad worshiped. It is Horus whose "entire orbit is the flame coming from the blazing of his two eyes." Horus lights the sky with the help of his "two plumes, he performs perfectly his duties." The two plumes are Isis and Nephthys, the two eyes are the fully functioning Eye of Horus, and words such as "orbit" again point to molecular formation.

Ba-2 is Atum, Amun, Osiris "who is before his left eye according to the putting in order due to Thoth." This is the "ba-soul who is in his left eye," the one that "determines the divisions of time, months and years when he comes." (75) As mentioned, the left eye or arm of Lambda is responsible for human creation or the origin of time as we know it.

Ba-3 is Amun, Shu, the one who directs the winds for the bark, who causes "heaven to be in a rage, the sea in a tempest." In his name of "Horus with the brave arm," he maintains his "son on the throne of his father." (75-76) The right arm of Lambda under cro control is responsible for the Horus species to which the Deceased transforms.

Ba-4 is destroyed.

Ba-5 is "she appears as a flame," and the rest of the passage is destroyed with only remnants.

Ba-6 is only fragments such as "He [unites himself(?)] with Re."

Ba-7 is nothing intelligible.

Ba-8 is "the ba of the(?) two skies." The words "the millions" is one fragment. There is no text on Ba-9 and Ba-10 due to the destruction of the wall (78). It seems very possible that the ten (10) bas represent the Great Ennead with the new Horus species as the tenth Ba. The fifth Ba is most likely Isis. The island of Philae was the center for worship of the goddess Isis during the Ptolemaic period of Egyptian history. Evidence suggests that Taharqa built an altar to Amun at Philae, where many monuments to Isis dominate the island. The Taharqa altar to Amun is the earliest evidence of structures on the island. (Parsons 1999) This would suggest that Ba-5 is Isis, the only female member of the Great Ennead and the major deity representative of the lactose nutrient medium that nourishes the Horus species.

All in all, the Edifice of Taharqa supports the interpretation of metasymbols derived from major Idea Strands in the Pyramid and Coffin Texts and the analyses of the Amduat, the Book of Gates, and the Book of Two Ways. The Edifice also provides evidence for phage morphology, through the depiction of tails on gods and the construction of the nilometer attached to the Edifice.

Matrix 24. Edifice of Taharqa

Architecture	Egyptian Sign	Possible Modern Science Parallel
	1) Amun, god of origins, Thebes 2) He whose arm is sublime; Primeval One of Two Lands 3) Elements in Amun = 30 4) NW corner of Sun-beetle	1) Higgs particle; mass-generation 2) cro control; lytic cyle 3) 30 bp prophage site on host chromosome 4) polar holes; transmembrane tunnel; true north
Nilometer	narrow, askew structure connected to Edifice	phage (head/tail) attached to bacterium
Edifice Court	2-walled court into Edifice	double membrane of host cell
Edifice	1) subterranean structure with 6 rooms in NW part 2) deities wearing tails 3) Two standards 4) Taharqa walking north	1) Host cell and northwest (true north) journey on circular chromosome 2) phage morphology 3) two promoters of phage Lambda 4) northern polar movement
West Staircase (A)	Great Stairway	staircase cusp
Antechamber (B) and Vestibule (C)	two rooms before Duat	LamB porin in double cell membrane
Chapel of Re (D)	1) Duat, 75 caverns 2) Taharqa wearing triangle kilt 3) blooming lotus 4) mysterious door out of Duat 5) Sun-bark towed by 4 jackals 6) Text: "jackals . . . overthrow" 7) Re setting in mountain of life or Duat 8) Thoth in bow of Sun-bark 9) "thy yesterday [state]" 10) sit down those who stand upon their tails 11) text describing Re's birth in sixth hour of night	1) Host cell chromosome 2) phage morphology 3) recombinant species from heart of matter 4) transmembrane tunnel; ring singularity 5) Integrase 6) cleavage reaction for 7 bp recombination 7) entry into earth-cell 8) DNA-directed RNA polymerase 9) return to origin of time or Early Universe 10) phage morphology 11) excision of prophage
Room E	1) Djeme and Reentrance rites 2) Wife of the God (Isis) 3) 2 outstretched arms or the Sublime Arm 4) Saving of standard 5) Palm, victory 6) earth quaking 7) presentation of tabernacle 8) the flood 9) perfect of turquoise 10) He is coming 11) Amun-Re and Taharqa 12) Wife of God shooting arrows 13) Acacia tree 14) Taharqa throwing 4 balls 15) white mace in Taharqa's left 16) Taharqa halts at Mound of Osiris 17) elevation of *tst*-support	1) excision of prophage 2) lactose nutrient 3) Lambda genome 4) Rightful Order for cro; Promoter-R 5) victory of vegetative lytic replication 6) SOS, excision, lysis indicator 7) excision of prophage 8) outflow of phage progeny 9) bioluminescence, hi-frequency blue light 10) excision 11) recombinant species 12) lactose and lysis indicators 13) tree of life of Lambda DNA 14) lysis indicator of phage progeny 15) lactose for left arm of Lambda genome 16) first stage replication stops; excision and second stage rolling circle replication 17) cro protein control of Promoter-right
Room F	1) Amun as Moon-god 2) full moon 3) 10 Bas of Amun	1) indicator of phage production 2) full phage rolling circle replication 3) Birth of recombinant species

20

The Book of the Dead and Theban Recension

BACK TO THE EARLY UNIVERSE BY CPT VIOLATION, QUANTUM TELEPORTATION AND WORMHOLE SHUNT

The origins of the Book of the Dead (BD) from the Ani Papyrus can be traced to the Pyramid Texts. By the early New Kingdom (c. 1550 BCE), the Book of the Dead was replacing the Coffin Texts. Also included for this analysis is the Theban Recension (TR) of the Book of the Dead, which does not appear in the Papyrus of Ani. Key Egyptian themes are present in both these works as Matrix 25 shows. The 88 signs in the Papyrus of Ani and the 85 signs in the Theban Recension support our model derived from the Idea Strands in the Pyramid and Coffin Texts. Because of these repetitive themes, this analysis will focus on textual references that have not been explored earlier in this work, so that we can apply Egyptian ideas to modern scientific theory and research.

The Sycamore of the Sky

In Plate 16 of the Book of the Dead, the imagery for Chapter 58 depicts Ani and Tutu standing before three trees and drinking from a pool of water. The central tree is distinctive from the other two in that it has a long trunk from which six branches sprout. Both of the shorter trees on each side have nine branches, suggesting the Two Enneads, the left Eye of Seth and the Right Eye of Horus, two seeds for two different but related species. From the central tree hangs two Songstress-serpents, which suggest Isis and Nephthys. The text for Chapter 58 states, "I shall cross to the Mansion of Him who finds faces." So it seems possible that this vegetative image of a central tree with six (6) branches represents the Mansion of the Six, or the six contested operator sequences that can produce the human species or the human-phage species of many faces. The text also states, "you shall give me a jug of milk, a Shens-loaf, a Persen-loaf, a jug of beer, and a portion of meat in the Mansion of Anubis," indicating the presence of milk or lactose in the Mansion.

The next image in Plate 16 is the sycamore of the sky that guarantees the Deceased will have water and air in the afterlife. The text for Chapter 59 states that the Deceased has guarded the Egg, a reference to the birth of the Horus lineage from the excision of the prophage at the *LacZ* gene seat. In Plate 10, the Sun-god is depicted as the Great Cat, cleaving a serpent at the base of a tree. The related text in Chapter 17 informs us that Re is the Great Cat because he was "catlike in what he did" on the night of the war with the rebels. This references cro protein's surreptitious conquest of the operator sequences of the Lambda genome for the birth of the Horus lineage. So, the function of tree imagery is to convey the idea of the Tree of Life or water (outflow of recombinant phage progeny), that is, the Lambda DNA molecule, controlling human creation (cI) and human-phage creation (cro). Thus, the Great Cat cleaves the Apopis-serpent at the base of the tree of life. This simply means that the LexA repressor protein is prevented from bonding to the operator sequences, which in turn prevents the cI repressor protein from binding. Thus, the catlike cro protein beats cI protein to the operator sequences, and the DNA tree of life produces recombinant phage progeny that ascend into the starry heavens.

The Mounds of Osiris

In Chapter 149, we encounter the 14 Osirian mounds composed of 11 green and three (3) yellow mounds. When the prophage excises, it reverses its path through seven (7) gates or the 7 bp branch migration. Fourteen (14) Osirian mounds signify the 7 base pairs (14 bases) through which the prophage excises. Recall that the Lambda prophage is lodged on the host chromosome in a central 15 bp region between *b-gal* and *bio* operons. Chapter 150 references this region and names each base pair in this 15 bp region where the prophage is lodged. What appears as an Egyptian discrepancy of numbers in Chapters

149 and 150 is actually a thorough account of the prophage region.

The Lack of Love-making

In Chapter 175 of the Papyrus of Ani, the primeval Atum tells the scribe Ani that he receives "spirit-being instead of water, air, and lovemaking." Atum assures Ani that the duration of his life will be "a lifetime of millions of years" and that the "earth shall return to the Primordial Water, to the surging flood, as in its original state." This suggests that Ani is alive in the Early Universe before the creation of the earth.

This idea of no love-making suggests the cloned status of the recombinant species, whose potential forms remain in the earth-cell, as the Book of Gates claimed (Hour Eleven), so it cannot reproduce. The Papyrus text concludes with Atum explaining that Horus in the Bark of Millions is firm on his throne, and the soul of Seth is restrained, again emphasizing no matter or human creation.

Parity Invariance

Parity invariance means that the probability of a particle occurring is exactly the same as the probability of the same process occurring with the position vectors and directions of travel of all particles reversed. Although this property is true for strong and electromagnetic interactions, it is not true for weak interactions. (Quinn 2003) In Chapter 152 of the Theban Recension, Osiris rises and turns himself from his left side to his right, which is a 180 degree turn. Parity reversal turns up to down, left to right, and front to back. We discussed this same process relative to biological molecules in Part Two, when the Deceased turned from left to right for insertion into the Lambda vector. Now, we observe Osiris performing the same 180 degree turn from left to right, indicating a left-handed molecule. Because of this parity reversal, Osiris rises or the prophage excises, activating the lytic lifestyle, and Osiris is represented as upside-down and inside-out. A reaction between subatomic particles is "CP violating" if the reaction produces a different result when the electrical charges of the particles are changed to their opposites (C or charge) and the mirror image of the particle trajectories is used (P or parity). We could say that Osiris is now a left-handed biological molecule that behaves differently than a right-handed molecule, and so is the Deceased. So it may be that this left-handed feature shows that the origin of the recombinant species is related to the underlying asymmetry of weak interactions, which violate charge and parity (CP).

Recall that the Deceased is present with his double, suggesting the idea of a quark and antiquark pair that had enough time to restore to a pion, possibly due to less particle interference and cold temperatures at the northern polar region. This process is CP violating. The CPT theorem, with its three parameters of charge, parity and time reversal, is a basic precept of particle physics. According to the theorem's logic, if there is a violation of C, there most likely will be a violation of P and T. Experiments at CERN and Fermilab have confirmed that CPT violation is evident in the puzzling neutral kaons that decay into two pions after a lapse of time greater than the typical decay period. (Sidharth[2] 1998)

Fermion Transformation to Boson with Halo

The pion, a quark and antiquark pair, is an interesting particle. In 1935, Hideki Yukawa postulated the existence of the pion, proposing a mechanism for the strong force and that the pion should be a massive particle. Like the electromagnetic field composed of virtual photons, Yukawa proposed the strong field consisted of a cloud of virtual pions. He predicted the correct mass of the pion, which was found in cosmic rays in 1947, and he was awarded the Nobel Prize in 1949. Not only does the pion contain a significant amount of glue (Perry 2000), but it also remains a Nambu-Goldstone boson that acquires a halo while propagating through the Early Universe. (Chang 1994; 1993) When a symmetry is spontaneously broken, the result is a massless particle called a Nambu-Goldstone boson. Yet, at zero temperature the pion is not massless, but possesses a mass of 135 *MeV* due to electroweak breakdown, giving rise to primordial quark mass. However, at high temperature, when electroweak symmetry is restored, the pion will manifest its Nambu-Goldstone boson nature and be physically massless. Chang claims that this results in the pion propagating in the hot Early Universe with a halo. Pionic halo states result in heavy nuclei with neutron excess, the balance between repulsive pion-nucleus and attractive Coulomb force leading to halo-like 1s- and 2p-states with small widths (Friedman and Soff 1985; Toki and Yamazaki 1988). The halo is a threshold phenomenon characterized by loose binding of valence and nucleons due to quantum mechanical tunneling.

Is it possible that the Deceased, as he tunnels into the earth-cell from the extra-cellular medium (polar cap or cusp), has transformed from a fermion (particle that makes up matter) to a massless weak nuclear boson with a halo? In Chapter 169 of the Theban Recension, the Deceased claims that he is the fourth of four mighty gods, suggesting a transformation to a time before matter creation or cI protein control, correlating to a time 10^{-10} after the Big Bang, when the weak nuclear bosons were massless and the weak nuclear force had an infinite range like that of the photons (electromagnetic force) and gluons (strong force). This suggests that the Deceased's original movement to the polar cusp, where atoms move slower because of cold temperature, allowed enough time to restore to an unstable pion, which in turn, transformed into a boson due to UV irradiation and symmetry breaking. In this very real process of parity reversal, the Egyptian texts indicate that not only parity is violated, but also time. Let's look at textual references showing a movement back to the Early Universe.

The Early Universe of Atum

The first-born god Atum plays an important role because he is the origin and final destination of the Deceased in the afterlife. As a self-emerging creator god, Atum laid a foundation in Maat (Rightful Order) and made every form. So, we could say the Deceased is journeying back to the Early Universe before the foundation of forms or the original DNA generated the Sun and stars (Lambda source in our model) and the earth or human creation. This was a time before the great battle between cro and cI protein for control over the operator sequences of the Lambda genome, which resulted in a cI victory or matter creation, that is, a time before the weak nuclear bosons became massive and lost their infinite range (10^{-10} sec.).

One indication of this movement backward in time is Chapter 175 (BD), where we learn that Atum will destroy all he has made, and that the "earth shall return to the Primordial Water, to the surging flood as in its original state." The surging flood can be compared to the primordial sea of seething photons, gluons and other elementary particles. However, the surging flood in its "original state" suggests a timeframe of the Planck or Inflation era or some time between 10^{-43} and 10^{-12} seconds before the Big Bang (see Figure 20.1). Like Atum who is self-created, theory claims the universe is self-creating. It grew out of an indeterminate sea of potentiality or quantum vacuum. This cosmic singularity or origin was the point of infinite density and infinite temperature. (Schombert 2002) We could say this cosmic singularity was the center of a great expanding well of space that can be compared to the Sky Goddess Nut, whose name is Great Well (BD178).

The texts also inform us that Yesterday belongs to Ani (BD17), and Ani creates the primordial water (BD85). Along with this, the Deceased is "Yesterday, one who views a million years" (TR42), and he reminds us, "Yesterday, which is pregnant with the one who shall give birth to himself at another time, belongs to me" (TR64). This locates the Deceased somewhere in time before Atum's human creation. Yet, according to the texts, the Deceased seems to have a grip on all time before the human creation (10^{-43} seconds to one billion years after the Big Bang), for the Hymn to the Sun claims that Re shines forth from the Primordial Water, Horus is kindly, and Ani vindicated.

In addition, the Deceased states that when the Two Lands are united, he passes into the "midst of the Milky Way" and does not die again (TR176). Recently, a NASA and University of Illinois team of scientists discovered the presence of a sugar molecule, glycolaidehyde in a large cloud of gas near the center of our galaxy (Bridges 2000). The sugar formed of carbon, oxygen and hydrogen, a chemical precursor to life, can combine with other molecules to form sugars. Recall that the chemical composition of lactose is carbon, oxygen and hydrogen, elements necessary not only for life, but also for the energy metabolism of the recombinant Horus species, that is, the Deceased passing into the Milky Way, the way of lactose. Even the Egyptian story about the Benu Bird lends credence to the idea that the Deceased has gone back to the Early Universe, possibly to a time just before the Big Bang.

History of the Universe
from the Official String Theory Website
http://superstringtheory.com

10^{-43} sec.	Planck Era and Inflation Era
10^{-12} sec.	Radiation fills Universe; Big Bang begins.
10^{-11} sec.	Quarks outnumber antiquarks; quarks equaled antiquarks until Universe cooled
10^{-10} sec.	Weak nuclear bosons become massive and lose infinite range
10^{-4} sec.	Quarks and gluons no longer are free, but confined in mesons and baryons that make up our Universe
1 sec.	Proton to neutron ratio fixed at 7 protons to every 1 neutron
100 sec.	Protons, neutrons form nuclei of H, He, lithium, deuterium
10,000 yrs.	Matter dominates over radiation
500,000 yrs.	Protons, electrons form H, He, lithium atoms
1 Billion yrs.	Hydrogen gas makes first stars
2-13 Billion yrs.	Lifespan of star is 2-13 billion years, during which time it produces heavier elements; star dies, ejecting heavier elements in supernova explosion. Dead star becomes white dwarf, neutron star or black hole

Figure 20.1

The Benu Bird

Inflationary cosmologists view the more than 100 billion galaxies as nothing more than quantum mechanics (Greene 2004, 308), that is, what is above is what is below. Physicist Brian Greene of Columbia University explains the theoretical inflationary period just before the Big Bang in the following manner:

> A long time ago, when the universe was enormously dense, its energy was carried by a Higgs field perched at a value far from the lowest point on its potential energy bowl . . . A Higgs field perched above its zero energy value can provide an outward blast driving space to swell. (2004, 284-285)

Greene explains that the powerful Higgs or inflaton field, the field that generated a massive gravitational repulsion to inflate, caused the universe to swell by a huge factor similar to a molecule of DNA becoming roughly the size of the Milky Way galaxy in a time much less than the blink of an eye. This resulted because the Higgs field did not reach its lowest energy configuration as the universe cooled, and it became trapped in a higher-energy configuration. Caught on this plateau, the Higgs field supercooled, exerting a repulsive gravitational force that drives space to expand.

This idea of the primordial Higgs field *perched* on the plateau of a potential energy bowl is similar to the Egyptian idea about the Benu Bird *perched* on the primeval mound as a manifestation of Atum or Re as the creator deity. The Benu Bird is depicted in Plate 7, and Chapter 17 (BD) recounts that Atum was alone on the Primordial Waters. The text then asserts that Yesterday belongs to the Deceased and that he knows Tomorrow. In answer to the question "What does it mean?" the text explains that Yesterday is Osiris and Tomorrow is Re, when the foes were destroyed and Horus ruled. From the Deceased's perspective as Atum or Re, he is the Benu-bird on the Higgs field mound of time, looking toward the future creation of earth. Similarly, and in a less confusing manner, Chapter 122 (TR) informs us that the Deceased receives everything, for "the whole of it has been given to me." He has "come out as a Benu-bird" and has "alighted on the beautiful tree which is in the middle of the island in the flood" (TR189), and it is here that the Deceased dwells with the "potent noble dead."

Even the earliest Pyramid Texts reinforce the idea of the Deceased's ascension to "the primeval hill of the land in the midst of the sea, whose hand no earthlings have grasped" (PT484). The Deceased states, "I was born in the Abyss before the sky existed, before the earth existed" (PT486), and that he is "one of this great company which was born aforetime in On" (486). Aforetime for the Deceased is the future of Yesterday, which can only be a movement back to the Early Universe.

In his Commentary to the Book of the Dead, Ogden Goelet, Jr. (1994, 159) notes that Herodotus may have made the error that equated the Benu Bird with an Egyptian Phoenix. Unlike the cyclic Phoenix that singes its wings on the flaming Sun and dies repeated fiery deaths, the Benu Bird perches on the primeval inflation mound, a metasymbol of an event before the Big Bang, when the universe was whole and the forces within it unified. Still, one wonders, how does the Deceased move backward in time to a low-entropy event before the Big Bang? This violates the second law of thermodynamics, stating that any real process can only result in an entropy increase.

Quantum Teleportation and Left-to-Right Movement

In 1993, a team of physicists from IBM, the University of Montreal, the Technion-Israel Institute of Technology, and Williams College found a theoretical way to use quantum mechanics for teleportation. The general idea of teleportation is similar to faxing data: something is scanned to extract its information, and then the data is transmitted to the receiving location to construct a replica. The team of physicists showed that teleportation was possible, but only if the original is destroyed and no information about the quantum state is known. However, the state can be known through a special feature of quantum mechanics called entanglement. Quantum entanglement means that two particles have common properties. If two photons are entangled, then measuring one photon's spin around an axis forces the other distant photon to have the same spin. (Greene 2004, 115)

With this information, scientists transferred a quantum property such as polarization state from one photon to another by producing pairs of entangled photons through parametric down-conversion and by using two-photon interferometry for analyzing the entanglement. (Bouwmeester et al. 1997). The experiment required a pulse of UV-light traveling left to right through a nonlinear crystal to create the entangled pair of photons A and B. Reflected back through the crystal, the pulse created two more photons, C and D. Photon D was then polarized to a specific X state, and a beam splitter was used to verify a photon acquiring X's polarization.

The process of quantum teleportation is similar to what happens to the Deceased in the afterlife. The Deceased travels to the polar cusp to be polarized to a specific state of alignment. He then merges with the Lambda crystal, experiences UV irradiation, and becomes entangled. The texts advise the Deceased, who bonds to the Sun-god, to make a 180 degree turn from his left to his right, a reversal of parity. The texts also advise Osiris to make the same change (TR152). Information, or the DNA instructions of the Deceased Sun-god, then travels to the Osiris receiving location to construct a replica by means of RNA transcription, replication and translation to protein. It seems as if we have all the ingredients for quantum teleportation: UV radiation, the crystalline Sun-god, the desired left-handed rotation of the Deceased that is imprinted on Osiris due to the magic of faster-than-light nonlocality.

Spooky Magic

Einstein called nonlocality "spooky action at a distance," whereas the Egyptian idea of *Heka* or magic in the universe seems to be equally appropriate, for the nonlocal Deceased claims that magic has been given to him "more swiftly than a shadow" (BD24). Further, if we perceive the Deceased and his double as a two-qubit system (entangled pairs composed of Deceased/Double and Sun-god/Osiris), then it is also possible that the emphasis on opening the mouth four times may relate to the four Bell states that can be realized in quantum teleportation. For example, a qubit is a quantum system that can be in one of two states; a two-qubit would have four states, which are entangled pairs. Does this mean it is possible for the Deceased to be teleported back to the Early Universe?

Maybe, because if wormholes are possible, then a faster-than-light particle may be transmitted back to the Early Universe. As mentioned, in Hour Twelve of the Amduat, the Sun-god travels through a serpent from its tail to mouth. We compared this to the holes located at the cell poles for releasing phage progeny that prompted researchers to theorize a transmembrane tunnel out of the cell. (Witte et al. 1999) Recall that using Sethe's interpretation of *b33* as "hole," Pyramid Text 291 states, "Your honour is removed, O white hole, by him who came forth from the *fnt*-snake." One way a wormhole could be generated is if a black hole is attached to a white hole. A theoretical white hole spews forth matter, and this process could be described as one coming forth from a snake or wormhole. Further, after talking with Hawking, Andrew Strominger (1993) investigated CPT, finding that in two dimensions, weak CPT invariance can be restored in a sector of Hilbert space by including the possibility of white hole formation/evaporation, viz., the time reverse of black hole formation/evaporation.

Could this nonlocal tunnel, this wormhole, also indicate a movement back in time to the Early Universe? Wormholes are allowed by the mathematics of general relativity (Greene 2004, 462), and some physicists think that the quantum fluctuations of the gravitational field could produce tiny wormholes in the fabric of space (466). Physicist Kip Thorne has investigated this possibility by asking the question, "Can highly advanced civilizations build wormholes through hyperspace for rapid interstellar travel and machines for traveling backward in time?" (1994, 483) First, the wormhole must be held open by exotic material with a negative energy density. Vacuum fluctuations of the electromagnetic field is a form of exotic material, but whether or not these fluctuations can hold a wormhole open is unknown (498). So Thorne decided to compute the behavior of circulating vacuum fluctuations to see if they would destroy a wormhole. He discovered that the fluctuations were infinitely intense for a short period of time at the instant when it is first possible to use the wormhole for backward time travel. Thorne concluded, "the laws of quantum gravity are hiding from us the answer to whether wormholes can be converted successfully into time machines." (521)

However, in the Egyptian afterlife, human bodies are not going through wormholes; recombinant phage progeny are. What if there were another source of exotic material with gravitationally-repulsive negative energy available to hold the wormhole open long enough to make it a quantum time machine for a molecule? Solar physicists have found negative energy waves in the solar atmosphere. In particular, in magnetic flux tubes, there are kink surface modes with negative energy. For coronal loops, they found that only very high-speed flows can produce negative energy slow body modes. In solar wind flow structures, both slow and fast body modes have negative energy. (Joarder et al. 1997) It may be possible that the Deceased Sun-god is a negative energy source that may hold the transmembrane tunnel or wormhole open for travel back to the Early Universe.

If this doesn't work, physicist Robert Lull Forward notes that a heavy atomic nucleus in a strong magnetic field could elongate into a cylinder to create a time machine. Gamma rays would allow information to be sent back in time. (Wikipedia) So our Twelfth Hour Amduat serpent may represent an elongated heavy nucleus or time tunnel through which the Sun-god and his millions travel back to the Early Universe. Egyptian textual references and modern physics indicate that this may actually be possible.

The Negative Confession

It may then be possible that the negative confession of the Deceased signifies the idea of negative energy. Three of the Deceased's confessions suggest time travel:

> O Burning One who came forth backwards, I have not told lies.
> O He-whose-Face-is-behind-him who came forth from his hole, I have not caused (anyone) to weep.
> O Ihy who came forth from the Primordial Waters, my voice was not loud.

"Coming forth backwards" suggests the idea of going faster than light or backward in time. If you watched an object coming toward you faster than light, you would see it going away from you, and then it would appear near to you at the end of its journey before the light arrived from farther off, telling you of its coming. (Calder 1979, 108) "He-whose-Face-is-behind-him who came forth from his hole" suggests the same idea of backward time movement from a wormhole, while "Ihy coming forth from the Primordial Waters" points to the early Big Bang era. These indicators of faster-than-light time travel backward suggest that the Egyptians were aware of the importance of a confession or admission of negative energy.

The Positive Confession

By comparing Egyptian ideas to discoveries in modern physics, we can unveil the Pharaohs' enormous understanding of the earth, sun, stars and cosmos. First, the Egyptian movement of the Deceased and his double to the northern polar region of earth suggests the long-lived kaon decay into two pions that violates CPT symmetry and ultimately transforms into a massless boson wearing a halo. Because kaon decay violates time reversal, time has a backward direction of flow, which is also evident in the funerary texts.

Second, the texts describe copying events within a context of nonlocality that suggests the potential for quantum teleportation, a process very similar to spontaneous RNA transcription and replication events on the quantum level. More interesting and in line with T violation, the texts and images suggest a movement back to the Early Universe, possibly by means of a wormhole or extended atomic structure acting as a time machine. This idea is supported by the presence of negative energy structures in coronal loops and magnetic flux tubes, implying the supramolecular Sun-god may have the potential to hold open a wormhole in time with exotic matter or negative energy.

Third, the creation in the afterlife of the recombinant species is related to the underlying asymmetry of weak interactions, which violate charge, parity and time (CPT). So it seems that we can reevaluate these ideas by saying that the Deceased's movement to the polar cusp results in a backward time movement to the Early Universe at the Planck-length.

Fourth, from our perspective on earth, we could date the first competition between cI and cro proteins to the birth of our solar system 4.5 billion years ago. The competition between cI and cro proteins is actually the competition between photosynthesis and chemiluminescence. Production of cI protein results in our world and photosynthesis, whereas cro protein production results in chemiluminescence or weak force interactions important in the energy-generating processes of stars. However, because of the human element, cro production results not in chemiluminescence, but in a bioluminescent life-form that may restore the equivalence of matter and antimatter. According to physicists, supernova data indicate that ordinary matter, such as ourselves, is 4% of the mass/energy of the universe, with dark matter comprising 21% and dark energy 75% (Harvard Smithsonian Center for Astrophysics 2004). Apparently, the Pharaohs have come up with an afterlife strategy based on real physics to restore us to the Early Universe. The first stage is a time-reversed movement of one's consciousness to the first prokaryote (3.8 billion years ago), within which a Lambda genome resided as a prophage. Here at the Lambda genome under cro control, a new recombinant species is born, which then tunnels out of the host cell, traveling backward in time to the Early Universe. A modern geneticist might say that the Lambda chromosome has systematic affinities across several genes for two particular lineages, whereas a physicist might say that this supersymmetry is similar to every fermion having a boson twin and the ability to become it through the mysterious kaon decay.

Nonetheless, the catalyst for transformation is the Deceased's presence at the northern polar cusp for spontaneous symmetry breaking. It may be that without thermal agitation at the pole, a ground state is achieved in which the particle spins point to a single direction due to the presence of iron nuclei at the cusp. In ferromagnetism, the spins tend to align spontaneously without any applied field, and this is a quantum mechanical effect due to the Pauli principle. Put simply, two electrons with the same spin cannot lie at the same position, so their repulsion lowers their electrostatic energy, inducing the electrons to align. The Pharaohs may be indicating this synchronicity by the constant presence of the Deceased's double (particle/antiparticle pair). Exactly how ferromagnetism, symmetry breaking, and temperature at the northern cusp contribute to the long range order of the Deceased's transformation from fermion to boson must be posed by this researcher as an Outstanding Question for further investigation.

Still, in light of the Deceased's movement backward in time in the black hole Duat, one wonders if the Pharaohs knew what to expect when spacetime ceased to exist near the singularity. Did they know that space and time would become unglued? ruptured? Did they know that spacetime is tightly interwoven like a piece of wood (space) impregnated with water (time)? According to Kip Thorne's (1993, 477) application of this analogy:

> the singularity and the laws of quantum gravity that rule it are like a fire into which the water-impregnated wood is thrown. The fire boils the water out of the wood, leaving the wood alone and vulnerable; in the singularity, the laws of quantum gravity destroy time, leaving space alone and vulnerable. The fire then converts the wood into a froth of flakes and ashes; the laws of quantum gravity then convert space into a random, probabilistic froth.

The Deceased states, "I am that oar of Re with which the Old Ones are rowed.

I will be neither burnt up nor scorched." He continues (TR63B), "I am that equipped oar with which Re is rowed when the Old Ones are rowed and the efflux of Osiris is upraised at the Lake of Flames which does not burn." Remarkably, the Pharaohs use an analogy similar to Kip Thorne's, but the Deceased is not burned in the flames through which the efflux of Osiris or the recombinant species is upraised. What is amazing is that Kip Thorne and the Pharaohs used the same metaphor—water-impregnated wood or an oar in fire—to describe the dynamics of a singularity. Despite 5000 years of time, twenty-first century man still uses the same metaphors to explain scientific ideas.

Another indicator of the Pharaohs' understanding of black and white holes is the cone-shaped Upper Egyptian White Crown, a fair representation of a white hole. Also referred to as green, the Red Crown sports the Fibonacci series spiral, suggesting the exponential growth of Nature. With the emphasis on the whole Black Eye and White Eye of Horus and the Double Crown, it is evident the Deceased travels through a black hole to a white hole to exist in an Early Universe, where the galaxies are bluer and brighter than they are today.

Matrix 25. Book of the Dead (Faulkner) D = Deceased = Ani

Chap.	Egyptian Sign	Possible Modern Science Parallel
30B	Ani is righteous in the great balance; no sin; follows Horus	right order of cro protein
1	Ani will be at opening of caverns for Inert One; rebels crushed; Ani will protect Osiris' left arm	excision of prophage
22	Ani is Osiris; rises from Egg in secret land	excision activating rolling circle replication
21	Ani is pure and desires mouth	wormhole mouth
72 Rubric	Ani can act as primeval nine gods of Duat	high energy core elements from supernovae
17	1) Yesterday belongs to Ani 2) Ani is Atum, Re 3) Ani is self-created 4) Ani restores Eye after injury 5) Ani journeys to Rosetjau or Osiris 6) Field of Reeds are provisions 7) Re embracing Osiris 8) Wadjet, Lady of Devouring Flame, is Re	1) existence in Early Universe 2) nonlocality 3) molecular self-assembly 4) cro control of operator sequences 5) *LacZ* gene where prophage lodged 6) nutrient medium 7) molecular bonding for replication 8) nutrient medium of genome is lactose
147	1) Ani makes own light 2) 7 gates of Rosetjau 3) in bark "as he circles the horizon"	1) internal light or photoreactivation process 2) 7 bp branch migration for excision 3) horizon of black hole
146	10 portals with names such as O Veiling, Great Embracer, Mistress of Heat	portal protein rings that surround DNA after it is pumped into prohead (similar to Hour 8 of Amduat)
18	1) Seth/rebels guarded, destroyed 2) Horus-with-no-Eyes-in-his-Forehead 3) Hacking earth; vindicating Osiris 4) Night of secreting forms	1) cI production very low 2) phage morphology 3) cleavage for 7bp branch migration 4) cI beating cro to Lambda operators
23	Bonds of Seth restricted Ani's mouth (or ability to utter words)	lysogeny due to restricted inert DNA
24	1) D is Atum-Khepri; magic is given to him 2) Sun-bark roped to North Wind goes to Island of Fire	1) quantum effects such as nonlocality 2) Lambda prophage on host chromosome; North Wind or high energy elements
26	1) Geb opens his jaws and Ani's eyes 2) Geb extends Ani's legs; Sekhmet stretches me out 3) Ani is not restrained at portals of West	1) reconnection; DNA recombination 2) stretching near event horizon of black hole; DNA strand stretching 3) penetration into host cell
30B	Ani's heart must not oppose him before Keeper of Balance or make his name stink to those who make men	choice for cro protein production
61	Ani came forth from flood	phage progeny
54	1) Ani is Egg; Rivals united 2) sweeten the state of the Two Lands	1) cro protein control; recombinant species 2) lactose medium for Lambda genome
29	Get back, you messenger of any god	no transcription other than lytic lifestyle
27	Ani vindicated in West, domain of Eternity	cro control; lytic lifestyle

Matrix 25. Book of the Dead

Chap.	Egyptian Sign	Possible Modern Science Parallel
58	1) You shall separate head from head 2) Ani to Mansion of Him who finds faces 3) Ani requests jug of milk, bread, beer	1) concatemer cleavage; phage morphology 2) phage morphology 3) lactose nutrient; Maltose Transport system
59	Ani guards Egg which he grows with	recombinant species; rolling circle replication
44	Ani's neck is Re and his speech is known	transcription for lytic lifestyle
45	Ani is Osiris	molecular bonding for rolling circle
46	Those who flash with swaying heads	phage progeny
50	4 knots on Ani	DNA nucleotides
93	Ani does not want to be seized by rebels	advocate of cro control, lytic lifestyle
43	Ani is knit together and given a head	phage head assembly; lytic lifestyle
89	Ani's soul wants his corpse gods dragged in bark	re-creation of matter through cro protein frame dragging around black hole
91	Ani can enter any gate in/out of West	entry through LamB gates; exit out of cell
92	1) Ani desires his beauty on vertex of Re 2) O Far-strider whose legs extend	1) insert in Lambda vector 2) phage penetration; movement over horizon
74	Ani ascends to sky though he is inert	viral clone; no reproductive power
8	Ani is Re; his head is sealed	phage head packaging
9	Ani opens Duat to see Osiris	LamB porin to prophage site
10	Ani equips a myriad	recombinant phage progeny
15	1) Rebel fallen, knife severed his spine 2) Sole One existed before mountains, plains	1) cro control over cI 2) Early Universe existence
Osiris Hymn	1) Isis embraces Osiris 2) Osiris face is like shining sun-disk	1) lactose nutrient for prophage 2) phage morphology
Hymn to Sun	Re shines forth from Primordial Water, Horus is kindly, Ani vindicated	First creation in Early Universe
133	Ani is golden image like sun-disk	phage morphology
134	Apopis conquered, Ani is Horus	LexA repressor cleaved; lytic lifestyle
18	1) Osiris binding with cloth 2) no offerings for Children of Impotence	1) translation to protein 2) no glucose for human creation
86	1) Seth in bonds 2) Ani pure on great tomb-plateau	1) minimal cI production 2) flat universe geometry
77	1) Ani reassembled as gold falcon upon pointed stone 2) Ani receives barley	1) phage morphology 2) Maltose Transport for lactose passage
78	1) House of Darkness (Duat) 2) Messenger is in shape of Horus 3) Messenger lands at Mansion of Great Dead One, the Lord of Weariness, Osiris 4) wardens of Mansion of Osiris rise up	1) abyss of host bacterium; black hole 2) phage morphology 3) prophage on host chromosome 4) excision of prophage induced
85	Ani creates primordial water	phage progeny as Early Universe plasma
83	1) Ani grows as a plant 2) Ani clads himself as tortoise 3) Ani is 7th of 7 uraei coming into being in West	1) vegetative lytic replication 2) phage morphology; pointed stone, crystal 3) reference to 7 Lambda operons
84	Ani is Wild Bull in writings	DNA transcription, replication of Lambda
81A	Ani is pure lotus	heart of matter, Calabi-Yau space

Matrix 25. Book of the Dead

Chap.	Egyptian Sign	Possible Modern Science Parallel
175	1) Ani has palette and inkpot of Thoth 2) Atum will destroy all he has made; earth returns to Primordial Water, to the surging flood in its original state 3) Atum restrains Seth	1) transcription in host cell 2) movement to Early Universe or past singularity 3) minimal cI protein production
125A	Ani sinks bark of enemies	No DNA transcription for humans
125	Negative Confession	indicator negative energy; exotic matter
42	Ani is Re, Hathor, Anubis, Neith, etc.	nonlocality
155	Raise yourself Osiris	excision of prophage
156	Isis has magic	creative potential through lactose
166	Ani's head will not be taken forever	phage morphology
151	1) Hapy gives Ani his head eternally 2) Ani reverses steps of One Hidden of Face	1) phage morphology 2) reverse integration of prophage
110	Ani pacifies Conbatants	insertional inactivation of cI gene
185	those who come in millions and millions	millions of phage progeny
186	Great Bark of Osiris crosses water of truth	phage progeny to Early Universe
Art	the ellipses present in Plates 1,3,10,11, etc.	In Black Hole theory, a photon sphere is an ellipsoid; horizon of spinning black hole is an ellipse

Matrix 26. Theban Recension D = Deceased

Chap.	Egyptian Sign	Possible Modern Science Parallel
4	To pass on upper road of Rosetjau	Maltose Transport for lactose passage
5	D lifts arm of Him who is inert	excision of prophage
7	Passing the dangerous coil of Apopis	LexA repressor protein
12	Re guards secrets of gates on neck of Geb	6 LamB gates at cell pole for phage Lambda
17	1) Re was catlike 2) Two Lands united 3) Potent Ram Re	1) cro beat cI to rightward operators 2) full Lambda genome under cro control 3) Ram pressure of high energy sun particles
20	1) night of battle with rebels 2) Heritage of Horus and property of Osiris	1) cro versus cI protein 2) cro control of DNA operators
34	Standard of Vegetation	vegetative lytic replication of Promoter-R
38B	1) ways encircling Celestial Waters on path of bark of Atum 2) Apopis has fallen down	1) path to Early Universe into black/white holes 2) LexA repressor protein cleaved
41	Doorkeeper of City of the Bee in West	phage progeny compared to pollen
42	1) D is Yesterday, viewing a million years 2) D's shape is turned upside-down 3) no child who treads Yesterday's road 4) D opens door in sky and will not die again 5) Where is sky? Earth? Offspring rebuffed 6) D passes time on road opened up 7) D is small golden baboon, no arms/legs	1) existence in Early Universe 2) parity violation 3) no creation of children; species is cloned 4) path in/out of black hole/white hole 5) existence in Early Universe; no humans 6) movement out of spacetime dimensions 7) recombinant phage species
62	D gets cold water, crosses sky, has eternity	cold, high-energy plasma; escape from earth system
63A	Chap. for drinking water and not being burnt by fire; D is oar of Re rowing Old Ones and will not be burned	avoiding thermal chemical reactions at a singularity where time and space rupture
63B	Oar of Re rowing Old Ones and efflux of Osiris upraised at Lake of Flames that does not burn	avoiding thermal chemical reactions at singularity
64	1) D says Yesterday belongs to him 2) Moored Ones who drag in Re 3) Circumvallation of earth 4) Lord of Millions of earth	1) existence in Early Universe 2) phage Lambda at LamB porin 3) earth's barrier; magnetosphere 4) recombinant phage progeny
65	D is reborn, but guarded Seth/Pig is loosed	lysogeny returns to cell; SHH gene active
66	D is Horus and has landed on vertex of Re in prow of his bark in Primordial Water	phage morphology; D is recombinant species in Early Universe
67	Open tomb to release those in sunshine	recombinant phage progeny escape cell
71	1) 7 knots, arms of balance on night of setting Sacred Eye in order 2) Day of dooming the robber	1) 7 operons of Lambda genome; lytic cycle 2) cro control over Lambda operators
79	D is Atum who made sky and what exists	movement to Early Universe
94	D is equipped with writings of Thoth	transcription of Lambda DNA by host cell polymerase

Matrix 26. Theban Recension

Chap.	Egyptian Sign	Possible Modern Science Parallel
95	1) D acted on behalf of Isis 2) D helped to make strong knife of Thoth	1) lactose nutrient 2) Insert for recombinant phage transcription
98	Fetching ferryboat at polar region/ladder	insert into Lambda vector at LamB
99	1) escape from evil land where stars fall upside down 2) You can bind on heads, make necks firm 3) You shall not repel me from Milky Way	escape from earth and gravitational field 2) phage head/tail assembly 3) lactose nutrient; escape to stars
101	Re is hale if he passes by Eye with pupil	journey through black hole to white
105	Those in horizon receive amulet if white	white light, white hole
106	Bring me loaves from your polar waters	nutrient rich poles of cells
108	Stoppage in Sacred Bark; Apopis swallows 7 cubits but Seth makes him vomit them up	LexA repressor controls Lambda operons but is cleaved (cI inactivation, SOS)
109	D knows northern gate of sky	northern escape from cell/hole
110	1) D shines on day of Milk goddess 2) D knows deep holes of snake	1) lactose nutrient medium 2) in electric field, hole is mobile vacancy in sea of electrons
118	D born in Rosetjau and is unique	recombinant phage species
119	the one purified by your own efflux	efflux of phage progeny
122	D comes out as Benu Bird	Higgs Field perched on inflaton field before Big Bang in Early Universe
123	1) D hails Atum 2) D is in Mansion of Him of double face	1) movement to Early Universe 2) full (Seth/Horus) operation of genome
125	1) Hall of Justice 42 gods 2) D sets balance in Silent Land	1) self-cleavage of LexA; 42 genes alive 2) restores cro control and protein level
127	Earth opens caverns to D	DNA chromosome of host cell
128	1) D saves Osiris alive today 2) To Osiris: May you be with them in your mummy-form	1) excision of prophage 2) phage morphology (large mummy head and tail stalk)
130	1) D hates storms, heaping up of water 2) D dispels cloudiness 3) D is not boatless; hears Re's word	1) substorms; bowshock of magnetosphere 2) clear plaque of lysis 3) insert in Lambda vector for transcription
131	D drives off Old One at bright place limits	Promoter for Repressor Maintenance
135	D dispels cloudiness	clear plaque
136A	Lotus-bark in dockyard of gods	incoming Lambda at LamB porin
136B	Fire concentrated behind Re whose face is wiped into his sacred lake	Lambda high energy elements
137A	7 gates of Osiris	7 bp branch migration for excision
144	1) I am one who creates a multitude 2) Face is Great One; hinderparts 2 crowns	1) phage progeny 2) phage morphology; molecular structure
149	1) Make my head firm for me 2) 14 Mounds (11 green, 3 yellow)	1) phage head assembly 2) 7 bp excision path
150	15 Mounds named	15 bp prophage insertion site on chromosome
152	Osiris turns from left to right	180 degree parity reversal

Matrix 26. Theban Recension

Chap.	Egyptian Sign	Possible Modern Science Parallel
154	my head is not removed from my neck	phage morphology
158	Chapter for golden collar on throat of D	phage morphology; sheath topped by collar
161	Tortoise dead; he in sarcophagus is stretched out; 4 sky openings (NWSE)	Lambda prophage; black hole stretching; 4 event horizons
164	Dwarf before and after	quantum existence
169	1) D is 4th of 4 mighty gods bringing water 2) D's vision is cleared in House of Darkness 3) D shall be inducted into Ennead	1) gravity/antigravity 2) rebirth as recombinant phage species 3) movement to first creation; Early Universe
170	Thoth has book of sacred words	recombinant phage DNA transcription
174	Go out from sky Great Gate; D raises Atum	release of phage progeny in Early Universe
176	I pass pure into midst of Milky Way	escape from earth system; Early Universe
178	1) making the head firm 2) Nut as Great Well	1) phage head assembly 2) well of universe generated from a singularity of infinite mass or energy
182	Re revives heart of Osiris Osiris refashions mankind	molecular bonding; prophage excision; birth of recombinant progeny
189	D alights on beautiful tree in middle of island in flood with potent noble dead	movement to Early Universe

Objective 10 completed: The Book of Two Ways, The Edifice of Taharqa, and the Egyptian Book of the Dead, including the Theban Recension, support the interpretation of metasymbols derived from the major Idea Strands in the Pyramid and Coffin Texts and the analyses of the Amduat and the Book of Gates.

V

The Many Faces of a Legacy

Perhaps we may ask ourselves where this passionate quest for truth
can lead us. Science advances with great strides; astonishing discoveries
issue each day from its laboratories; by its bold theories
it opens out for us wonderful new vistas on the mystery of things.
Will it then soon lift the veil of Isis,
make us definitely penetrate into the secrets of nature,
give an assured answer to the great metaphysical problems
which for so many centuries vex the soul of man?

Louis de Broglie
Nobel Laureate, Physics 1929
from *Physics and Microphysics, 1955*

21

Lambda-Genesis

THE EGYPTIAN MODEL OF HOW MATTER IS CONSTRUCTED WITHIN A BLACK HOLE

The folding of cI protein to its native conformation results in *Homo Sapiens Sapiens* trapped in the earth system, while the folding of cro protein results in the recombinant *Homo Sapiens Lambda* reversing time into an Early Universe. In the Egyptian afterlife, the action happens within the energy landscape of a protein folding funnel or the earth-cell's vortex. However, in the quantum world of proteins and nonlocality, separate locations are the same locations, so the protein folding funnel is not only the earth-cell's vortex, but it is also a representation of the Planck length Early Universe. According to String Theory, this Early Universe can be described as a quantum foam of ten dimensions containing microscopic black holes that are continuously created and annihilated with no cause or effect. (Schombert 2002) According to the Amduat, the Book of Gates and the Egyptian Book of the Dead, the protein product of the transformed Deceased ultimately travels through a transmembrane tunnel into the chemiluminescent realm of an Early Universe. This release from the earth-cell vortex results from the merger of the Deceased into the Sun-god, a Lambda vector for the journey through the host cell.

In contrast, if cI protein beats cro to the operator sequences, a cI product blooms in the macrocosmic earth system of photosynthesis and matter. The failure to merge with the Sun-god vector brings a second death, what amounts to a recycling of one's immortal part back to our fermion mirage-world, our hologram of hell, that is, the upside-down earth system of photosynthesis and cI protein products.

The Cosmic Subway

In the quantum domain, the earth-cell's vortex acts as a gateway to a cosmic subway back to the Early Universe. First, DNA damage or magnetic reconnection creates a tear in spacetime. The recombinant species, as exotic matter with negative energy, travels into the spacetime tear of a spinning vortex or a quantum mechanical Kerr black hole. Recall that mathematician Roy Kerr found that a rotating black hole would eventually collapse to a ring, not a point. Traveling to the ring results in large but finite gravity and access to an Einstein-Rosen bridge or wormhole on the scale of the Planck length, leading to a mirror universe. So when the recombinant species enters the Duat or earth-cell and leaves by a transmembrane tunnel, the Pharaohs are describing the process of an exotic species relocating by an Einstein-Rosen wormhole to a quantum mirror universe.

The current cosmological view of our universe is that it is a huge black hole (Gribbin 2001, 88). Some cosmologists believe that a singularity forming inside a black hole universe can give birth to a baby universe. In Egyptian science, the path through the spinning vortex of the earth-cell is the same path as a protein folding to its native conformation in an energy landscape funnel. Both these processes point to the dynamics of a black hole singularity, as do the Egyptian textual references. Current theory states that material falling into a singularity in our spacetime can be shunted through a kind of spacetime warp that emerges as an expanding singularity in another spacetime of four dimensions at right angles to the familiar four dimensions of our spacetime. The funerary texts point to this idea when the Deceased Sun-god enters the black Duat or the folding funnel where cro protein folds into the recombinant species. The tunneling movement of the recombinant cro species out of the black-hole Duat into the Early Universe results in an expanding singularity at the scale of the Planck length, a white hole. The Egyptian texts emphasize that this *evolutionary shunt* into the Early Universe only happens by a specific pathway linked to merging with the Sun-god. Within the energy landscape of the earth-cell's vortex, we can assume that other figurative pathways result in severe gravitational pressures and/or a recycling of the elements back to the earth system of matter, possibly in the form of plants, animals or humans.

Dark Energy

Dark energy is a hypothetical energy and pressure that uniformly fills space. Similarly, dark matter is matter suffused through space, exerting gravity but not emitting light. According to recent measurements of the cosmic microwave background and Chandra observations that agree with results from the Hubble Space Telescope, our universe consists of 4% visible matter, 21% cold dark matter, and 75% dark energy (Harvard Smithsonian Center for Astrophysics 2004). Both visible (4%) and dark matter (21%) account for 25% of our universe's critical density, whereas dark energy accounts for 75% and causes the universe's expansion to accelerate. This means that humans are part of the 4% composition of protons, neutrons and electrons in the universe.

The question arises, is the recombinant species dark energy? Scientists only understand some of the properties of dark energy. It is a repulsive force responsible for the acceleration of the universe; it is related to vacuum energy density; it is distributed homogeneously in the universe. Relative to this, Brian Greene (2004, 301) explains cosmic evolution as follows:

> Early on, the energy of the Universe was carried by the inflaton field, which was perched away from its minimum energy state. Because of its negative pressure, the inflaton field drove an enormous burst of inflationary expansion. Then, some 10^{35} seconds later, as the inflaton field slid down its potential energy bowl, the burst of expansion drew to a close and the inflaton released its pent-up energy to the production of ordinary matter and radiation.

Greene explains that spatial expansion slowed until about seven billion years ago, when it became weak enough for the gravitational repulsion of the universe's cosmological constant to dominate. Thus, the current rate of spatial expansion is increasing.

Reviewing these dynamics from the Egyptian perspective, it seems that the transformation of the Deceased from fermion to boson could represent the creation and emergence of dark energy into the Early Universe. Operating as an outward gravitational push, increasing expansion of the universe, dark energy would then drive the acceleration of the universe. As the texts indicate, the King's head and back are of lapis lazuli (CT294), and he makes lapis-lazuli grow (PT319). To the Pharaohs, lapis lazuli represented the night sky. Put simply, the black-hole Duat operates similar to an engine that pumps dark energy into the Early Universe through an Einstein-Rosen bridge, causing the entire cosmos to expand, making lapis-lazuli grow. As discussed earlier, the recombinant phage progeny reproduce at exponential proportions. At the same time, this black-hole engine uses and recycles matter within the nets of its (the earth's) gravitational field.

In light of the process, a transformation to upgrade from common matter (4%) to a more abundant form of dark energy (75%) may be a reasonable choice for an afterlife consciousness trapped within the earth's magnetospheric system, or worse, trapped within an *E. coli* host organism according to the Pharaohs. As Brian Greene says, "the stuff of which we're made is like flotsam on the cosmic ocean" (2004, 301). In line with this idea, physicist Lee Smolin has indicated that at best we may be a by-product of black hole processes, and at worst, we may be parasites (Gribbin 2001, 231). The Pharaohs reiterate the ideas of Greene and Smolin in the simple statements of the Deceased Sun-god: "I will not eat faeces. I will not drink urine," (CT186, 191-195) and "I ask for a brain" (CT243).

Nonetheless, the Deceased in the afterlife can choose to become *Homo Sapiens Lambda* by the creative union with the Lambda Sun-god, who journeys along the guided diffusion path of the maltose transport system to the Osiris prophage site. According to the Emerald Tablet of Hermes Trismegistus, this results in the Deceased becoming the *glory of the whole world*, or possibly the dark energy present in our expanding universe as defined by the Deceased's desire to become the four winds of the sky (CT297). For simplicity, we can refer to the Egyptian model of matter creation outlined in this thesis as *Lambda-Genesis*. The major precepts of the model based on an interpretation of over 870 signs are:

1. What is above is like what is below.

Egyptian science compares the entry of solar wind and high energy particles into the earth's magnetosphere as equivalent to the process of an incoming phage Lambda attaching and injecting its DNA into a bacterial host cell. The high energy elements come from supernovae explosions. This knowledge enabled the Pharaohs to identify a cosmic process similar to the lysis/lysogeny decision pathway of bacteriophage Lambda.

2. Lambda structure is imprinted on our Universe.

Relative to this cosmic model, approximately 3.8 billion years ago, Lambda lysogeny, resulting from cI protein production in the prokaryotic earth-cell, activated the transition to eukaryote development and photosynthesis. Prior to that time, the original Lambda structure, as signified by cro protein control and chemiluminescence, was imprinted on the universe.

3. Evolutionary merge into Lambda results in Homo Sapiens Lambda. The Lambda model predicts that at human death, a transformation pathway for species diversification and genetic survival exists, if the Deceased chooses to insert into what might be called an incoming phage Lambda that activates the lytic lifestyle. This results in a journey into the earth-cell that creates a bioluminescent life-form that uses lactose as an energy source. This *evolutionary merge* results in the recombinant species *Homo Sapiens Lambda* that is shunted into the Early Universe. Pathways also exist for recycling back to a photosynthetic life-form by means of thermal heat reactions in the earth-cell.

4. The earth-cell exhibits the energy landscape of a protein folding funnel. Accordingly, Lambda entry into the host earth-cell causes DNA breaks. Single-stranded DNA activates the SOS response of the earth-cell, and RecA cleaves the repressor proteins LexA and cI. Cleavage of the LexA repressor protein activates the LexA regulon, de-repressing 42 genes. Cleavage of Lambda cI repressor induces the existing Lambda prophage to excise. Phage DNA degradation occurs, and recombinant phage progeny escape from the earth-cell through a transmembrane tunnel.

5. The protein folding funnel has the properties of a quantum mechanical Kerr black hole. The black Duat with its circles, horizons, spheres, tunneling, and places of dragging, exhibits the properties of a quantum mechanical Kerr black hole. The *evolutionary shunt* of *Homo Sapiens Lambda* into an Early Universe results from 1) fermion-to-boson transformation, 2) CPT violation, 3) biosynthesis as a left-handed particle, 4) negative energy, and 5) movement through an Einstein-Rosen bridge, where the species emerges with the quantum consciousness of the Deceased as Hawking radiation or dark energy, the Cosmological Constant, what Einstein called Lambda.

Obviously, the emergence of the Deceased from the black-hole Duat does not result in information loss. "The King attains the limit of the horizon" (PT 275), where modern theory postulates that evaporation occurs just outside the horizon. An apparent horizon forms and unravels, releasing the so-called Hawking radiation that carries valuable information. In his recent speech before the 17th International Conference on General Relativity in Dublin, Stephen Hawking said that information is not lost, but can escape from a black hole to remain in our universe. In the original approximation he was using, the black hole radiation was completely thermal, carrying no information. Hawking explained the release of information as follows:

> So what would happen to all that information locked inside a black hole that evaporated away and disappeared completely. It seemed the only way the information could come out, would be if the radiation was not exactly thermal, but had subtle correlations. No one has found a mechanism to produce correlations, but most physicists believe one must exist . . . My work with Hartle, showed the radiation could be thought of as tunneling out from inside the black hole. It was therefore not unreasonable to suppose that it could carry information out of the black hole.

These comments by Hawking about the radiation not being exactly thermal and tunneling out of the black hole suggest the bioluminescent *Homo Sapiens Lambda* that tunnels out of the black-hole Duat, which seems to evaporate. One could say the species was not exactly thermal but lukewarm (cold virus, thermal human), one reason for its emergence from the black hole. Applying the subtle correlations of Egyptian knowledge, information escapes due to three more factors. First, rotating black holes have two event horizons and two photon spheres. When the Deceased enters the black hole from the axis of rotation at the North Pole, he encounters only one photon sphere because the spheres (or riverbanks) are joined. Second, the evolutionary merge with Lambda influences the reaction diffusion kinetics within the hole for a different product. Third, the supramolecular Deceased moves past the ring singularity through a wormhole to the Early Universe, that is, a movement to the past through a white hole with two horizons.

From the perspective of the Pharaohs, the earth returns to "the Primordial Water," it evaporates in "the surging flood, as in its original state" (BD175). "Where is the sky? Where is the earth? Their offspring are rebuffed and they are disunited" (TR42). Yet, the Deceased and his entourage survive as a recombinant life-form in our Early Universe.

22

The Supersymmetric Tree of Life

A LIBATION FOR STRING THEORY

Egyptian science supports T-Duality, the String Theory idea that our universe looks the same at Planck-length scales. String theory maintains that during the Planck era, the universe had ten dimensions that collapsed into three spatial dimensions and one time dimension when the era ended. What is above in the Sun-earth system mirrors what is below in the quantum world, that is, the whirling web of earth's magnetic field lines is similar to a dense tangle of strings in a quantum mechanical black hole.

As physicist Fred Alan Wolf explains, if the earth contained its same mass but began to shrink, the gravitational factor would increase, and one would experience a pulling apart, a stretching that might be described as "I am stretched out straight" (CT218) or a stretching of bones or limbs (CT365). Once the earth shrank to a radius of about one half a centimeter, the earth would become a black hole. (1988, 147-148)

String theory asserts that an elementary particle is a tiny, vibrating string. When a string falls into a black hole, more of its vibrations become visible. As physicist Leonard Susskind (2003) states, "The string spreads and grows, just as if it were being bombarded by particles and radiation in a very hot environment. In a relatively short time the string and all the information it carries are smeared over the entire horizon." Information is not lost, for it is radiated back out (Hawking radiation), and String theory accounts for this. Yet, what the Pharaohs are telling us is that a quantum mechanical black hole in which a string grows and spreads is a protein folding funnel based on Lambda genetics. A black hole radiates away its mass and vanishes in the same way a protein folds to its native conformation in its energy landscape funnel that vanishes. Apparently, information is carried away by the protein product and deposited in the Early Universe. It is not lost forever behind the horizon. Energy, mass and information come out as Hawking radiation, viz., dark energy. The information falling into a black hole has microreversibility, for it becomes available in the Early Universe. But, the Pharaohs explain that this only happens by means of a specific pathway.

The funerary texts proclaim that this preferred path aligned to Nature's designs is one of chemiluminescence, and that fermions or the building blocks of matter can become bosons or force particles at human death. Thus, the Egyptian texts suggest that Nature is supersymmetric. Two very different kinds of particles are related, for every fermion has a boson twin, and vice versa. Even the Egyptian idea of the quantum heart of matter, which they symbolize by the lotus, is similar to the Calabi-Yau shape, where String theorists posit that the extra six dimensions are curled up. As mentioned, one way a fermion becomes a boson is when a quark and antiquark restore to a pion. This happens as long as the quark and the antiquark do not annihilate. (Close 1989, 397)

The pion plays a role in strong interactions and can be used as a building block for developing a mass spectrum (Sidharth 1998[2]). Aware of this, the Pharaohs advise the Deceased to journey to the northern polar cusp for transfiguration and the high-energy, creative union with the Sun-god. This ultraviolet union with Sun particles and other high-energy cosmic elements at the cusp may energize ionospheric particles at unification mass of ~10 to the 15th power GEV/c^2 allowing unification of strong, weak, and electromagnetic forces. It may also generate a microscopic black hole, that is, the Duat. Still, the wealth of Egyptian wisdom does not stop here, for they had an amazing science that we have only recently discovered in the twentieth century.

Our Reflection in the Mirror

Relative to black hole formation and growth within, the Egyptian evidence clearly describes a scientific model for the afterlife that mirrors bacteriophage genetics and the lytic lifestyle of phage Lambda within a protein folding funnel landscape. In the Prologue to the Book of Gates it is written that all men, gods, cattle and worms are brought before the hidden seat. Lodged on the host chromosome, the Lambda genome is the proverbial Tree of Life, for according to the Pharaohs, it has the potential to confer both human existence and a recombinant form of viral-human life. Put simply, the hidden seat or Lambda genome generates both *Homo Sapiens Sapiens* and *Homo Sapiens Lambda.* Human existence and the world we experience result from the lysogenic lifestyle. Transfiguration to an everlasting species is the subsequent possibility, if the Deceased is at the nutrient-enriched polar cusp (H, He, C, O, Fe, Li, S) for an afterlife *evolutionary merge* into the Lambda Sun-god and transduction through the host bacterium. Thus, we have the idea of two seeds, the twin births, the two Enneads, fermions and bosons. This grouping of nine Ennead deities may represent the quark model of nine possible combinations grouping themselves into an octet and a singlet, the quantum structure of electroweak interactions in physics, for which Murray Gell-mann received the Nobel Prize in Physics in 1969.

But, what we also must remember is that the spinning vortex of the earth-cell, as described by the Pharaohs, fits the criteria for a spinning Kerr black hole. It has outer and inner horizons or Double Gates (CT48), along with angular velocity as defined by language indicating dragging (Rosetau), circulating (CT265, 551), circles (Amduat), and art depicting spheres. In modern black hole physics, polar coordinates in two dimensions or lines of constant distance are called circles; in three dimensions, lines of constant distance are called spheres. Again, the Pharaohs have outpaced us with their knowledge. Further, the texts describe and depict wormholes, white holes, future and past singularities. The Deceased's ability to move through a white hole is related to his left-handed helicity, the parity change activated at the pole because of the presence of iron nuclei and the merge into the Sun-god, a composite of high energy cosmic elements. By crossing four event horizons, the Deceased moves through a black hole into a white hole or past singularity. Crossing the first outer horizon, time and space reverse: space becomes a stream and time becomes spacelike. If you stayed here, you would eventually crash into the hole's future singularity. Crossing into the inner horizon, space and time reverse again, becoming normal. (Wolf 1988, 165-66) But the Deceased conquers the horizon (CT256) and descends "into the lustral basins," which suggests the effects of light at a singularity. Entering the past singularity, the Deceased crosses two more horizons and emerges as dark energy in the Early Universe. Today dark energy is referred to as the cosmological constant, what Einstein called *lambda.*

Einstein first proposed the cosmological constant symbolized by the Greek letter *lambda*, as a mathematical fix to the theory of general relativity, which predicted the universe must either expand or contract. Because Einstein thought the universe was static, he added the term to stop the expansion. Today this cosmological constant represents a gravitationally-repulsive dark energy that is accelerating the expansion of the universe. Recent supernova results suggest that *rho(vacuum)* = *0.75*rho(critical)* = $6*10^{-30}$ *gm/cc.* The ratio of the *rho(vacuum)* to *rho(critical)* is called *lambda.* Put simply, dark energy comprises 75% of our universe.

All in all, the Egyptian model seems reasonable and supports tenets of String Theory and black hole theory, including Hawking Radiation. The macro-level earth spin system represents a quantum cell, where proteins fold to their native conformation in a folding funnel landscape with Kerr black hole dynamics. Folding of cI protein results in movement through a black-hole to a future singularity of photosynthesis. Cro protein folding results in a movement through a black hole to a white hole past singularity by means of CPT violation. The preferred option recommended by the Pharaohs is the cosmic, bioluminescent option for species re-invention rather than a photosynthetic recycling of elements for planetary humans.

The Macrocosmic Competition

Energy can be discarded in two ways. Photosynthesis is the reaction where molecules in green leaves capture the Sun's energy, converting the light into carbon dioxide and water, then into carbohydrates, producing the by-product of oxygen. Chemiluminescence, the emission of light by an atom or molecule that is in an excited state, however, is the chemical reaction that dominates the universe. Whereas photosynthesis produces both light and heat such as a burning candle, chemiluminescence produces light without heat—cold light. For chemiluminescence to occur, the excited molecule needs time to generate a photon of light, so that its excitation is not transferred to the neighboring molecules in the form of thermal motion. (Atkins 1991, 206) This happens in outer space where the temperature is three degrees above absolute zero or three degrees Kelvin. Outer space is actually teaming with molecules. As of April, 2003, the National Radio Astronomy Observatory reported 123 interstellar and circumstellar molecules comprised primarily of hydrogen, nitrogen, carbon and oxygen, the major elements in a human being. Circumstellar species include NaCl, SiC, MgCN and FeO. (Wootten 2003)

One way of winning the macrocosmic competition is for the viral Sun to envelope the prokaryotic subkingdom of earth in a process similar to phagocytosis. If one were sitting in the bucket of the Big Dipper and had Egyptian

Death-vision, one would see the monstrous magnetic field net of the Sun enveloping our tiny earth-cell. After all, we exist because of the advent of oxygen and eukaryote development, events the Pharaohs believe can be traced to the repression of a group of operons in a lysogenic Lambda genome lodged in a prokaryotic cell. This repression allowed the advent of oxygen-generating photosynthesis and life as we know it. The de-repression of these operons fosters the Egyptian goal of the "translation of the Blessed." In the chemical battleground of the funerary texts, the victory goes back to Horus or cro translation to protein rather than Seth or cI. The Deceased is then transfigured or cloned for ascension into the heavens with a chance of survival as *Homo Sapiens Lambda.*

As physicists know, two-dimensional Hilbert space is very large, suggesting that classical states such as ours are rare. Neither the Copenhagen Interpretation with reliance on the measurements of classical observers, nor the Many Worlds Interpretation with its enlarged focus on the splitting quantum domain can establish the correspondence between the quantum and classical worlds, although String Theory has potential. Egyptian science also has potential, for it infers that the emergence of classical reality and the resultant transition of consciousness from prokaryote to eukaryote development is a sequential outcome of a phage Lambda infection of the first prokaryote lysogen. On the other hand, human death returns consciousness to the origin of classical reality or a quantum state where consciousness, which resides in our genetic essence, can choose to insert into a phage Lambda vector for transduction into a host cell. This pathway activates the SOS response of the lysogen, excises its Lambda prophage, and produces human-phage progeny, while not lysing the cell, but rendering it invisible by a CPT violation back to the Early Universe. In other words, phage Lambda made us what we are today (fermions) and what we can become tomorrow (bosons).

The transfigured Deceased is a unique outcome with recombinant DNA, and the clone in its entirety may retain a semblance of the classical human consciousness, albeit at a deeper, more perceptive level. The Deceased claims he is one of four gods Atum begot (IS57). As dark energy, he represents antigravity in the quantum world, the inversion of gravity in an Early Universe of unified forces. The Egyptian scientists had a sophisticated knowledge of the whole system that centered on choices made by the individual consciousness at the molecular level. The classical apparatus, that is, the world as one knew it, was no longer an option for the transfigured DNA creation, now photon-like with a lifetime approaching infinity. The Pharaohs believed that this system-based choice for transfiguration was preferable to recycling ad infinitum on the prokaryotic subkingdom of earth, a minute thermal bubble battered by the solar wind, its destruction imminent in time and leaving no host cell for transduction of the remaining human heritage.

Three-Fold Model of Egyptian Afterlife

1. Transfer and release of high energy cosmic/solar particles through the earth spin system.

   a) What is above is below = T-Duality (String Theory)
   b) Earth spin system = one-celled organism exhibiting Lambda decision circuit

2. Phage Lambda infection of *E. coli* host cell for prophage excision and lytic lifestyle.

   a) folding of cro protein in energy landscape funnel
   b) protein folding funnel has dynamics of black hole/white hole

3. Journey into a protein folding funnel or Kerr QMBH through Einstein-Rosen bridge to the Early Universe.

   a) entry at North Pole encounters only one photon sphere
   b) presence of high energy particles and iron nuclei at pole

      1) flips Deceased 180 degrees into left-handed particle (CPT violation)
      2) quark/antiquark restore to a pion
      3) left-handed helicity influences Deceased's entry into black hole
      4) Deceased travels through four horizons or wormhole

   c) Deceased becomes Hawking Radiation = Dark Energy = Cosmological Constant = Lambda

Figure 22.1

23

From Here to Eternity through Egyptian Science

WHO WE ARE: FROM FERMION TO BOSON WITH A HALO

Egyptian science not only offers the Deceased knowledge of the guided diffusion path to Eternity, but it also gives living human beings knowledge of who we are, is there life after death, and how does our universe function. The Egyptian ideas support the String concept of T-Duality, an idea claiming that a dual universe exists at Planck-length scales similar to our large universe. What is above is like what is below. The operations of the solar wind and earth mirror chemical activities in the quantum world. The earth's flowing magnetosphere mirrors the activities of a living, one-celled organism:

- Magnetic reconnection in the magnetosphere is similar to DNA recombination in the cell;

- Antiparallel north and south IMF or bidirectional jets of plasma mirror antiparallel directions of DNA;

- The staircase cusp signature of magnetic reconnection is similar to the bursty merging caused by phage adsorption and DNA injection at the LamB porin;

- The interchange or "kink" instability of magnetic reconnection is similar to the thymine dimer "kink" in the DNA double helix;

- Solar FTEs moving into a polar site of magnetic reconnection mirror the activity of phage Lambda injecting its DNA into the polar LamB porin of a host cell;

- A magnetospheric substorm that pinches off a plasmoid is similar to cellular binary fission that pinches off a new bacterial chromosome;

- Ions frozen on the earth's magnetic field lines are similar to nucleotides frozen on a DNA molecule;

- Iron core of earth's magnetosphere is similar to iron embedded in the center of the DNA double helix at certain loci;

- The dynamics of magnetic flux ropes are similar to the activity of iron-containing siderophores in a cell;

- The HLBL and LLBL of the magnetosphere map respectively to non-MBP-binding lactose transport and MBP binding channels in the maltose transport system of *E. coli.*

As a mirror model of a one-celled organism, the Duat also has the properties of a Kerr black hole. The earth's magnetosphere is actually a spinning vortex with mountainous barriers of plasma. At the quantum level, the mountains and valleys are energy landscapes depicting protein folding, ideally that of cro protein folding to its native conformation. This folding energy landscape is similar to a funnel, a vortex, a Kerr black hole with a ring singularity near which the Deceased exits, traveling on an Einstein-Rosen bridge to the Early Universe. Because the Sun-god is an exotic species with negative energy, the bridge stays open. Also, the Deceased's parity change results in a left-handed biological molecule, allowing him to orbit in the same direction as the black hole's spinning axis. Thus, the Deceased moves with the current, going faster than light. This advantage of left-handed helicity allows the Deceased to enter into the forbidden past Early Universe.

Related to this idea, B. G. Sidharth (1998) describes the electrons, the muons, tau particles, neutrinos and approximately the quarks as Kerr-Newman black holes. His Compton Radius Vortex model identifies the electron as a relativistic vortex rotating at the speed of light. In quantum mechanics, one can only calculate the probability of where particles will be found. The Compton wavelength is this spread in location. Sidharth states that near the Compton wavelength scales, electrons display a neutrino-type bosonization or low dimensionality. At the Compton wavelength, neutrinos and relativistic quarks are left-handed, while corresponding antiparticles are right-handed. All of this supports the interpretation of the Deceased as a left-handed particle that exhibits bosonization. Further, Sidharth states (1998[1]) fermions are primary and bosons can be treated as bound states of fermions. In this sense, quarks can be treated as quantum mechanical black holes (QMBH), and pions and other hadrons can be treated as bound states of quark and antiquark. He states:

> a pion can be considered an electron-positron composite because its Compton wavelength equals the classical electron radius which resembles the fact that the pion is a quark/antiquark composite. These could be incorporated into the above QMBH consideration to get a mass spectrum.

Once again, this relates to the decay of the Deceased and his double to a pion. Sidharth further states (1999) that just beyond the Compton wavelength, the particle corresponds to an electron; at scales less than or equal to the Compton wavelength, the particle corresponds to a quark; at scales greater than or equal to the Compton wavelength, it corresponds to a pion. At and within the Compton wavelength, negative energy dominates (1998[2]). This electron-quark-pion potential supports the description in this work of the Deceased's transformation.

Our Genetic Essence

It is also obvious from Egyptian science that after death, human consciousness resides in our immortal part, our genetic essence, whatever that is. Like the Tibetan Book of the Dead, the texts advise the Deceased to merge with the Sun-god in the afterlife. This *evolutionary merge* into a molecular assembly that operates like phage Lambda results in the recombinant species *Homo Sapiens Lambda.* The evidence suggests that the Egyptian Tree of Life is the Lambda genome. *Homo Sapiens Sapiens* results from the production of cI protein, whereas *Homo Sapiens Lambda* results from cro protein production. Thus, Egyptian science proposes that Lambda structure is imprinted on our universe. Mathematical proof for this claim may be Week's finding that the universe is shaped like a dodecahedron based on *Phi.*

The creation of *Homo Sapiens Lambda* happens within the natural time machine of the earth's magnetosphere, acting as a rotating quantum mechanical black hole gateway to a cosmic subway back to the Early Universe. The Deceased passes through four event horizons in this process. By escaping from the earth-cell, the recombinant species survives as a bioluminescent rather than photosynthetic life-form. In essence, Egyptian genetics advocates the reinvention of humans at the species level to enhance the world, rather than degrade it.

The recombinant species results from a fermion-to-boson transformation in a quantum mechanical black hole, an event that supports String Theory concepts such as supersymmetry and T-Duality, while showing that gravity can act at the quantum level. Therefore, Egyptian science claims the Pharaohs possessed an understanding of the unified four forces. Earlier we referenced Ngee-Pong Chang's research that the pion remains a Nambu-Goldstone boson and acquires a halo while propagating through the Early Universe (Chang 1994). As mentioned, the halo is a threshold phenomenon due to quantum mechanical tunneling, an activity of the Deceased that is evident in the texts. In heavy nuclei with neutron excess, a halo forms due to the balance between repulsive pion-nucleus and attractive Coulomb force. (Al-Khalili 2002)

Modern researchers consider the quantum halo a new form of matter that displays essential quantum features common to all microscopic matter. Haloes also aid understanding of element production in stars and supernovae. For example, isotopes are formed through the process of neutrons attracting protons and each other. The amount of neutrons determines the various isotopes, which come from the Big Bang, our Sun and exploding supernovae. When a star ends its life as a supernova, it uses up all its hydrogen, converts elements up to iron, then explodes, thrusting debris into space and leaving a neutron star. During the explosion, the collapse of the core creates a shock wave that accelerates neutrons that are created. These neutrons combine with nuclei of lighter elements to produce elements heavier than iron. The neutron-rich elements are returned explosively to interstellar space, where they form new stars. Some of these nuclei form a halo outside the core. Other kinds of haloes are formed by Borromean systems, two neutrons bound to a core with fields that partly overlap. The tendency to tunnel past the classical limit makes haloes bigger in the quantum world. (Thompson 2001) So what does this have to do with the self-assembled molecular structure the Deceased becomes?

First, the presence of hydrogen, helium, oxygen, nitrogen, iron and other elements at the enriched polar cusp may be evidence of cosmic ray acceleration of neutron-rich isotopes. Second, references to Re's sun-disk (Intro Hymn to Re, BD, Plate 1), "Re who is in his sun" (CT105), the Deceased needing "strong sunlight" (PT523), the "Sole One who glow in the sun" (BD2), and the Deceased not being "restrained or repulsed," but his flesh renewed by Re's beauty (BD15) suggest a self-assembled, neutron-rich, haloed carrier molecule that ferries the Deceased through the Duat's Double Ramgate. Additional references to Re such as "what the sun-disk encircles is bright because of you" (BD15), and "you are that golden image which bears the likeness of the sun-disk" (BD133) point to the idea of a halo. Not only does the Sun-god tunnel through two barriers into the Duat, but the supermolecule burrows out of the earth-cell by means of a transmembrane tunnel. It seems that the dynamics of halo formation apply to the Deceased Sun-god.

Third, the Orion region is a dense area of about 2,000 very young stars with elevated X-ray emissions that scientists believe arise from the stars' strong magnetic fields (NASA 2000). In the Theban Recension (64), the Deceased claims that he knows the depth and the composition of the blessed dead. He states, "That which is upon the shoulders of Orion is examined, being one-twelfth, strewing out what is united, as what one gives to another among them." Examining this statement, we discover that Betelgeuse, a red super giant on the shoulder of Orion, long ago burned the hydrogen deep within its core. It is an ancient star approaching the end of its life cycle. Recently, the Harvard-Smithsonian Center for Astrophysics (2000) reported the first direct evidence in Betelgeuse' pulsing chromosphere of streams of gas in opposite directions with velocities of 10,000 miles per hour. Like a human heart, Betelgeuse pulses, expelling gas from its surface out into space in one direction, while gas falls to the star in the other. Could this blown-off gas account for the Egyptian claim of one-twelfth strewing out from Betelgeuse on Orion's shoulder? Is this one-twelfth the acceleration of neutron-rich elements from Betelgeuse and Orion's giant, element-rich molecular clouds? Possibly Orion is the source of cosmic ray elements at earth's cusp. Put simply, the Deceased merging with the self-assembled molecular Sun-god at the cusp may be just the energetic bond the Deceased needs to transform from a fermion to a boson with a halo.

On Earth as it is in Heaven

Evidence such as the architecture of the pyramids and Taharqa's nilometer, the language of the texts, the large head and tubular stalk of the mummified form, and Egyptian drawings, showing deities wearing ceremonial tails and having spherical heads, point to phage Lambda morphology. Also, other indicators such as Egyptian directions for specific coding sequence, Herodotus' writings on the birth of Apis Bulls, and the distinctive Apis markings suggest the Pharaohs understood gene cloning. Further, the funerary texts as a whole provide evidence that the Pharaohs understood the lytic/lysogeny lifestyles of phage Lambda, along with the dynamics of horizontal gene transfer.

Two Ways

Within this Egyptian scheme, the alternative to merging with the Sun-god and becoming dark energy through a white hole past singularity is a recycling of human elements back into the earth system through a black hole future singularity. But, this alternative can be avoided. The Cairo Coffin 28083 Plan of the Book of Two Ways features a blue upper band or path that the Deceased should follow, rather than the thinner black band below. Within an *E. coli* cell, researchers have defined two figurative paths for the transport of substrate at the LamB receptor site. In one path, the substrate is bound to MBP protein, but in the case of lactose transport, the second path is accessed because MBP cannot bind the substrate lactose. Thus, the texts advise the Deceased to take the Plan's upper blue path, which is the lactose pathway. On the macrocosmic level, the HLBL mirrors the Plan's blue upper band, while the LLBL mirrors the Plan's lower black path, the one the Deceased should not take because the substrate is bound to MBP. Clearly, Isis is central to the transfiguration of the Deceased, for she represents lactose energy for the recombinant species.

Texts such as the Amduat and the Book of Gates have an indepth biochemical and bacterial genetic knowledge related to the lytic lifestyle of phage Lambda. Hour Twelve of the Amduat shows the supramolecular Sun-god's exit from the earth-cell Duat by means of an elongated serpent or transmembrane tunnel. The Book of Gates also mentions passage through the serpent Khepri. This tunnel-exit points to passage through existing holes at cell poles discovered by modern researchers, where Lambda progeny escape from the cell without lysing it. It also suggests movement through a quantum mechanical Einstein-Rosen bridge. In addition, the New Kingdom Book of the Dead and Theban Recension offer more support for the Lambda lytic lifestyle that results in *Homo Sapiens Lambda*. However, these funerary texts support other modern scientific concepts such as CPT violation in weak interactions, fermion-to-boson transformation, the Higgs field, quantum teleportation, and a movement back to the Early Universe.

It is evident that the funerary text corpus is unified in its presentation of Egyptian science, which is embedded in over 870 metasymbols, a city of signs paralleling the achievements of twenty-first century space physics, bacterial genetics, biology, quantum physics and new chemistry. The *evolutionary merge* of the Deceased with the Lambda Sun-god may result in an *evolutionary shunt* out of the earth system into an Early Universe. Instead of the earth and its inhabitants being our community, the Pharaohs have mapped a path to the starry heavens that inflates the entire universe as our matrix of existence. From the twin seed of the Lambda genetic heritage, one's life through death can expand from human self-concern to a cosmic consciousness embracing the entire universe. With the knowledge of Egyptian science, humanity can re-invent itself as a species, overcoming our present limitations such as overpopulation, nuclear war, poverty, global warming, and the ongoing mass extinction of species necessary for human survival. As promised, the Egyptian funerary texts offer humans knowledge for an evolutionary adventure that could allow one's deepened consciousness to exist in the Milky Way galaxy when the Sun becomes a red giant and destroys the earth five billion years from now.

24

The Marriage of Religion and Science

WHY THE PHARAOHS DESERVE THE NOBEL PRIZES

Homo Sapiens Lambda has also been referred to as the attainment of the "light body." World religions and sacred traditions are well aware of this transcendent bioluminescent body (see Figure 24.1), referred to in its various guises as "the diamond body," the "superconductive body," the "solar body," the "ultra-human," and the "resurrected body of Christ the Light." All of these names can be neatly summarized by Nietzsche's *ubermensch* or "overman" and ancient Egypt's "the radiant one" or *akh*.

Similarly, we see the quantum phenomenon of haloes on Christ, Mary, the saints, the Buddha, Krishna and others. It is also interesting that besides having spin, Kerr black holes pulsate at frequencies that produce bell-like tones (Thorne 1994, 293-96), a possible scientific reference explaining the emphasis on bells in religious ceremonies. According to the Egyptian texts, on the quantum level, the immortal body is self-created from high-energy cosmic elements, pre-existent as the Lambda prophage in the earth-cell, and an available evolutionary path for human transfiguration.

The Judaeo-Christian tradition also references Osiris, the Lambda prophage on the bacterial host chromosome in the hymn *Crux Fidelis* that is sung on Good Friday:

> Faithful cross! Above all other,
> One and only noble Tree!
> None in foliage, none in blossom,
> None in fruit thy peer may be;
> Sweetest Wood, and sweetest iron,
> Sweetest Weight is hung on thee.
>
> (Juergens 1950, 359)

The *Faithful cross* references the *noble Tree*, the *Sweetest Wood,* that is, the Lambda genome or Osiris inserted at the *LacZ* gene (Isis) responsible for the lactose nutrient medium.

As humans, we must stretch to think and imagine in new ways, as we answer questions by seeing that Science and Religion is a marriage embedded in quantum phenomena. We must discover whether or not this chemical act of species rebirth is the final stage of human evolution or a new seed for the expansion of human intelligence. Jesuit priest and paleontologist Pierre Teilhard de Chardin simply stated that the same life animates both Religion and Science. In the *Phenomenon of Man* (1959), he traces the rise of consciousness from the cell to *Homo Sapiens*, claiming that by death a man can escape from entropy and become the super-man, *an organic superaggregation of souls.* He considers this outcome an offshoot of the evolutionary tree of consciousness, what he refers to as *a new step in the genesis of the mind.* To achieve this, one must give up his ego or his personality, a familiar echo from the Tibetan Book of the Dead, which also emphasizes the importance of merging with the Light. Pierre writes that *each ego is destined to be forced convulsively beyond itself into some mysterious super-ego.* (1978, 38) He describes this process in the following prayer to Lord Jesus:

> What I discern in your breast is simply a furnace of fire, and the more I fix my gaze on its ardency the more it seems to me that all around it the contours of your body melt away and become enlarged beyond all measure, till the only features I can distinguish in you are those of the face of a world which has burst into flame. (131)

Then Pierre writes, "Lord, lock me up within you." At this point, it seems as if he is merging with either the Egyptian Lambda Sun-god or, as the pre-Buddhist Bon civilization of Tibet would say, *a great mass of light, the Buddha of Immortal Light* (Rinpoche 1975). What is remarkable about the Judaeo-Christian tradition, the Tibetans and other creeds is that they have preserved Egyptian religious ideas 5,000 years old that harbored an amazing science, describing the final option for higher evolution of human consciousness.

All Religions are One Science

From John White, "Enlightenment and the Body of Light"
What is Enlightenment. Spring/Summer, 2002, 93-94.

Judaeo-Christian	resurrection body	**Tibetan Buddism**	light body
Tantrism	*vajra* body	**Vedanta**	superconductive body
Gnosticism/Neoplatonism	radiant body	**Mystery schools**	solar body
Ancient Egypt	luminous body/*akh*	**Sufism**	supracelestial body
Taoism	diamond body	**Kriya yoga**	body of bliss
Hermetic Corpus	immortal body	**Emerald Tablet**	Glory of the Whole Universe
Rosicrucianism	diamond body of the Temple of God	**Old Persia**	indwelling divine potential
Mithraic Liturgy	perfect body		
Philosophy of Sri Aurobindo	divine body	**Philosophy of Teilhard de Chardin**	ultra human

Figure 24.1

Now, we can trace the rise of human consciousness on an evolutionary circle, beginning with the first prokaryotic lysogen 3.8 billion years ago that harbored a Lambda genome for eukaryotic evolution. To this viral world-heart we return for a second option—resurrection with its prophage as *Homo Sapiens Lambda.* Thus, Osiris is the Alpha and the Omega. So it is that the Pharaohs professed a religion of science that was emulated, but misunderstood by religious traditions.

Why the Pharaohs deserve the Nobel Prizes

All the following discoveries, to name a few, occurred in Egypt 5,000 years before modern efforts:

Literature

- For the visionary force of maintaining 3,000 years of hieroglyphs and art that housed an imaginative poetry of Being
- For creating immortal characters that inspired future sacred traditions and great literature
- For noble themes that transcend time and space because they are carved in stone for posterity

Medicine

- For millenniums of work devoted to cloning a Cosmic Being, an afterlife transfiguration that preserves human consciousness, while making all men equal
- For their cosmic vision of human evolution to a being beyond human, a solution for species survival to ultimately conquer problems of global warming, nuclear war, overpopulation, species extinction, and the cooling of the Sun
- For their effort to embody a courageous attitude toward death through the knowledge that death is a passage to a Planck-scale universe where the Sacred and the Scientific are merged
- For the discovery that proteins have intrinsic signals that govern their transport and localization in the cell
- For their discoveries concerning the replication mechanism and the genetic structure of viruses long before Delbruck, Hershey and Luria
- For discoveries concerning genetic recombination and organization of the genetic material of bacteria
- For determining the structure of DNA before Watson and Crick

Chemistry

- For discoveries concerning channels in cell membranes, the properties of molecules and chemical reactions
- For work in atmospheric chemistry, particularly the self-assembly of molecules within the earth's magnetosphere
- For fundamental studies of the biochemistry of nucleic acids, with particular regard to recombinant-DNA
- For discoveries in the field of chemistry related to the structure of proteins

Physics

- For elucidating the quantum structure of electroweak interactions in physics
- For discoveries in Space Physics regarding the function and dynamics of the Sun-earth-star system
- For determining the physics of black holes and wormholes before Einstein, Hawking and Thorne
- For envisioning facets of String Theory before Robert Witten: the nature of strings, supersymmetry, and T-Duality
- For revealing the dynamics of fermion to boson transformations and CPT violations
- For elucidating the Lambda worldheart that is the seat of creation imprinted on our universe
- For identifying that QMBHs are energy structures within which proteins fold to their native conformation

Yet, the Isis Thesis is not only a study of the wise Pharaohs' Nobel Prize-winning scientific knowledge in Physics, Chemistry and Medicine, but it is also a story of immortal characters and noble themes that are mirrored in the works of the world's greatest creative artists. *The Road from Orion* is a story about testimonials from the works of creative artists supporting this argument's interpretation of Egyptian science.

25

The Forgotten Hero Journey

REMEMBERING OUR LOST BIRTHRIGHT

Literary critic Northrop Frye has designated the single mythic pattern or archetype from which all literature and myths arise. Put briefly, this monomyth describes the birth of the hero, his sacred marriage, and his violent death and final defeat that results in the return to chaos. The pattern of this classic hero journey is similar to the chemical reaction of lysogeny that is played out on a quantum stage, a circling ad infinitum that results in the defeated hero, expulsion from paradise, and the triumph of the Powers of Darkness.

Yet, the Pharaohs suggest a different monomyth, a forgotten hero journey. The Deceased slays the dragon, wins the Lady and does not suffer death and defeat by the Powers of Darkness. The story of John Friedman and Lucia Farrell in *The Road from Orion* sheds light on the Pharaohs' monomyth. It reveals clues and evidence from great art, myth, literature, philosophy, music and the creative genius of madmen that reflect the science of the forgotten hero journey. One cannot doubt that the nostalgia we feel when reading great literature, viewing impressive art or listening to noble music, is simply a reminiscence of our lost birthright, a legacy preserved by the Pharaohs. Because of this, the story—although not experimental proof, but based on historical facts, great ideas and works of art—is an integral part of the evidence related to the Isis Thesis from Time's honored writers, philosophers, musicians, artists and genius madmen.

In consideration of their amazing scientific legacy, one marvels at the Pharaohs' ability to see into the quantum world and understand the classical and quantum mechanics of Nature. Lifting the veil of Isis reveals the next level of cosmic evolution for human consciousness, while demystifying the whole process of life, death and the journey beyond. Whatever the Pharaohs did to access the quantum-spiritual state, they tapped into a base of comprehensive wisdom that enabled them to deliver the afterlife knowledge in a language of Being woven with beautiful metaphors and intrinsic knowledge.

26

The Path on Earth Back to the Early Universe

WHERE THE ROAD FROM ORION DEAD-ENDS

The path the Deceased follows through the earth-cell can be traced along the Nile River on ancient maps of Egypt. The journey begins at Abydos, the site of the famous Egyptian Gap of entry into the Duat. From here, the Deceased proceeds north along the Winding Waterway of the Nile River to Sais near Giza, the site where Osiris is lodged. Then he exits into the mouth of the Nile that opens into the Mediterranean Sea, that is, the primordial waters of the cosmos and starry Nut.

At this point, we can reconsider the meaning of the Opening of the Mouth Ceremony that emphasizes the importance of repeating words and ceremonies four times. The Deceased is "true-of-voice" (*ma'a-kheru*) (Goelet 1994, 153) and has been found worthy at the judgment of cro and cI proteins levels. Because of his true status, the Deceased has opened the mouth four times. First, he opened the mouth by merging with the Lambda Sun-god. Second, he opened the mouth of the Duat by entering the earth-cell. Third, he opened the mouth of Osiris by excising the prophage and activating the Horus species. Fourth, he opened the mouth out of the Duat to enter the Early Universe. He has broken iron four times as the Pyramid Texts advise.

From the QMBH perspective, the Opening of the Mouth ceremony with its emphasis on four times signifies the movement of the Deceased across four horizons. He passes through the black hole's outer event horizon into the inner event horizon, then through the white hole's outer and inner event horizons. When the earth opens its mouth for the Deceased (CT4), the mouth is a reference to the mouth of a wormhole, which is comprised of a black hole and white hole. Put simply, the Deceased journeys through four mouths or horizons to emerge in the Early Universe. This quantum wormhole magnetic field configuration depends on the Deceased as the polymerase complex plowing straight through the DNA, instead of circulating or transcribing around it. Thus, plowing straight through the DNA is not the template for the topological condensation of ordinary matter, viz., human beings. It is the template for a movement of genetic information between remotely related species—a horizontal gene transfer of eukaryotic DNA mediated by a virus. Still, mysteries remain about this act.

Iron, a silvery-white transition metal with its 26 protons and 30 neutrons, is a necessary element in magnetic fields and DNA. It is essential for humans as it is the chief constituent of hemoglobin, which carries oxygen in blood vessels. In the atmosphere, iron-containing particles scatter sunlight back into space and cause cooling. Oliver Manuel, a professor of nuclear chemistry, believes iron, not hydrogen, is the Sun's most abundant element. Although some of the Sun's hydrogen heat moves to its surface, Manuel believes that most of the heat comes from its exploded supernova core that still generates energy from within the iron-rich interior. (University of Missouri-Rollo 2003)

Astrophysicists assert that iron is created in the center of massive stars and expelled when the stars explode as supernovae. Iron and other heavy elements then mix with interstellar matter and form new stars and planetary systems. Recently, Professor Gunther Hasinger and Dr. Stefanie Komossa of the Max-Planck Institute and Dr. Norbert Schartel of the European Space Agency made a strange discovery. Using the European X-ray satellite XMM-Newton, they observed a young quasar containing a three times larger iron fraction than our own solar system which is much older. This quasar was observed at a time when the universe was only 1.5 billion years old, whereas our Sun formed 9 billion years after the Big Bang. The scientists determined an iron abundance in the central region of the quasar. This is unusual because the creation of iron takes at least 1.5 billion years to produce the metal abundances of our Sun. The scientists then theorized that a mysterious iron factory may exist in the Early Universe. (Max-Planck Institute 2002) One is forced to conclude that primordial iron is essential to all life-forms, cosmic and human. As Isis states about the knitting together or translation to protein of the Deceased, "this iron shall be brought for him" (PT669), and the Deceased has "stellar iron" (CT666).

Scientists theorize that the Early Universe was composed of hydrogen, helium, and lithium. These primordial gasses generated giant stars that lived about 3 million years and then exploded, spewing carbon, oxygen and iron into the void at great speeds. The first supernova explosions were violent and seeded the cosmos with metals. Near the end of their lives, the stars searched for energy, burning carbon and oxygen to form heavier and heavier elements until they reached iron, an element that cannot be fused to create energy. The supernovae then exploded, thrusting up to 100 solar masses of iron into the interstellar medium. (Harvard-Smithsonian Center for Astrophysics 2003)

Some scientists think that the highest-energy cosmic rays originate in other galaxies distant from our Milky Way. However, researchers from the University of Chicago and the Los Alamos National Laboratory challenge that idea, suggesting that these ultra-high energy events originate in our galaxy (Olinto et al. 1999). They propose that these events are due to iron nuclei accelerated from young, strongly magnetic neutron stars. These iron nuclei traverse the supernova envelope without significant losses. According to Olinto et al., these cosmic ray protons of iron ejected with energies $\sim 10^{20}$ eV reach the earth after some diffusion through the galactic and halo magnetic fields, but they do not point out their source. Surrounding the young stars in the constellation Orion is gas and dust of carbon, silicon and iron produced by earlier stars (Comins 2000, 107). The stars in Orion span the entire range of star types, so perhaps the source of cosmic rays on earth is from Orion.

In the quantum Egyptian afterlife, the Deceased accepts Orion's staff of rank and journeys on the guided diffusion path to Eternity through the black-hole Duat. But remember, there is no path because the point particle is spread out over the nonlocality region. If the ultra-high energy iron nuclei that arrive at earth are from Orion, then that cosmic ray is actually a line extending from Orion to earth because one cannot define a point in space in a quantum vacuum since its state is all of space. The Pharaohs would have us believe that we can access this nonlocal *Road from Orion* to earth—an ultra-high energy wave of core elements–by going to the polar cusp or true north. This energization and magnetic alignment, this attunement as the philosopher Heidegger would say, *guarantees to us humans a passage to those beings that we ourselves are not, and access to the being that we ourselves are.* Here the geometry of our universe is flat or two dimensional, and "the great plain of iron on which your gods stand" (CT479) stretches before us. So it seems there could be an invisible magnetic field stretched across the cosmos, an iron-rich network or bloodline uniting an invisible, starry Everybeing a million cubits tall in a living universe. As Dr. Faust would say,

Whoever ignores
The elements' cores
Their energy
And quality,
Cannot command
In the spirits' land.

Epilogue

Even though hieroglyphic translations and wall drawings depict Egyptian ideas dating to the Pyramid Texts, the funerary corpus as a whole is unified in its presentation of scientific thought. In fact, this scientific knowledge becomes more precise as it evolves from the Old Kingdom to the New Kingdom, equaling our twenty-first century understanding of how our universe operates. And yet, many outstanding questions remain. I urge scientists to review these texts, using and expanding the decoded 870 signs to examine the many faces of the Egyptian legacy. If knowledge is power in the afterlife as the Pharaohs attest, then we can be consoled by the wisdom of the Deceased who proclaims, "To me belongs Yesterday, I know Tomorrow."

Outstanding Questions

1. *E. coli* RNA polymerase does not transcribe through Z-DNA (Peck and Wang 1985). Does Polymerase IV or V and RecA protein transcribe through Z-DNA?

2. Do the interrelated processes of cAMP/CRP, the lac operon and the SOS response activate the lux genes resulting in luminescence and a related photoreactivation process?

3. Does phage Lambda undergo a transition from the hexagonal to a star-shaped configuration similar to phage T4?

4. In light of the genetics in this thesis related to phage Lambda and *E. coli,* what is the genetic significance of the twelve caverns, the numerical values, and the images in the Book of Caverns?

5. How does ferromagnetism, symmetry-breaking, and temperature contribute to the Deceased's long range order of transformation from fermion to boson?

6. As dark energy, the Deceased may represent antigravity, the inversion of classical gravity in a hot Planck length Early Universe of unified forces. Are the four forces in the classical world simply an inversion of the four unified forces in the Planck length world?

7. After death, human consciousness resides in our immortal part, our genetic essence. What is it?

8. What other mechanisms in our magnetosphere and our universe are similar to quantum phenomena?

9. What other scientific knowledge is hidden within the Egyptian signs?

10. The earth and its magnetosphere (and the attachment site of the *E. coli* chromosome surrounded by the cell membrane) approximates the String Theory idea of a three-brane wrapped around a three-dimensional sphere. Similarly, the activity of magnetic reconnection in the magnetosphere (or break-induced DNA recombination near the cell membrane) approximates the String Theory idea of a space-tearing conifold transition that collapses to a massless black hole and then transmutes into a massless particle, such as the Deceased's transformation to dark energy in a black hole/protein folding funnel. Is this evidence for String Theory?

11. Did the Pharaohs purposely limit the frontiers of the history of ideas by disguising their science in religious literature, or did they have a scientific rationale for keeping their knowledge secret?

Figure 26.1

Appendix

108 Idea Strands or Major Themes in the Old Kingdom Pyramid Texts and the Middle Kingdom Coffin Texts

IDEA STRANDS (IS)

PT = Pyramid Texts CT = Coffin Texts D = Deceased

No.	Pyramid Text	PT Idea Strand	Coffin Text	CT Idea Strand
1	260.390.694	Not falling upside down; King will not hang upside down	1.21.44.90.173. 181.184.200.201. 203.204.205.206.211. 214.220.343.367.417. 817.819.895.942.	Not going upside down
2	213.264.336.346.353. 373.425.429.431.436. 462.690.	King is not dead but alive King's corpse is rejuvenated King lives as Beetle	27.45.47.51.67.83. 152.258.265.326. 438.	D has power over death; D has not died
3	251.374.703	King is not opposed in horizon; earth gods will not seize King and are powerless	66.75.105.510.	Earth gods are powerless over D
4	361.422.	King will not die on earth among men; King will not	9.45.68.69.114. 245.256.344.359. 361.	D will not be annihilated or scorched; he will pass by the Valley and escape the place of execution
5	273.274.570.572.719.	King is eternal with ever-lasting limit; King is Osiris' heir; King will not die; King comes out of tomb	78.83.307.326.356. 402.423.458.758.	D is heir of Eternity and will not die again
6	218.258.273.274.307. 334.422.471.486.533. 539.565.673.	King is Osiris, oldest god; has Onite character; King is a god, son of god, messenger, one of Great Ennead; King is Re's blood, Isis' sweat; King is more than human, a celestial being	19.47.75.76.167. 169.173.185.205. 214.215.227.278. 307.	D is a god, Horus, Re-Atum, Shu, Re, Anubis, Atum, Osiris, Khopri
7	472.480.506.525.576. 582.587.646.686.718. 724.759.	King is magician; has new vision; King is saved by Osiris; King saves men from ill; King saves Eye from Seth; a god saves King from the obstructor due to power of repulsion on god's face	155.162.261.297. 396.397.847.932.	Savior; has power over 4 winds; is a magician, possessor of Right; Savior-god
8	217.335.467.470.488. 524.582.668.681.682. 704.	King is falcon; King's plumes are spines when he ascends; King is falcon landing on vertex of Beetle in bark in Abyss	147.148.149.272. 273.274.278.286. 287.292.302.303. 305.340.383.682. 691.	D is human falcon, phoenix, heron of lotus-tank, heron on desert plateau, a lotus-bird

No.	Pyramid Text	PT Idea Strand	Coffin Text	CT Idea Strand
9	305.511.517	Heir with no documents writes with big finger instead of little; King is flowing fluid, snake with many coils, scribe of god's book that states what is, the Eye of Horus that pours out a star; I am that pygmy	25.132.136.	D goes to regions of dwarfs
10	1.3.211.303.371.437. 442.483.535.578.588. 592.660.	King is first-born, conceived in Abyss, eldest one, born by dawn-light, conceived in sky	20.42.43.153.906	D is first-born, is Atum, will regain original shape
11	254.456.556.692C	King is Unique One, Bull of sky; the double crown	184.317.318.817. 820.827.	D is unique
12	263.266.463.466.488. 507.556.676.	King's offspring is dawn-light, Morning Star, dawn star; King is Lone Star in in east; King rises in 3 days as Lone Star	44.722.	Morning Star will set you in sky; D is Morning Star, Lone Star (*see also* IS 87)
13	304.311.470.568.	Bull of Re with 4 horns (NWSE); bend down western horn for King to pass; Re with 4 winds that are gentle or destructive; King drives away storms; Bull of Sky bends down horn for King to pass	21.162.184.355.	D has power over winds of heaven or bulls of sky; no pestilent streams
14	508.522.539.	King comes to stairway to ascend to 2 mothers, 2 vultures on mountain who nurse him; King asks Vulture to open way for him; King's head is a vulture	350.365.399.416. 658.667.	D is equipped by vultures; D goes to side of West at stairway to lotus-bark; goes up the stairway to crew of bark
15	421.437.441.470.483. 513.519.523.575.610.	King ascends to half-light at pole; Re calls king as Horus from zenith of sky; King goes to northern gods, fair place where Re walks; King stands at Great Polar Region with sun-folk and takes seat in bark; King ascends from Geb's vertex; King needs strong sunlight in sky; King is Anubis	62.132.255.343. 347.848.	D goes to Unwearying Stars, the horn or cusp, portal, Pole where Re appears
16	267.271.304.306.333. 478.480.508.530.536. 539.572.586A.610.	King ascends stairway to Re; King ascends Re's ladder to Duat; Western ladder or stairway	4.21.62.66.68.76. 162.297.399.416. 510.517.704.964. 1030.	D ascends ladder or stairway to Re and bark

No.	Pyramid Text	PT Idea Strand	Coffin Text	CT Idea Strand
17	268.459.519.	Re appears to King and Great Ennead shines; King ascends/descends into Great Valley; King gets ferryboat to obtain cold water at polar quarter of Imperishable Stars	275.305.486.648.	D splits mountains, soars between 2 mountains where Re appears, broken mountain; magic created mountains knit firmament
18	528.697.	King boards bark which Ennead rows; King rows by Unwearying Stars	398.400.401.403.	D finds ferryboat
19	37.38.272.469.503.510.	King's jaws fastened; splits iron of Upper/Lower Egypt; Abyss portal opens to King; iron firmament doors open for King in bark; earth opened; movements of Abyss and sunlight revealed; King sits on throne of She who preserves justice	4.62.105.108.109. 143.223.275.510. 827.	Geb/earth opens jaws/mouth so D becomes Osiris; split mouth, open doors of tomb, open doors of Geb, split mountains; opening Duat or West, splits iron or what is joined; D sees opening up
20	275.322.437.483.610. 611.717.	King opens double doors; sky, earth, doors are open for Horus; lotus-doors open for Seth; doors of Geb/earth open for King; celestial portal to horizon open for King; Double Ramgate unbolted for King who enters House of Protection and Geb protects	24.48.91.107.147. 217.297.416.901. 1007.	D opens portals, gates of horizon, gates of blue one, secret gate, double barrier, double gate
21	224.225.412.472.482. 487.531.553.662	King turns himself about, raises himself left to right; King takes ferryboat to other side; King on Horus mission goes to other side; King as Great Bull crosses over to Re's pure places	1.51.214.219.255. 327.341.	D raises himself from left to right side of riverside; ferries across to other side
22	555.611.	King's ropes are knotted; King asks Thoth to take him from south to north of Winding Waterway; King enters into Geb and waters are joined together, hoed lands united	132.136.144.168. 169.170.171.172. 219.622.	D finds ropes, broken cord, knots them, joins river-banks
23	520.654.	King sees 4 with locks on temples, backs, foreheads, tops with dancing tresses and threatens to tear out top tresses which are lotus-buds in swamp garden if he doesn't get a ferryboat	154.219.310.1003. 1007.1011.	D knows a braided lock is made for humans; tearing out braided tresses, owning or eating braided locks, and disordered tresses

No.	Pyramid Text	PT Idea Strand	Coffin Text	CT Idea Strand
24	252.264.320.374.412. 438.442.470.516.518. 587.617.675.	King is on bark, ferries east to where god fashioned him; King is self-created or son of unknown mother; King is not begotten by father or born by mother; King's father is Great Wild Bull; King is foundling with no parents; King's birth is unblemished in 2 Lands on right side of Osiris; King unites with gods in On	75.76.131.136.137. 141.142..144.146. 317.335.341.648. 823.854.	D on bark is self-created god; D assembles family, is self-created Khopri
25	263.264.265.266.359. 437.481.483.509.571. 610.684.	King ferries to eastern horizon on Winding Waterway; King travels Winding Waterway in north of sky crossing sea below sky; King ferries across on reed-floats to east side of sky in north star region near Moon; King crosses lake, iron firmament; King is star crossing sea below sky's underpart; King goes on sky underside with stars on Winding Waterway	18.29.57.72.129.130. 163.175.241.288.482.	D moves from West to rise in East; D crosses sky, lake, Winding Waterway, lake of sky; goes down western path; Great Bear marks path to Western Horizon
26	263.264.265.266.473. 481.504.519.609.691A	Day-bark sets down sky's reed-floats for Re who crosses them to horizon; Night-bark brings reed-floats to King, who crosses them to Re then Horus in horizon; King and Re go to horizon on 2 reed-floats	132.136.144.168.169. 170.171.172.188.562.	D finds and knots ropes severed in flood; finds broken cord; joins the riverbanks
27	518.573.659.674.676. 690.718.	Causeway of Happiness is north of pools of Field of Offerings; clear place for King at causeway beneath firmament; stand up at causeway as Geb; King is cleansed by Celestial Serpent in causeway in meadow	(See IS no. 25 for CT references on Winding Waterway)	
28	226.233.234.237.240. 293.298.384.385.386. 387.502.	Re sees monster snake; monster lie down/crawl away; 4-coiled Monster; son-of-earth monster snake dies for what it sees	52.266.1094.1099.	Be gone monster; D is Atum and Re and monster is on belly; D saves Re from Apep
29	733.	Panic appeal to Thoth for protection against snake attacking in night	284.	Great Lady (Isis) of Desert rescues Re from Apep
30	227.241.285.332.390.	Monster snake, scorpion turns around since Seth is beheaded (Great Black Bull); serpent vomits brick, poisons itself; King escapes serpent; venon fails	335 Part II.414.435. 436.	Eye conquers monster; D makes Apep impotent, drives off bull-snake; venom fails

No.	Pyramid Text	PT Idea Strand	Coffin Text	CT Idea Strand
31	229.230.581.	Atum makes serpent crawl away; serpent goes into hole for 2 knots of Elephantine were for Horus; save King from not holding back the living and hindering the gods	473.644.689.681. 752.1053.1100.	D fells, drives off, attacks Apep
32	227.382.	Serpent slides into earth/hole; snake ploughs earth	467.	D knows holes of snakes and is saved
33	378.381.384.385.388.	Horus tramples snake in sky or centipede on earth; great centipede goes down; King as Great Fetterer makes snake crawl away; snake's head is cut up and Seth cuts it up	885.	viper in sky; monster
34	239.	White Crown goes on after swallowing or absorbing the Great One (Apopis)		
35	213.249.334.665.682.	King gives orders to living with lotus-bud sceptre; King is lotus bloom at Re's nose, a golden flower; King is heavenward heron	44.48.162.184.228. 292.377.399.400. 510.682.703.	D is lotus-haunting heron on lotus bark going to lotus tanks
36	319.	King causes lapis-lazuli and Upper Egypt plant to grow	135.	D is greenstone or papyrus-amulet
37		(see Idea Strands asserting D is every god)	275.703.	D assumes all forms
38	273.274.310.	Atum begot King; What is done to Atum is done to King	45.132.136.153.252. 266.424.442.709.906.	D is Atum
39	253.259.405.439.475. 570.	King is hand in hand with Re; King is Re; King is greater than Re; King has Re's nature	133.248.266.341. 442.991.	D is Re
40	570.	King is firmly bound at waist to Re	60.75.162.	Re causes gods to follow; D merges with Re; D builds bark to sail to lotus tanks
41	273.274.370.	King assembles his spirits; Horus attaches to King and his children	131.136.141.143. 146.	D assembles his family
42	639.	(According to Faulkner in PT 639 (p.264), the Eye of Horus is feminine)	44.312.316.954.958. 971.1000.1011.1101. 1143.1146.	D is Eye of Horus, the Lady of All; Isis is Sole Eye, Mistress of Enneads, Lady of All, Great Lady, Sacred Eye

No.	Pyramid Text	PT Idea Strand	Coffin Text	CT Idea Strand
43	639.	Eye of Horus is feminine or Isis	148.182.294.332. 411.605.	D is Isis; son of milk goddess
44	4.101.357.362.510. 595.664.664A.	Isis gives King his heart, protects him, reassembles him, protects throne; King is pure by breath of Isis; Horus brings Isis' heart and vice versa; Isis gives King a heart in middle of earth	6.28.44.248.252. 286.526.	Isis makes fair ways for D, fashions him, follows after Eye; D seeks Great Lady, is son of Isis; Isis gives heart
45	406.413.437.461.483. 503.610.676.	Bring King Isis' milk, flood of Nephthys; Isis as Great Mooring-post calls to King, removes impediments; Earth opens and King sits on throne named "She who preserves justice"	68.148.182.239.246. 252.276.284.	Isis is Great Lady, Lady of Provisions, Mistress of Old One and Great Mooring-post for ferryboat; Isis is Great Lady of Desert, and Lady of Horizon
46	41.42.146.211.268. 269.337.470.578.661. 663.	Milk from Horus' breast, from Isis the milk provider's breast; take Eye of Horus, 2 bowls of sacred milk; King nourished with milk so he gives bread; Isis/Nephthys suckle King; milch-cows cry for King when he ascends; King takes milky fluid in Isis' breasts	75.96.175.259.265. 301.344.402.468. 546.622.648.695. 820.858.862.924. 979.982.993.	Isis as milk-goddess suckles White Bull; milk of red cow; references to Milky Way; rise up wearing White Crown; gods live by sweet savour; white bird, sweet milk, milk of Bulls; milk goddess suckles D who lives on milk; D is son of Great Lady
47	222.269.356.357.364. 468.477.480.505.511. 532.593.628.631.694.	King descends in Night-bark with Nephthys and rises in Day-bark with Isis; Isis and Nephthys support/protect/strengthen; Isis conceives King; Nephthys begets King; Isis and Nephthys find and revive King; Nephthys gives King a heart; Isis reassembles Osiris	45.148.181.229.236. 238.1128.	Strength of D is power of Isis; Seed of Osiris in Isis' womb; D will not upside down for Isis rows; Isis gives breath to and removes limpness from Inert One; Isis raises Osiris; Isis in bow of bark
48	34.44.357.455.462.	Cream reconciles Two Gods; Re reconciles the Two Lords; Horus takes Seth's sweet Eye; King purified of evil on him with *zmn* (cream? PT34) for King sweetness is sweet and he raises up	133.312.354.924	Great Lady made 2 mansions; Horus allies with Isis; *smyn* splits mouth; D takes sweet Eye of Horus
49	524.665.665B.666A. 694.698.	King is Thoth in his Castle of the Mace; Thoth has Seth's knife; King is Thoth in authority over sky	249.277.	D is Thoth, becomes Thoth

No.	Pyramid Text	PT Idea Strand	Coffin Text	CT Idea Strand
50	367.477.	Thoth decapitates Seth and followers; Horus and Thoth raise Osiris and make him stand before Two Enneads; Thoth cuts off heads of those opposing King when he comes to Osiris	231.277.	Thoth and Book split open mouth; three give orders at Eye in affairs of Thoth
51	479.505.524.	On left ladder side, Thoth's wing gleams with Eye of Horus; King clad with Thoth's garment with Isis in front, Nephthys behind King before stairway; Thoth protects Eye	254.	arm of D is Thoth
52	210.270.448.511.	King crosses sky with Re and Thoth; Thoth ferries King over to other side; Thoth reassembles King, removing what was on him; King is guided to Great Throne Horus made that Thoth brought into being		
53	347.403.413.457.460. 494.496.535.536.553. 576.663.667A.676.679.	King's mouth is incense, lips myrrh; Flood is in King's lap; King has water, inundation; irrigation ditches flooded for King; cool water is great flood issued from king; water/flood from Two Enneads provides bread/beer for King; those presiding over Ennead live on Great Flood; Osiris cut up has no efflux; Osiris risen has efflux, flood; King has water, flood, efflux, milk from Isis; King will not putrefy or rot; King's water, flood, efflux issuing from the putrefaction of Osiris is his; efflux from Osiris during inundation	69.292.334.341. 362.833.857.997. 1082.1087.	Efflux missing from Left Eye due to full power of Osiris; D eats flood-water of of Inundation-god in Island of Double Lion; D's smell is incense, oil is efflux; D is winding Nile, quenches thirst with flood of Osiris; cold water is efflux from Osiris; Seth's Great Flood is enclosed; D causes efflux of Osiris to rise; the Word contains efflux of Osiris
54	412.468.524.532.535. 577.582.674.677.690. 694.701.	King's form is that of Anubis; King receives jackal-face; as Anubis, King will not rot; King is Anubis, Claimer of hearts; King is Anubis in authority over house; King as Anubis the Foremost of the Westerners	67.254.	D has jackal on shoulders; D's mouth is Anubis
55	255.256.260.294.310. 313.540.587.589.683.	King is Horus who is strong despite injury; King sits on Horus' throne; King is Horus who must beware of lion	1.46.107.110.150. 255.362.458.1016.	D is Horus

No.	Pyramid Text	PT Idea Strand	Coffin Text	CT Idea Strand
56	219.256.260.301.468. 524.570.592.599.724.	Enneads restore Osiris; King's strength is Horus' Eye; Horus refashions King by bringing great healed left Eye; whole Eye of Horus is dreadful White Crown and powerful Red Crown; King wears White Crown, the Eye of Horus that is strong; King is master of Green Crown; Eye issues from King's head as magic Upper Egyptian/Lower Egyptian Crowns; King bears Eye of Horus wearing White Crown; Enneads rejoice	42.43.64.71.97.107. 133.205.233.316. 858.	Horus gives D his Eye, Eye of Great Lady, white Eye of Horus; D is Eye of Horus
57	260.570.573.576.684. 738.	King is 4th of 4 gods bringing water; King is 4th Imperishable Star; King is 1 of 4 gods watching over Upper Egypt; Kinng is 1 of 4 Geb made; King is 1 of 4 Atum begot; King is 1 of 4 gods issuing from Geb's vertex	1.122.123.125. 311.	D is 4th of 4 gods, 4th of 4 uraei
58	254.273.274.390.407. 485.505.509.619.675. 737.	King judges Two Contestants; King is between Horus and Seth; judgment at Mansion of Horus; King sits between Two Enneads to give judgment; King stands between 2 great gods, Two Enneads giving judgment; King heads Two Conclaves to judge gods; King judges Enneads	75.277.280.344. 464.622.682. 1125.	D judges secret matters & rivals in Mansion of Six; D enters judgment hall, judges Rivals, Contestants, and pacifies Combatants
59	81.268.271.319.439.	Eye of Horus awakes and Two Lands bow, shine; King unites, rules Two Lands, southern and northern	7.75.357.647.	Two Lands triumph & reduce to order; D crosses Two Lands with limb and rules
60	36.210.357.412.422. 511.515.553.665A.676.	Purification of King; mouth pure; King is Foremost of Westerners; King heads Two Conclaves; Re guies King to Two Conclaves to Osiris' throne; Upper/Lower Egyptian Conclaves bow to King	27.68.84.255.1003.	D purifies self, & is head of the Two Conclaves
61	284.285.287.294.394. 400.551.	Lion within lion; Lion is endangered and throat of King's heart lengthens; go away lion; King as Horus must beware of lion; lion behind lion in life; King needs food or he and Double Lion are hungry; retreat lion	1.113.153.173.242. 248.250.276.292. 357.383.438.453. 510.906.1000.1003.	References to Double Lion and Island of Double Lion

No.	Pyramid Text	PT Idea Strand	Coffin Text	CT Idea Strand
62	558.569.666A.	King stops the stopping of the Eldest God; King cannot be stopped; Thoth has Seth's knife and has implanted an obstacle against Seth's actions	160.391.1063.	Mountain serpent stops Crew of Re; night of stopping movements; crystal mountain of Bakhu with serpent; path prepared for Re when he halts
63	273.274.306.319.394. 408.409.539.	King is Bull of sky, enduring bull; 2 bulls are now an ibis (Thoth); King is Bull of On, of Ennead; King's spine is Wild Bull	15.31.32.36.51.76. 84.85.86.87.88.181. 191.201.204.208. 212.218.251.260. 267.	D is begotten by Bull, is Apis, the Double Bull, Bull of West, Bull of the Ennead, Bull of Great One, Bull of Kenzet
64	282.	Strong bull injured	15.36.261.	Bulls of sky, Bull in midst, Bull of Great Ones; pull off bonds of bull
65	250.438.502C.581.725.	Re heads Cavern of Abyss; Great Cavern of On is open for Horus; caverns complete before 4 gods; King's cavern is Broad Hall; cavern or chapel open for King	149.151.170.317. 486.	D is taken to his cavern; cavern is opened; bulls led to caverns for D; serpents depart caverns for D; caverns of Hathor are broken open
66	130.535.541.	Take those who rebelled; cut off heads of Seth's followers; smite Seth	92.311.335.358.	Battleground of gods is Island of Fire; night of battle dividing the Eye; fighting of Rivals; Seth the Rebel in stormy Two Lands
67	369.412.485A.566.615.	Seth's evil smell; King does not tread on corruption of Osiris; King exhorts Horus not to leave him boatless; King and Thoth are not boatless; son of Atum is not boatless	168.182.	Putrefaction is left boatless; Horus brings boatless Eye to land (saves it from putrefaction; boatless means putrefaction, no replication template
68	524.562.	King blocks Seth's roads and escapes messengers; Eye of Horus will not fall to Seth's rage	49.51.113.157.464.	Seth conspiracy, injury by brother; Osiris calls Seth an Eyebreaker; anger of Seth; Seth injures Eye of Horus

No.	Pyramid Text	PT Idea Strand	Coffin Text	CT Idea Strand
69	57S.59A.161.283.524. 570.652.691B.	Take Eye of Horus that Seth snatched; do not rob; Seth took Eye; Seth gouged out Eye; Seth snatched Eye; Horus brings Osiris what Seth took; take/protect White Eye from Seth	16.106.237.252.303. 304.335.414.691. 856.	Theft/robbery references; what is taken, what is missing; magic power is missing, beard is missing; reckoning with robbers; Seth snatched half of Eye of Horus
70	213.224.225.306.424. 676.	Rule hidden seats in Mounds of Horus and Seth; King occupies Mounds of Horus and travels about Mounds of Seth; King travels Southern/ Northern Mounds	111.468.701.	D owns fields in Great mound; D makes upper mounds strong and and lower mounds prosper; unites the lands
71	262.356.475.482.532. 593.610.	King not stopped by Great Ones of Castle of Mace on Milky Way; King as Horus is greater than Seth due to a superior nature; King rises for Horus is victor; Horus stands up against Seth; King is stronger than Seth	11.12.14.149.154. 303.338.405.	Overcome Seth's confederacy; D is great falcon that crushes his foe; D builds up injured Eye, defeats Seth's conspiracy; Horus vindicates
72	61.126.135.301.327. 355.372.413.477.497. 524.539.578.665.675. 688.695.697.	Take Seth's foreleg Horus tore off; take Seth's Eye or meat of forepart; Horus is Ready Fighter; Thoth's messenger loves King and brings Thoth's arm; arm of King as Horus rules land; Horus cuts foes' arms off; King eats foreleg, haunch, rib-joints; King comes to Osiris who rises and King eats limb of foe; get rid of 2 arms of Seth; King takes Eye from Seth; King is announced to Re as one having left arm raised; King's arms are before him; arms of Seth are loosed; King drives off hidden Nine; arm upraised in the East	100.154.246.249. 254.314.356.357. 358.363.398.648.	Arm cut off, extending of arm by the Destroyer, arm of Horus, arm of Thoth, separation of foreleg, power over Seth's limb, joy of seeing god's limb, original giving of arms; greet left arm of Osiris; Seth's Eye rescued
73	570.571.	King will not commit Seth's crime: he will not eat Eye of Horus or limb so that Osiris dies; King escapes death as does Seth	335.	Seth laps up corruption and putrefaction
74	511.	King's right hand supports sky, left hand supports earth	296.414.	Left hand of Osiris obeys; Entourage of Re of right hand and left hand

No.	Pyramid Text	PT Idea Strand	Coffin Text	CT Idea Strand
75	136.227.277.342.367. 519.	Take severed heads of Seth's followers; black bull's head severed; Bull/Seth with injured testicles; nome of black bull serves King; Seth decapitated by Thoth; take harpoon to cut off heads of fores in Field of Offerings	311.	D is strong to cut off heads; great battle reference
76	29.31.39.43.54.56.57A. 74.130.135.160.301.356. 357.423.519.	Eye of Horus is whole, is placed in King's mouth; take 2 Eyes of Horus (black/white); take Seth's Eye; take those who rebelled; take Eye rescued from Seth; King brings Horus healed left Eye; efflux issues from King whose name is "Fresh Water"; Fields of Rushes/Offerings inundated, full of water	69.96.101.102.189. 205.235.316.362. 551.858.859.934.	Left Eye will not be destroyed, but will putrefy with no efflux due to full power of Osiris; Osiris remade with with efflux, water springs of Mansion and no inertness with efflux; become Eye of Horus; quench thirst with efflux of Osiris; full Eye replaces empty Eye; take two complete Eyes
77	57J.106.364.680.681.	Take 2 Eyes to dilate heart; join/unite 2 Eyes to Osiris which expand heart; Horus attaches his Eye to King; Re crowns King as Horus and sets his 2 divine eyes	431.	Inert One ascends from Abyss
78	576.578.	King hates inertness and sleep; King's embrace prevents inertness	74.80.111.204.235. 237.297.312.399.	Horus is limp, patricians inert; Garden of Silent One; inert ones are in flood; may you never be inert; Osiris is limp Great One; Osiris sleeps, Great Dead One; D detests efflux of earth/humans
79	412.452.686.	King as Horus hates sleep, inertness; Evil on King is is destroyed; Horus saves Eye from Seth	14.52.56.74.327. 330.465.874.	Horus triumphs over dispute, is no longer inert or an unconscious god; Great Inert One stands up on his side, is victorious in Field of Offerings; no shouting; Osiris inert; inert ones

No.	Pyramid Text	PT Idea Strand	Coffin Text	CT Idea Strand
80	82.356.368.	Thoth brings Eye of Horus, turns back Seth's followers; Thoth reassembles King	107.242.260.271.	Thoth presides over God's Booth, heals Eye, is potent; D is Thoth/Ibis
81	68.73.148-151.311. 344.348.357.455.510. 577.	Take water in Eye of Horus, take ferment in face, take ferment which issued from you; Re is Great Flood of of Great One; King hails Great Flood, leader of sunfolk; King is Fresh Water; flood of purification from Osiris; Horus is rowed on Great Flood; Lord of wine in flood	72.107.149.169. 189.235.317.318. 431.485.	D is Horus, has floodwater, springs of water, is Great Flood, is happy on flood banks, is Nile-god Lord of Waters, has efflux and will inert, devours Inert One, is not inert or destroyed
82	79.162.186.190.273. 274.301.317.351.352. 605.	Paint in green an uninjured Eye on Osiris/King's face; take/protect green Eye from Seth; King swallows Green Crown; Horus, Lord of Greenstone; King brings greeness to Great One's Eye; a green living rush; King grows with greeness; King receives green eye paint for filling empty Eye with full Eye	302.305.817.	D is Falcon with greenstone wings; D is Nile to make Two Lands green
83	57M.57N.97.199.215. 259.260.606.673.	Take Eye of Horus so Seth does not destroy; take sole possession of Eye; demand Eye from Seth; reversion of Eye of Horus and offering; remove Horus' injury and Seth's mutilation; thrones of Geb revert to King; Seth bears King aloft forever; Seth bears burden of King	32.154.164.287. 303.316.318.451.	D as Horus will dispel Osiris' pain, build up injured Eye, cure god of sufferings, drive out secret trouble, slay Seth conspiracy, join Two Brothers, restore Osiris
84	260.355.364.367.368. 447.452.485C.	King/Horus' limbs reassembled; puts a stop to affair in On; King's head knit to his bones; Horus and Thoth reassemble King; Nut the Great Protectresss purifies King and gives head, heart and reassembles him	106.175.241.255. 256.938.	Osiris and D's limbs reassembled, knit together
85	217.222.357.368.432. 454.	King embraces Sun-god; Atum embraces King; King embraces Re, Horus, earth/all things; Nut as Great Well protects King; King encloses in his arms every god, their lands, possessions, is great and round as a circle		

No.	Pyramid Text	PT Idea Strand	Coffin Text	CT Idea Strand
86	215.262.268.328.329. 504.509.555.667C. 685.700.	King ascends to sky with Horus/Seth in Castle; no opposition from Castle of Mace; King takes crown from Two Enneads, who tremble as King becomes star; King destroys ramparts of Shu; issues from between Two Enneads; King takes White/Green Crowns; King is reborn, waters of life are in sky/ earth, 2 mountains split; reborn King rises on right side, lifts upon left	11.44.132.341.422. 758.1013.	D takes possession of crown, arrives at Castle seat, has seat in Mansion of Sunrise in On, has seat between the Two Enneads; Re rises from Eastern double gates
87	214.261.268.313.323. 325.355.358.360.361. 419.437.461.473.479. 481.485C.504.519.536. 553.554.662.	King descends on iron bands in Horus' arms, rising to stars; King is at eastern side of celestial vault; King ferries across to Field of Rushes; King/Re bathe in Lake of Rushes; Horus bathes in Field of Rushes; at dawn; King goes up in Field of Rushes; King crosses sky to Field of Rushes; sky doors open for resurrection; King as Horus rises as human substrate slips into furnace heat; brick drawn from tomb; King lets go of knotted bonds; King/ Horus is Morning Star; King is removed from conflagration	151.156.160.161. 164.274.279.288. 343.722.724.832. 995.	D descends into lustral basins; shining Red Crown in bowl; D bathes in basin of Abyss; at sky's Eastern Gates; Re exits from gate in middle in Field of Rushes; way is middle sky for D; descent to Bank of Rushes; become Morning Star; eastern side of celestial vault; join land to land at ramp; 2 knots/Twins go to middle of East
88	669.	Isis describes King's reborn form: he is a being with no arms or legs, but the iron, the *Hnw*-bark shall be brought	20.294.	D established in original shape; D has back of lapis lazuli, gold belly and neck
89	438.519.548.554.619. 674.691B.758.	King's translation or "caused to be one belonging to the lords of veneration"; King's translation to Blessed One, to possessor of honor; King's stern-warp is coiled; King has jackal face, Celestial Serpent middle, hinder parts like a Broad Hall; King is knit together; has spines on arms of Thoth, sharp knife from Seth; Osiris has jackal front, Celestial Serpent hinder parts, spine is door-bolt; King lies down in coil	167.169.239.251. 259.279.421.	D is Eyeless One, the Great Flood, Lord of Faces or or centipede-faced; D is Glitter-bird; hinder parts of D's back, legs on shoulders, spinal cord is in nest of children

No.	Pyramid Text	PT Idea Strand	Coffin Text	CT Idea Strand
90	266.319.504.565. 685.720.	King is 3rd in On; King is 3rd at accession; King's 3rd is Sothis; King is 3rd of 2 with him; King's 3rd orders offerings after King reborn; Osiris is 1 of 3	187.198.277.1181.	D is 3rd of Osiris of of 3 Osiris portions; D is 3rd of ascend-ing gods; D is head of 3 in Thoth affairs; D sits on Eye as 3rd
91	211.338.501.	King gives bread due to nourishment from milk-goddess Iat; King eats Horus' and is not hungry; 3 meals for King	70.71.137.149.153. 164.165.166.181. 189.203.215.729. 1011.	Bread is issued from Eye of Horus; eats bread, beer on on bark; D is Bull having Bread in On (4 in sky, 3 in earth); lives on 7 portions in On; 9 portions from Great Ennead
92	205.409.	King has quintet of meals in Mansion; 5 meals (3 sky, 2 earth)	75.201.1006.	D judges Mansion of Six; D is Bull owning 2 portions Geb, 3 portions Re
93	409.437.627.667.667A.	King lives on tree of sweet things/censing on earth; King has his earth-attackers; King's food is in Lakes of Turquoise in Field of Offerings; King's food is bread in Broad Hall	165.175.278.	Re eats meal of Great Goddess; pools of Re's Field of Offerings; D eats
94	224.225.414.477.515. 597.603.675.682.690.	King clothes his body, puts bright cloak on and is clad in Eye of Horus; King comes to Osiris, eats limb, clothes Osiris; King puts on intact Eye of Horus in Weaving-town; knit on King's head, gather members; King wears cloak out of Mansion; Horus weaves his booth, Seth spreads awnings	271.334.467.468. 485.486.487.608. 691.728.837.862.	D sees Unclothed One, knits 6-weave cloth; puts on cloak, weave dress, fringed garment; D clothes Great One; D is clad in woven Eye of Horus and D clothes Osiris
95	476.	King tells scribe to destroy writings, asks Re to replace scribe with King	392.397.425.430. 458.688.	D breaks pens of Vulture-god and smashes inkpots of Vulture; Outcast's messengers have no power over D who is Horus
96	215.250.273.274.302. 309.327.364.375.388. 437.460.471.506.524. 529.537.570.576.577. 593.659.675.678.690. 697.734.	Seed of god lives through his word; King bears god's book, sends messages; King's word on earth annulled and he flies away from men to sky; King sends messages for Re; messengers of Horus, Seth, Thoth love King; Word of Horus; (Continued)	253.254.258.295. 312.329.334.351. 387.404.405.422. 460.533.538.540. 654.695.849.954. 959.967.976.987. 1067.1087.	To become Re-Atum's scribe, a scribe of Re/Osiris; D has speech of those in authority; D's writings are in 2 Fields of Offerings to reassemble D; (Continued)

No.	Pyramid Text	PT Idea Strand	Coffin Text	CT Idea Strand
96	(Continued)	Horus shatters snake's mouth so snake has no messenger; King has messengers; King speaks word; King is Great Word; King escapes messengers of Osiris for Seth, bringing his words to Re; King advises Gate-keeper to act against messenger; Re favors King's speech; hear word of King; King has writing in register; Great Word from Thoth for Osiris; Osiris seed is in Isis; Word of Re; King is messenger to Osiris; King breaks pens, shatters inkwells; King is messenger of great god; hear the word Horus said to Osiris		D is lst seed of Re and in charge of of Word of God; D is Great God's messenger/scribe of record of Maet; D opens chest of writings; D's seed is that of Bull; Thoth's ritual book; D sends god's word to a god; word is in darkness, Osiris
97	38.56.214.257.325. 413.419.424.483.509. 537.584.669.670.676. 723.	Split iron of mouth; iron bowl of Seth's Eye; descend on iron bands; King cleaves iron; King's iron bones; King sits on iron throne at cool water pool; King enters bark and iron doors open; Isis says iron will be brought to King to knit him together; mouth split with iron fingers; King rises on his iron bones, golden members	159.223.474.479. 666.816.991.	Iron walls of Field of Rushes; splits iron, iron on hands of Re, receive offerings on great iron plain; magic of D is stellar iron, sharp, strong iron on D's mouth; cut away iron
98	32.33.423.436.452. 460.510.515.518.519. 537.662.670.676.	Horus issues from cold water; King receives cold water like Horus; King has cold water, flood, fluid issuing from Osiris; great flood of cool water from King, who receives jar of Re's cold water at polar region; King gets ferryboat to get cold water at polar quarter; King's iron throne at cool water pool; King cleansed in Lake of Cool Water; cold water in Busiris	61.62.64.267.344. 345.346.570.833. 895.926.936.	Cold water; great cool room; Horus cleans D in cold water; cold water of those in sunshine are open; cold water is efflux of Osiris; give/take cold water
99	350.352.627.	Turquoise of stars; King's food in Lake of Turquoise in Field of Offerings	336.468.486.	lst blue fire portal means blackness; D has blue eyes, is Lord of Turquoise; Hathor ascends in Turquoise
100	20-23.32.37.38.39. 46.87.93.110.219. 223.273.274.318.	4 times, fasten jaws, split iron of mouth or Upper & Lower Egypt; Eye of Horus placed in King's mouth; King eats Eye; take, eat, absorb Eye of Horus, the offering cake, morning meal, bread; King eats men, lives on gods; King swallows intelligence of gods and 7 uraei	934.935.	Eat Eye of Horus; take Eye of Horus

No.	Pyramid Text	PT Idea Strand	Coffin Text	CT Idea Strand
101	25.50.176.215.263. 268.347.390.410.436. 440.467.468.469.534. 677.684.688.726.	Presence of King's double; King is Geb's double; King and double shall live; star-gods have companions; King's double eats with him forever; Pyramid/temple or or Mansion of Horus for King and double; lift King's double to Double Lion-god for King is reborn; King's double escorts him	13.251.255.261.268. 269.304.467.530. 666.674.824.936.	If double remains, D does not die; promoting a man's double; D is greatest of owners of doubles; D's double is present; pure double; D joins with double as god of the field; content double; D goes with double
102	215.491.	You are a double; if King dies, double has power, for King is 3rd of 2 gods ascending as as falcons who descend to earth as pair of serpents	378.381.445.474. 586.	Destroying doubles; D's double is protected; acclamation to D's double
103	359.372.506.	King goes to castle for owners of doubles, is god of those who have gone to their doubles; Horus drives doubles of fores away; King is double-maker	265.341.344.428. 581.	Doubles of Great Ones circulate; doubles be joined in peace; those who have gone to their doubles; D has seen doubles on fair path guiding; D travels path of owners of doubles
104	214.262.422.466.500. 619.666B.	Beware lake; Great Lake striking power misses King; beware foul-smelling House of Soul		
105	265.266.303.473.481. 504.507.515.519.609. 691A	Net; set down reed-floats for D to Re	343.477-481.	Iron floats in sky; iron weights on earth; escape from net
106	271.290.324.326.334. 336.368.369.373.600. 603.667.667A.667C. 735.	Face of god is open to me; One face falls on another; Geb gives you your head; collar for front on neck of Re; King greets Sun-god and grasps his tail; King grasps root of tail; gods knit together King; receive your head; tail growing in Lakes of Osiris; King's essence in Pyramid forever; knit head, take head; he has appeared upon the Stone; King's face is among the coils	95.96.239.251.260. 267.276.422.499. 573.656.765.817.	Vertex of Re; Vertex of Ennead; on my Mistress and Lord of faces, centipede-faced; King is he of Pyramidion; Lord of Heads; many faced

No.	Pyramid Text	PT Idea Strand	Coffin Text	CT Idea Strand
107	216.219.273.274.302. 325.365.366.368.412. 437.442.446.452.459. 466.472.502A.510.515. 519.	Orion, Sirius and King swallowed by Duat; dweller in Orion; King is son of Sirius; King's limbs in womb of Nut; mother Nut; King reaches sky as Orion; Duat grasps King at place where Orion is; King has come as Orion; King is companion of Orion; King issues from creating of waters; King is clothed by stars; Sirius is active, going forth, censing the bright ones	44.61.280.399.258. 335.482.469.689.	D protected by Orion, Sirius; Orion lifts up bark; D grasps orion; Orion and Great Bear ready; Nut bore D; Orion warrants D
108	258.261.474.511.581.	King ascends on wind, is flame moving in wind Geb brings to King, the gods who are in sky; King will have abundance of North wind; Osiris brings wind to to strengthen North wind	46.62.75.81.83. 162.330.297.934.	D receives breezes of North wind, runs with wind; Shu begot men; power over winds of heaven; Shu strews sky with beauty; becoming winds; winds bring Eye to Deceased

GLOSSARY

Aker: earth-god represented as a pair of lions or sphinxes back-to-back
Akh: in the afterlife, the transfigured deceased often identified with light
Amun: ancient creator deity of city of Thebes; self-created
Anubis: black jackal-headed god who guided the deceased in the afterlife
Apis: sacred bull worshiped at Memphis; earthly manifestation of Ptah
Apopis: serpent-demon and enemy of the Sun-god
Atum: primeval, self-created Heliopolitan god of origins
Ba: a nonphysical component of an individual, often depicted as a human-headed bird; appears most often in afterlife texts
Benu-Bird: a creator deity represented as a heron resting on the primordial mound that first emerged from the waters
Bes: dwarf deity with lionlike face associated with the child Horus
Cubit: linear measurement of 20.6 inches
Dismembered One: the dead Osiris before resurrection
Double Lion: solar lion deities back-to-back
Ennead: company of nine gods
Eye of Horus: torn out by Seth, restored by Thoth and the Deceased
Geb: god of the earth, the product of Shu (air) and Tefnut (moisture)
Hathor: cow goddess associated with fertility; called "Mistress of the West"
Horakhty: "Horus of the Horizon," sun-god with falcon head; often combined with Re as Re-Horakhty
Horus: a major ancient deity; living King was identified as an earthly Horus and the dead King as Osiris; Seth was the rival of Horus
Isis: member of the Heliopolitan Ennead; wife and sister of Osiris
Ka: a person's vital life-force, born with him and resembling him exactly
Khepri: scarab or dung beetle representing the transforming Sun-god
Maat: goddess of truth, justice and cosmic order
Mounds: the 14 mounds or regions of the Elysian Fields
Neith: ancient creator-goddess worshiped at Sais in the Egyptian delta
Nephthys: sister of Isis and Osiris, consort of Seth
Night-bark: boat of Sun-god that sails through Duat
Nun: the primeval waters merging toward creation; often presented with Atum
Osiris: god of the realm of the dead; always shown in mummy wrappings; brother and husband of Isis; member of Great Ennead; equated with Deceased Pharaoh
Ptah: chief god of Memphis; primeval creator-god encompassing the world
Re: falcon-headed Sun-god who created the world
Red Crown: royal crown of Lower Egypt
Rosetjau: "place of dragging;" reference to Duat
Sekhmet: Lioness-headed goddess suggesting destructive power; consort of Ptah
Seth: brother and murderer of Osiris; rival of Horus; also the god who guards the Sun-god from the evil serpent Apopis
Supports of Shu: columns of air supporting the sky at the four cardinal points
Sothis: Sirius the Dog-star as a goddess
Thoth: scribe of the gods; god of wisdom and learning depicted as an ibis or a baboon; mediator between Seth and Horus; restores Eye of Horus
Uraeus: symbol of royalty
West: region where Sun sets; land of the dead
White Crown: crown of Upper Egypt

REFERENCES

Asterisk (*) denotes university course or tutorial

Abedon, S. T., T. D. Herschler, and D. Stopar. 2001. Bacteriophage latent-period evolution as a response to resource availability. *Appl. Environ. Microbiol.* 67:4233–4241.

Achenbach, L. 2002. Dept. of Microbiology, Southern Ill. Univ. at Carbondale. Microbiology 460. "Bioluminescence." www.science.siu.edu/microbiology/micr460/460%20Pages/460.biolum.html.

Ahn, Eun-Joo, G. Medina-Tanco, P. L. Biermann, and T. Stanev. 1999. The origin of the highest energy cosmic rays. Do all roads lead back to Virgo? November 8, arXiv:astro-ph/9911123v1.

Albright, R. A. and B. W. Matthews. 1998. Crystal structure of lambda-cro bound to a consensus operator at 3.0 angstrom resolution. *J. Mol. Biol.* 280:137

Anfinsen, C. B. 1959. *The molecular basis of evolution.* New York: John Wiley & Sons, Inc.

*Ansari, A. and J. F. Marko. 2001. Univ. of Illinois at Chicago. Physics 450: Molecule and Cell Biophysics. www.uic.edu/classes/phys/phys461/phys450/ANJUM04.

Araya, P., M. Rosemblatt, P. Valenzuela, and H. Murialdo. 2001. Bacteriophage lambda DNA packaging enzyme: identification of four structural domains of the gpNu1 subunit using limited proteolysis. *Biol. Res.* 34:(3–4). www.scielo.cl/scielo.php?script=sci_arttext&pid =S0716976020010003000008&Ing=es&nrm=iso#37.

Atkins, P. W. 1991. *Atoms, electrons, and change.* New York: W. H. Freeman and Co. Scientific American Library, #36.

Baranska, S., M. Gabig, A. Wegrzyn, G. Konopa, A. Herman-Antosiewicz, P. Hernandez, J. B. Schvartzman, D. R. Helinkski, and G. Wegrzyn. 2001. Regulation of the switch from early to late bacteriophage lambda DNA replication. *Microbiol.* March, 147(Pt3): 535–47. http://mic.sgmjournals. org/cgi/content/full/147/3/535?view=full&pmid=11238961.

Bell, C. E., and M. Lewis. 2001. Crystallographic analysis of lac repressor bound to natural operator O1. *J. Mol. Biol.*, 312:921–926.

Benford, M. S. 2002. Implications of plant genome research to alternative therapies: a case for radiogenic metabolism in humans. *Journal of Theoretics.* 4–6. www.journaloftheoretics.com/Articles/4-6/MSB.pdf.

*Bergman, R. 1999. University of Hamburg Depart. of Biol. Porins. www.biologie.uni-hamburg.de/lehre/bza/kanal/porin/eporin.htm.

Bernhardt, T. G., W. D. Roof, and R. Young. 2000. Genetic evidence that the bacteriophage *phi*X174 lysis proteins inhibits cell wall synthesis. *Proc. Natl. Acad. Sci. USA.* April 11, 97 (8): 4297–4302.

Blasi, P., R. I. Epstein, and A. V. Olinto. 2000. *Astrophys. J.* 533:L123. http://arxiv.org/abs/astro-ph/9912240.

Bohm, D., and B. Hiley. 1993. *The undivided universe.* London and New York: Routledge.

Bohr, Neils. 1963. *Essays, 1958–1962, on atomic physics and human knowledge.* New York: Wiley.

Bouwmeester, D., J.-W. Pan, K. Mattle, M. Eibl, H. Weinfurter, and A. Zeilinger. 1997. Experimental quantum teleportation. *Nature.* Dec. 11, 390:575–579. http://deutsche.nature.com/physics/43.pdf.

Bridges, Andrew. "Scientists find sugar in space, building block of life." news release. June 16, 2000. www.space.com/scienceastronomy/astronomy/sugar_000615.html Accessed June 19, 2004.

Brody, T. B. 1996. Biological Overview of gene *adar.* http://flybase.bio.indiana.edu/allied-data/lk/ interactive-fly/hjmuller/adar1.htm.

Brown, D. M., editor, et al. 1992. *Egypt: land of the pharaohs.* Alexandria, Virginia: Time–Life Books.

*Brown, M. 2000. Swarthmore College. http://physics.Swarthmore.edu/html/faculty/SSX/faq.html.

*Budd, T. 2003. St. Lawrence Univ., N.Y. Introduction to Cell Biology, BIO 250. DNA repair systems. http://it.stlawu.edu/~tbudd/repair.html.

Budge, E. A. W. 1905. *The Egyptian heaven and hell.* Unabridged republication of original full work. New York: Dover Publications, Inc., 1996.

Budge, E. A. W. 1904. *The gods of the Egyptians, Volume I–II.* Unabridged republication of original full edition. New York: Dover Publications, 1969.

Buechner, M., A. H. Delcour, B. Martinac, J. Adler, and C. Kung. 1999 Ion channel activities in the *Escherichia coli* outer membrane. *Biochimica et Biophysica Acta.* Abstract. 1024:111–121.

*Bull, H. 2003. Univ. Saskatchewan, College of Medicine. Micro 216.3. Genetic exchange assays, lambda x lambda crosses, single-strand gap recombination. www.usask.ca/medicine/microbiol/bull/mar-25- 6.pdf.

Cai, D., Y.-T. Li, T. Ichikawa, and K.-I. Nishikawa. 2001. Visualizing magnetotail field topology in a three-dimensional particle simulation. *Proceedings of ISSS-6*:1–4. www.copernicus.org/ISSS6/abstracts/isc0007.pdf.

Cairns, J., J Overbaugh, and J. H. Miller. 1988. The origin of mutants. *Nature.* 335:142–145.

Calder, Nigel. 1979. *Einstein's universe.* New York: Greenwich House.

*Caltech Div. of Geological and Planetary Sciences. Genesis Web Science Doc. G. "Solar Wind Properties." www.gps.caltech.edu/genesis/DocumentG.html.

Campbell, A. 1962. Episomes. *Adv. Genet.* 11:101–145.

*Cann, A. 2004. University of Leicester. Course BS 2024 Microbiology II. Lecture Notes: Virus Structure. www-micro.msb.le.ac.uk/224/Structure224.html.

*Carnegie Mellon Univ. Department of Biological Sciences. Course 03-441 Molecular Biology of Prokaryotes. "Controlling gene expression by RNA degradation." http://info.bio.cum.edu/Courses/03441/RNAdegradation/RNADegControl.html.

Catalano, C. E., D. Cue, and M. Feiss. 1995. Virus DNA packaging: the strategy used by phage lambda. *Mol. Microbiol.* June;16(6): 1075–86.
Cattell, C., J. Crumley, J. Dombeck, J. Wygant, and F. S. Mozer. 2002. Polar observation of solitary waves at the earth's magnetopause. Abstract. *Geophys.Res. Ltrs.*, 29(5).
www.agu.org/pubs/sample_articles/ae/2001GL014046/0.shtml.
Cattell[1], C., J. Dombeck, J. Wygant, M. Goldstein, W. Keith, A. Fazakerley, J. F. Drake, M. Swisdak, M. Andre, E. Lucek, and A. Balogh. 2004. Cluster observations of solitary waves in association with magnetotail reconnection. Space Physics at the Univ. of Minnesota.
http://ham.space.umn.edu/cattell/jgr_sw/1oct_sw_paper_cattell.pdf.
Cattell[2], C., J. Dombeck, J. Wygant, F. S. Mozer, and M. Andre The role of waves in magnetotail dynamics. Electric Field Instrument on the Polar Spacecraft.
http://lepefi.gsfc.nasa.gov/~polarefi/publications/cattell_proc.pdf.
Chandler, M. O., S. A. Fuselier, M. Lockwood, and T. E. Moore. 1999. Evidence of component merging equatorward of the cusp. *J. Geophys. Res.* 104(A10): 22623–33.
Chandra, N. R. Department of Physics, Indian Institute of Science, Bangalore, India. Protein Informatics, RecA. http://physics.iisc.ernet.in/~dichome/course/assign.htm
Chang, Ngee-Pong. 1995. Chiral restoration in the early universe: pion halo in the sky. *Nucl. Phys. Proc. Supp.* 43:308. http://arxiv.org/PS_cache/hep-th/pdf/9503/9503119.pdf
Chang, N. 1993. Braaten-Pisarski action, disoriented chiral condensate, and chiral symmetry nonrestoration. http://arxiv.org/PS_cache/hep-ph/pdf/9309/9309253.pdf
Chardin, P. Teilhard de. 1959. *The phenomenon of man.* London: Wm. Collins Sons & Co., Ltd. New York: Harper & Row, Publishers, Inc.
Chardin, Teilhard de. 1978. *The heart of matter.* San Diego, New York: Harvest Book, Harcourt, Inc.
Chen, J. , T. A. Fritz, and K. Kudela, Cusp: A new acceleration region of the magnetosphere, *Czech. J. Phys.*, 49, No. 4a, 667–674, 1999.
*Cristoffersen, R. 2004. Life Science Computing Faculty. MCDB/BMSE 293 Survey of Computational Methods in Biochemistry and Molecular Biology. Handout: Principles of Protein Structure, Comparative Protein Modelling and Visualization by J. Cooper, J. Walshaw and Alan Mills.
http://tutor.lscf.ucsb.edu/course/winter/mcdb293/handouts/proteinstructurecourse.pdf.
Chubb, R. T. 2002. Structural studies of Xis-DNA recognition in bacteriophage lambda. *J. of Analytical Sci.com.* http://www.analytical-science.com/Journal/nuclearmagneticresonance_2002.htm.
Cingolani, G., S. D. Moore, P. E. Prevelige, Jr., and J. E. Johnson. 2002. Preliminary crystallographic analysis of the bacteriophage P22 portal protein. *J. Structural Biol.* 139:46–54.
www.ncbi.nlm.nih.gov/entrez/query.fcgi?cmd=Search&db=PubMed&term=Prevelige+PE.
Cirlot, J. E. 1971. *A dictionary of symbols, second edition.* New York: Philosophical Library, Inc.
*Clark, D. P. 1999. Carbon and energy metabolism. Southern Illinois Univ. Carbondale. Micro 425: Physiology & Biochemistry of Microorganisms. www.science.siu.edu/microbiology /micr425/425Notes/04-C&Energy.html.
Close, Frank. 1989. "The quark structure of matter" in *The new physics,* edited by Paul Davies. Cambridge University Press.
Cold Spring Harbor Laboratory. 2001. "Histone Code" joins genetic code as critical determinant of chromosomal inheritance: study reveals key properties of silent versus active DNA." news release, August 9, 2001. http://www.cshl.org/public/releases/grewal080901.html.
Comins, N.F., and W. J. Kaufmann, III. 2000. *Discovering the universe, fifth edition.* New York: W. H. Freeman and Company.
Cowley, S. W. H. 1996. A beginner's guide to the earth's magnetosphere. *Earth in Space.* (American Geophysical Union) 8(7). http://www.agu.org/sci_soc/cowley.html
Cox, M. M. 2001. Historical overview: searching for replication help in all the rec places. *PNAS.* July 17, 98(15): 8173–8180.
Cramer, P. 2002. Multisubunit RNA polymerase. *Current Opinion in Struct. Bio.* February, 12:89–97.
Creighton, T. E. 1990. Protein folding. *Biochem. J.* August 15, 270(1): 1–16.
Crowther, R. A., E. V. Lenk, Y. Kikuchi, and J. King. 1977. Abstract. *J. Mol. Bio.* 116(3): 489–523.
Czyz, A., B. Wrobel, and G. Wegrzyn. 2000. Vibrio Harvey bioluminescence plays a role in stimulation of DNA repair. *Microbiol.* 146:283–288.
Davidson, A., P. Yau, H. Murialdo, and M. Gold. 1991. Isolation and characterization of mutations in the bacteriophage lambda terminase genes. *J. Bacteriol.* 173(16):5086–5096.
Doi, A., R. Drath, M. Nagasaki, H. Matsuno, and S. Miyano. 1999. Protein dynamics observations of lambda phage by hybrid petri net. Japanese Society for Bioinformatics. *Genome Informatics.* 10:217–218.
Donaldson, L. W., J. M. Petersen, B. J. Graves, and L. P. McIntosh. 1994. Secondary structure of the ETS domain places murine Ets-1 in the super family of winged helix-turn-helix DNA-binding proteins. *Biochem.* November 22, 33(46): 13509–16.
Doxey, Denise M. 2002. Thoth. *Ancient gods speak: a guide to Egyptian religion.* New York: Oxford University Press.
*Doye, J. Depart. of Chemistry, Cambridge, United Kingdom. EnergyLandscapes.
www-wales.ch.cam.ac.uk/~jon/research/cluster_eland.html.
Doye, J. P. K., M. A. Miller, and D. J. Wales. 2003. Evolution of the potential energy surface with size for

Lennard-Jones Clusters. *J. Chem. Phys.* 111:8417–8428.
Doye, J. P. K., and D. J. Wales. 1996. On potential energy surfaces and relaxation to the global minimum. *J. Chem. Phys.* 105:8428–8445.
Duff, M. J. 2003. The theory formerly known as Strings. *Spec. Ed. Scientific American: The Edge of Physics.* 13(1): 12–17.
Dungey, J. W. 1961. Interplanetary magnetic fields and the auroral zones. *Phys. Rev. Lett.* 6:47–48.
Elbashir, S. J., J. Harborth, W. Lenderckel, A. Yalein, K. Weber, and T. Tuschi. 2001. Duplexes of 21-nucleotide RNAs mediate RNA interference in cultured mammalian cells. *Nature.* May 24, 411(6836):494–8.
Escoubet, C. P., M. F. Smith, S. F. Fung, P. C. Anderson, R. A. Hoffman, E. M. Basinka, and J. M. Bosqued. 1993. Staircase ion signature in the polar cusp: a case study. *Geophys. Res. Lett.* 19:1735–1738.
EurekAlert. Amer. Assoc. for the Advancement of Science. Contact: Bonner, Joseph. Rockefeller University. "Three-D images shed light on first steps of RNA synthesis." news release, May 16, 2002. www.eurekalert.org/pub_releases/2002-05/ru-tis051502.php.
European Bioinformatics Institute. Interpro Database of protein families. DRADA IPR000607. www.ebi.ac.uk/interpro/DisplayIproEntry?ac=IPR000607.
European Space Agency. "Cluster's new view of near-Earth space." news release, February 16, 2001. www.esa.int/esaCP/ESA6VTTM5JC_index_2.html.
European Space Agency. "Cluster captures a double cusp." news release. October 9, 2001.
Faraldo-Gomez, J. D. 2002. Computational studies of bacterial iron transport proteins: methodological aspects and application. PhD diss., Univ. of Oxford. http://sansom.biop.ox.ac.uk/josed/thesis/chapter1.pdf.
Fire, A., X. S. Xu, M. K. Montgomery, S. A. Kostas, S. E. Driver, and C. C. Mello. 1998. Potent and specific genetic interference by double-stranded RNA in *Caenorhabditis elegans. Nature.* Feb. 19, 391:806–11.
*Fitzpatrick, R. 2002. Univ. of Texas online graduate level lecture course. Intro. to Plasma Physics. Nonlinear tearing mode theory. http://farside.ph.utexas.edu/~rfitzp/teaching/plasma/lectures/node76.html.
Fogh, R. H., G. Ottleben, H. Ruterjans, M. Schnarr, R. Boelens, and R. Kaptein. 1994. Solution structure of the LexA repressor DNA binding domain determined by 1H NMR spectroscopy. Abstract. *Embo J.* Sept., 1, 13(17): 3936–3944. www.ncbi.nlm.nih.gov/entrez/query.fcgi?cmd=Retrieve&db=PubMed&list_uids=8076591&dopt=Abstract.
*Franzen, S. 2001. Intro. to Transport Phenomena. CH7951. http://chsfpc5.chem.ncsu.edu/CH795I/lectures/diffusion/index.htm.
Friedman, E., and G. Soff. 1985. Calculations of deeply bound pionic states in heavy and superheavy atoms. *J. Phys.G. Nucl. Phys.* Abstract. 11:L37–L42. Racah Inst. of Phys., Hebrew Univ., Jerusalem, Israel. Issue 3 (March 1985).
Friedman, Florence D. 2002. Akh. *Ancient gods speak: a guide to Egyptian religion.* New York: Oxford University Press.
*Frommert, H. and C. Kronberg. 2002. Univ. of Arizona SEDS. The Milky Way. www.seds.org/messier/more/mw.html.
Fujimoto, M., T. Terasawa, T. Mukai, Y. Saito, T. Yamamoto, S. Kokubun. 1998. Plasma entry from the flanks of the near-Earth, magnetotail: Geotail observations. *J. Geophys. Res.* 103:4391–4408.
Fuselier, S. A., D. M. Klumpar, W. K. Peterson, and E. G. Shelley. *Geophys. Res. Lett.* 16:1121.
Gardiner, A. 1927. *Egyptian Grammar, being an introduction to the study of hieroglyphs.* Cambridge, United Kingdom, Third Edition 1957.
Gee, H. "A journey into the genome: what's there." *Nature Science Update.* news release, February 12, 2001.
Gell-man, M. and Yuval Ne'Eman. 2000. *The Eightfold Way.* Cambridge, MA: Perseus Publishing.
Gilbert, S. F. 2000. *Developmental Biology.* Sunderland, MA: Sinauer Associates, Inc., Publishers.
Gimbutas, Marija. 1974. *The goddesses and gods of Old Europe 6500 to 3500 B.C.: myths and cult images.* Berkeley & Los Angeles: Univ. of California, 1982.
Goelet, O., Jr. 1994. Introduction and Commentary to *The Egyptian book of the dead* by R. Faulkner. San Francisco: Chronicle Books.
*Gonzalez, J. E. Fall, 2000. Univ. Texas at Dallas. Molecular Biology 5420. Lecture #9 Phage Lambda. http://nsm1.utdallas.edu/bio/Gonzalez/Lecture/Genetics/Lecture09.htm.
*Gonzalez, M. A. G. 1997. Ohio State, College of Biological Sciences. Bacteriophage Lambda. Excerpted from a course by Dr. Alan Cann, Univ. of Leicester, UK. www.biosci.ohio-state.edu/~mgonzalez/Micro521/Lambda/lambda_phage.html.
Gopaul, D. N., F. Guo, and G. D. Van Duyne. 1998. Structure of the Holliday junction intermediate in Cre-*loxP* site-specific recombination. *Embo. J.* 17(14): 4175–4187. http://snowwhite.med.upenn.edu/vanduyne/pdf/embo-17-4175.pdf.
Goswami, A. 1997. Consciousness and directed mutation: is there conscious choice in directed mutation, photocopies and related phenomena?: a quantum measurement theoretic answer. *Integrative Beh. Sci and Online Bulletin of Science within Consciousness.* www.swcp.com/swc/Essays/bio.html.
Greene, B. R. 1999. *The elegant universe.* New York: Vintage Books, A Division of Random House, Inc.
Greene, B. R. 2004. *Fabric of the cosmos: space, time and the texture of reality.* New York: Alfred E. Knopf.
Gribbin, John. 2001. *Hyperspace.* London: BBC Worldwide Limited and New York: DK Publishing, Inc.
Griffiths, J. Gwyn. 2002. Osiris. *Ancient gods speak: a guide to the Egyptian religion.* New York: Oxford University Press.
*Guffey, S. Z. 2002. Univ. of Tennessee, Div. of Biology. Biology 102. Summer. http://web.bio.utk.edu/guffey/sg102/July12.html.

Hameroff, S. and R. Penrose. Orchestrated objective reduction of quantum coherence in brain microtubules: the "Orch OR" model for consciousness. Univ. of Arizona. http://www.quantumconsciousness.org/publications.html#penrose.

Harari, D., S. Mollerach, and E. Roulet. 2000. Magnetic lensing of extremely high-energy cosmic rays in a galactic wind. *J. High Energy Phys.* 10(2000)047. http://www.iop.org/EJ/abstract/1126-6708/2000/10/047.

Harrison, P. 2003. "Nature's flawed mirror." *Physics World.* July. http://physicsweb.org/article/world/16/7/8 (accessed Sept. 30, 2004).

Harvard Smithsonian Center for Astrophysics. 2004. "Galaxy clusters and dark energy: Chandra opens new line of investigation on dark energy." http://chandra.harvard.edu/photo/2004/darkenergy.

Hasinger, G., N. Schartel, and S. Komossa. 2002. Discovery of an ionized FE K edge in the z=3.91 broad absorption line quasar APM 98279+5255 with XMM-Newton. Abstract. *Astrophys. J.* 573(2): L77–L80.

Hawking, Stephen. 2004. Speech at 17th International Conference on General Relativity and Gravitation, Dublin, Ireland. July 21, 2004. http://pancake.uchicago.edu/~carroll/hawkingdublin.txt.

Hawking, Stephen. 2001. *The universe in a nutshell.* New York: Bantam Books.

Hawking, Stephen. 1988. *A brief history of time.* New York: Bantam Books.

*Heapy, S. 2004. Univ. of Leicester. Course BS(IM) 2024: Microbiology II. http://www-micro.msb.le.ac.uk/224/bs224.html.

Hegner, M., S. B. Smith, and C. Bustamante. 1999. Polymerization and mechanical properties of single RecA-DNA filaments. *Proc. Natl. Acad. Sci. USA.* 96:10109–10114.

Heikkila, W. J. 1990. Magnetic reconnection, merging, and viscous interaction in the magnetosphere. *Space Science Reviews.* 53(1).

Heikkila, W. J., and J. D. Winningham. 1971. Penetration of magnetosheath plasma to low latitudes through the dayside magnetospheric cusps. *J. Geophys. Res.* 76:883.

Hendrix, R. W. 1998. Bacteriophage DNA packaging: RNA gears in a DNA transport machine. *Cell.* July 24, 94:147–50. www.cell.com/content/article/abstract?uid=PIIS0092867400814130.

Herbert A., and A. Rich. 2001. The role of binding domains for dsRNA and Z-DNA in the *in vivo* editing of minimal substrates by ADAR1. *Proc. Natl. Acad. Sci. USA.* October 9, 98(21): 12132–12137. Online: www.pnas.org.

Herbert, A. and A. Rich. 1999. RNA processing the evolution of eukaryotes. *Nature Genetics.* Abstract. 21:265–269.

Herbert, A. and A. Rich. 1996. Biology of left-handed Z-DNA. Minireview. *J. Biol. Chem.* May 17, 271(20): 11595–11598. JBC Online. www.jbc.org.

Herodotus. 1996. *The histories.* trans. Aubrey De Selincourt. revised John Marincola. London, UK: Penguin Books.

*Hewlett, M. 2000. Univ. of Arizona Biology Learning Center. Molecular Biology. MCB 411. Bacteriophage lambda: a complex viral operon; DNA recombination; Operons; Lambda Repressors. www.blc.arizona.edu/marty/411/Modules/lambda.html.

Hile, Jennifer, director of 30-minute documentary. National Geographic Channel. *The Hidden World of the Asmat.* September 30, 2003.

Hoffmann, M. A., G. Wrigge, and B. v. Issendorff. 2002. Photoelectron spectroscopy of Al_{32000}: Observation of a "Coulomb staircase" in a free cluster. *Phys. Rev.* B 66:041404(R).

Hogan, Jenny. "Hawking cracks black hole paradox." news release, July14, 2004. www.NewScientist.com/news/print.jsp?id=ns99996151.

Holliday, R. 1964. A mechanism for gene conversion fungi. *Genet. Res.* 5:282–304.

Hones, E. J. Jr., D. N. Baker, S. J. Bame, W. C. Feldman, J. T. Gosling, D. J. McComas, R. D. Zwickl, J. A. Slavin, E. J. Smith, and B. T. Tsurutani. 1984. Structure of the magnetotail at 200 Re and its response to geomagnetic activity. *Geophys. Res. Lett.* 11, 5.

Hornung, Erik. 1999. *The ancient Egyptian books of the afterlife.* Trans. David Lorton. Ithaca and London: Cornell University Press.

Houser-Wegner, Jennifer. 2002. *Ancient gods speak: a guide to the Egyptian religion.* New York: Oxford University Press.

Howard Hughes Medical Institute. "Human genome bears a virus related to HIV-1." news release, November 9, 1999. www.hhmi.org/news/cullen/html.

Huth, G. P. 2004. A new physics-based model for light interaction with the retina of the human eye: rethinking the vision process. www.ghuth.com.

*Illingworth, J. A. and P. J. F. Henderson. 1999. Univ. of Leeds. BIOC3390 Tutorials November 16 and 18, 1999. Molecular Motors: Flagella in *E. coli.* www.bmb.leeds.ac.uk/illingworth/motors/flagella.htm. Institut Pasteur. 2001. Colibri Database *E. coli K-12* genome. http://genolist.pasteur.fr/Colibri/genome.cgi. (accessed Sept. 30, 2004).

Jacob, Francois, and Jacque Monod. 1961. Genetic regulatory mechanisms in the synthesis of proteins. *J. Molecular Biol.* 3:318–356.

Jechlinger, W., M. P. Szostak, A. Witte, and W. Lubitz. 1999. Altered temperature induction sensitivity of the lambdapR/cI857 system for controlled gene *E* expression in *Escherichia coli. FEMS Microbiol. Lttrs.* 173:347–352.

Joarder, P. S., V. M. Nakariakov, and B. Roberts. 1997. A manifestation of negative energy waves in the solar atmosphere. *Solar Physics.* Dec., 176(2): 285–297. http://tbird5.astro.warwick.ac.uk/~valery/Offprints/jnr2.pdf.

Juergens, Sylvester, P., S.M. *"Crux Fidelis." The New Marian Missal.* New York: Regina Press. Imprimatur Francis Cardinal Spellman, 1950.

Jung, C. G. 1958. *Psyche & Symbol.* Violet S. deLaszlo, Ed. New York: Doubleday Anchor Books, Doubleday & Co., Inc.

Keith, W. R., J. D. Winningham, and O. Norberg. 2001. A new, unique signature of the true cusp. *Ann. Geophys.* 19:611, June.

Kihara, A., Y. Akiyama, and K. Ito. 1997. Host regulation of lysogenic decision in bacteriophage lambda. *Proc. Natl. Acad. Sci. USA.* May 27, 94(11): 5544–5549.

Kilbinger, M., and M. Hetterscheidt. Dark energy dominates the universe. *Institut fur Astrophysik und Extraterrestrische Forschung der Universitat Bonn* www.astro.uni-bonn.de/~webiaef/outreach/posters/darkenergy.

Kim, J. I., J. Heuser, and M. M. Cox. 1989. Enhanced recA protein binding to Z-DNA represents a kinetic perturbation of a general duplex DNA binding pathway. *J. Biol. Chem.* Dec., 25, 264(36): 21848–56.

Kim, M.-H. Y., J. W. Wilson, F. A. Cucinotta, L. C. Simonsen, W. Atwell, F. F. Badavi, and J. Miller. 1999. Contribution of high charge and energy (HZE) ions during solar-particle event of September 29, 1989. NASA/TP–1999–209320. http://techreports.larc.nasa.gov/ltrs/PDF/1999/tp/NASA-99-tp209320.pdf.

*Klevickis, C., James Madison Univ. Dept. of Integrated Science and Tech. www.isat.jmu.edu/users/klevicca/isat454/3CRO.HTM.

*Langeveld, W. 2002. Stanford Univ. High energy cosmic rays and Sun. http://www2.slac.stanford.edu/vvc/cosmicrays/crsun.html.

Lavaki, E., and T. Callaway. 2001. Ionophore effects on *Enterococcus faecium* and *Enterococcus faecalis.* NASA SHARP Plus Program. Southern Plains Agric. Research Center-U.S. Depart. of Agriculture.

Lehn, Jean-Marie, and Philip Ball. 2000. Chap. 12 Supramolecular chemistry. *New Chemistry.* Nina Hall, ed. Cambridge University Press.

Leopold, P. E., M. Montal, and J. N. Onuchic. 1992. Protein folding funnels: a kinetic approach to the sequence-structure relationship. *PNAS.* 89:8721–8725.

Lesko, Leonard H. 2002. *Ancient gods speak: a guide to Egyptian religion.* New York: Oxford Univ. Press.

Lewis, M., G. Chang, N. Horton, M. A. Kercher, H. C. Pace, M. A. Schumacher, R. G. Brennan, P. Lu. 1996. Crystal structure of the lactose operon repressor and its complexes with DNA and inducer. *Science.* 271:1247–1254.

Li, Xinlin. 2002. Radiation belts and substorm particle injections. Depart. of Aerospace Engineering Sciences, Univ. of Colorado. http://lasp.colorado.edu/~lix/paper/ICS6/ics6.pdf

Little, R. D., T. H. Platt, and C. L. Schildkraut. 1993. Initiation and termination of DNA replication in human rRNA genes. *Mol. Cell Biol.* Abstract. October, 13(10): 6600–13.

Liu, L. F., and J. C. Wang. 1987. Supercoiling of the DNA template during transcription. *Proc. Natl. Acad. Sci. USA.* 84(20): 7024–7027.

Lockwood, M., A Fazakerley, H. Opgenoorth, J. Moen, A.P. van Eyken, M. Dunlop, J.-M. Bosqued, G. Lu, C. Cully, P. Eglitis et al. 2001. Coordinated Cluster and ground-based instrument observations of transient changes in the magnetopause boundary layer during an interval of predominantly northward IMF: relation to reconnection pulses and FTE signatures. *Annales Geophys, Cluster First Results Special Issue.* Paper AG/2001/000105 July.

Lockwood, M., and M. F. Smith. 1992. The variation of reconnection rate at the dayside magnetopause and cusp ion precipitation. *J. Geophys. Res.* 97:14841–14847.

Lundin, R., and E. Dubinin. 1985. Solar wind energy transfer regions inside the dayside magnetopause - accelerated heavy ions as tracers for MHD-processes in the dayside boundary layer. *Planet Space Sci.* 33:891–907.

Luscombe, N. M., S. E. Austin, H. M. Berman, and J. M. Thornton. 2000. An overview of the structures of protein-DNA complexes. *Genome Bio.* Reviews. http://genomebiology.com/2000/1/1/reviews/001.

Lybarger, S. R., and J. R. Maddock. 2001. Polarity in action: asymmetric protein localization in bacteria. *J. Bacteriol.* June, 183(11): 3261–3267.

*Maber, J. 1999. Univ. of Leeds, UK. Depart. of Biochemistry and Molecular Biology. Introduction to Glycolysis. www.jonmaber.demon.co.uk/glyintro/page04.htm.

Malaise, Michel. 2002. Bes. *Ancient gods speak: a guide to Egyptian religion.* New York: Oxford Univ. Press.

*Maloy, S. April 26, 2000. San Diego State Univ. Microbial Genetics. Specialized Transduction. www.sci.sdsu.edu/~smaloy/MicrobialGenetics/problems/exchange/transduction/sptdx.html.

*Maloy, S. 2000. Univ. of Illinois at Urbana-Champaign. Micro 316. Microbial Genetics. Lambda attachment sites. www.life.uiuc.edu/micro/316/topics/phage/lambda-att-sites.html.

*Marcey, D. 2001. California Lutheran Univ. Online Macromolecular Museum. *Cro* repressor of temperate bacteriophages. www.clunet.edu/BioDev/omm/cro/frames/crotxt.htm#1.

*Marcey[1], D. H. M. Heerssen, and A. Downs. 2001. California Lutheran Univ. Online Macromolecular Museum. RecA protein: structure and biological function. www.clunet.edu/BioDev/omm/reca/frames/recatx.htm.

*Marcey[2], D., K. Flammer, and A. Downs. 2001. California Lutheran Univ. Online Macromolecular Museum. The *E. coli* porin proteins OMPF and maltoporin (*LamB* porin). www.clunet.edu/BioDev/omm/porins/pormast.htm.

Markey, Sean. "Universe is Finite, "Soccer Ball"-Shaped, Study Hints."National Geographic News, news release, October 8, 2003. http://news.nationalgeographic.com/news/2003/10/1008_031008_finiteuniverse.html.

Martin, W., and M. Muller. 1998. The hydrogen hypothesis for the first eukaryote. *Nature.* March 5, 392:37–41.

Massachusetts Institute of Technology News. "Evidence found that spinning black holes drag spacetime." news release, Nov. 6, 1997. http://web.mit.edu/newsoffice/nr/1997/blackholes.html.

Massachusetts Institute of Technology News. "Rich team finds role for Z-DNA." news release, August 16, 1995. http://web.mit.edu/newsoffice/tt/1995/aug16/40591.html.

Mathews, C.K., K. E. van Holde, and K. G. Ahern. 2000. *Biochemistry 3rd edition.* Benjamin/Cummings. D/B Pearson Education

Max-Planck Institute. "Mysterious iron factory in the early universe." news release. PRI SP 8/2002(68). www.mpe.mpg.de/pr20020708.html.

Maxwell, K. L., A. A. Yee, V. Booth, C. H. Arrowsmith, M. Gold, and A. R. Davidson. 2001. The solution structure of bacteriophage protein W, a small morphogenetic protein possessing a novel fold. Abstract. *J. Mol. Bio.* April 20, 308(1): 9-14.

McBride, D. R. 2002. Nun. *Ancient gods speak: a guide to the Egyptian religion.* New York: Oxford University Press.

*McClean, P. E. 1998. North Dakota State Univ. PLSC 731 Plant Molecular Genetics. Bacteriophage lambda vectors. www.cc.ndsu.nodak.edu/instruct/mcclean/plsc731/cloning/cloning3.htm.

McFadden, J. P., C. W. Carlson, R. Strangeway, and R. Moebius. 2003. Observations of downgoing velocity dispersed O+ and He+ in the cusp during magnetic storms. *Geophys. Res. Lett.* 30(18).

McKenzie, G. J., R. S. Harris, P. L. Lee, and S. M. Rosenberg. 2000. The SOS response regulates adaptive mutation. *Proc. Natl. Acad. Sci. USA.* June 6, 97(12): 6646–6651.

McManus, M. T., C. P. Petersen, B. B. Haines, J. Chen, and P. A. Sharp. 2002. Gene silencing using micro-RNA designed hairpins. Cambridge University Press. *RNA.* 8:842–850.

*McQueen, N. 2003. Californian State Univ., L.A. Dept. of Biological Sci.Powerpoint presentation of prokaryote expression. http://instructional1.calstatela.edu/nmcquee/Proexpression.2003.ppt

Meirav, U., and E. B. Foxman. 1996. Single-electron phenomena in semi-conductors. *Semiconductor Sci. Technol.* 11:255–284.

Merino, G., and H. A. Shuman. 1997. Unliganded maltose-binding protein triggers lactose transport in an *Escherichia coli* mutant with an alternation in the maltose transport system. *J. Bacteriol.* December, 179(24): 7687–7694. http://jb.asm.org/cgi/reprint/179/24/7687.

Meltzer, Edmund S. 2002. Horus. *Ancient gods speak: a guide to the Egyptian religion.* New York: Oxford University Press.

*Metzenberg, S. 2002. Department of Biology. California State University, Northridge. Recombinant DNA Techniques. Lecture 2 Bacterial Plasmids. http://escience.ws/b572/L2/L2.htm

Mitchell, M. S., S. Matsuzaki, S. Imai, and V. B. Rao. 2002. Sequence analysis of bacteriophage T4 DNA packaging/terminase genes *16* and *17* reveals a common ATPase center in the large subunit of viral terminases. *Nucleic Acids. Res.* 30(18): 4009–4021.

Moore, S. D., and P. E. Prevelige, Jr. 2001. Structural transformations accompanying the assembly of bacteriophage P22 portal protein rings *in vitro*. *J. Biol. Chem.* March 2, 276(9): 6779–6788.

Moore[1], S. D., and P. E. Prevelige, Jr. 2002. Bacteriophage P22 portal vertex formation *in vivo*. *J. Mol. Biol.* 315:975–994.

Moore[2], S. D., and P. E. Prevelige, Jr. 2002. A P22 scaffold protein mutation increases the robustness of head assembly in the presence of excess portal protein. *J. Virol.* October, 76(20): 10245–10255.

Moore, T. E., and M.-C. Fok. 2002. The dayside reconnection X line. *J. Geophys. Res.* 107(A10): 1332, doi:10.1029/2002JA009381.

Moore, T. E., M. O. Chandler, C. R. Chappell, R. H. Comfort, P. D. Craven, D. C. Delcourt, H. A. Elliott, B. L. Giles, J. L. Horwitz, C. J. Pollock, Y.-J. Su. 1998. Polar/TIDE results on polar ion outflows. *NASA Publications.* http://satyr.msfc.nasa.gov/studies/publications/98Moore-GM109-outflows/00.TIDEpolarIonOutflowCR.pdf.

Morimatsu, K., M. Takahashi, and B. Norden. 2002. Arrangement or recA protein in its active filament determined by polarized light spectroscopy. *Proc. Natl. Acad. Sci. USA.* September 3, 99:11688–11693.

*Mosher, R. 2003. Wagner College, New York. MI522. Bacteriophages. http://www.wagner.edu/faculty/users/rmosher/MI522Lecture7.pdf.

Mozer, F. S., S. D. Bale, and T. D. Phan. 2002. Evidence of diffusion regions at a subsolar magnetopause crossing. *Phys. Rev. Lttrs.* July, 89(1). http://lepefi.gsfc.nasa.gov/~polarefi/publications/prlv89n1.pdf.

Mulcahy, S. 1997. The thermodynamics of protein unfolding. Fourth Industrial Biochemistry. www.csn.ul.ie/~stephen/reports/unfolding.html.

*Mulligan, M. E. 2003. Memorial Univ. of Newfoundland. Biochemistry 4103, Prokaryote Gene Regulation, Lambda. www.mun.ca/biochem/courses/4103/PDF/Lambda6.pdf.

*Mulligan, M. 2002. Memorial Univ. of Newfoundland. Biochemistry 3107. Bacterial RNA polymerase. www.mun.ca/biochem/courses/3107/Lectures/Topics/RNAP_bacterial.html.

*Mulligan, M. 2001. Memorial Univ. of Newfoundland. Biochemistry 3107. Site-specific recombination. www.mun.ca/biochem/courses/3107/Lectures/Topics/Site_specific_Recomb.html.

Mysliwiec, K. 2002. Atum. *Ancient gods speak: a guide to the Egyptian religion.* New York: Oxford University Press.

NASA Magnetospheric Consellation Mission. DRACO. 2001. Understanding the global dynamics of the structured magnetotail. May Report. http://stp.gsfc.nasa.gov/missions/mc/STDT_Final/MC_STDT_0401_Screen.pdf.

*NASA[1] Space Technology 5. Solar Storms. http://nmp.jpl.nasa.gov/st5/SCIENCE/storms.html.

*NASA[2] Polar Wind Geotail. International Solar Terrestrial Physics. The tail of the magnetopshere #23. www-spof.gsfc.nasa.gov/Education/wtail.html.

*NASA[3] Polar Wind Geotail. International Solar Terrestrial Physics. The Magnetopause #19. www-istp.gsfc.nasa.gov/Education/wmpause.html.

*Nave, C. R. 2003. Zero potential. Hyperphysics. Depart. of Physics and Astronomy, Georgia State University. http://hyperphysics.phy-astr.gsu.edu/hbase/electric/elepe.html.

Nelson, J. R., C. W. Lawrence, and D. C. Hinkle. 1996. Thymine-thymine dimer bypass by yeast DNA polymerase *zeta. Science.* Abstract. June 14, 272(5268): 1646–9.

Neudegg, D. A., S. W. H. Cowley, K. A. McWilliams, M. Lester, T. K. Yeoman, J. Sigwarth, G. Haerendel, W. Baumjohann, U. Auster, K.-H. Fornacon, and E. Georgescu. 2001. The UV aurora and ionospheric flows during flux transfer events. *Annales Geophysicae.* 19:179–188.

Newell, P. T., and C.-I. Meng. 1992. Mapping the dayside ionosphere to the magnetosphere according to particle precipitation characteristics. *Geophys. Res. Lett.* 19:609–612.

Newell, P. T. U.S. National Report to IUGG, 1991–1994. *Rev. Geophys.* Vol. 33 Suppl. www.agu.org/revgeophys/newell01/node5.html.

Newell, P. T., and C.-I. Meng. 1991. Ion acceleration at the equatorward edge of the cusp: low-altitude observations of patch emerging. *Geophys. Res. Lett.* 18:1829–1832.

Nicholl, D. S. T. 2002. *An introduction to genetic enginnering, second edition.* Cambridge: Cambridge University Press.

Nomura, M. 1999. Engineering of bacterial ribosomes: replacement of all seven *Escherichia coli* rRNA operons by a single plasmid-encoded operon. *PNAS.* March 2, 96(5): 1820–1822.

Ochman, H., J. G. Lawrence, and E. A. Groisman. 2000. Lateral gene transfer and the nature of bacterial innovation. *Nature.* May 18, 405(6784): 299–304.

*O'Connor, J. J., and E. F. Robertson. University of St. Andres, Fife, Scotland. 2003. History of Measurement. The MacTutor History of Mathematics Archive. www-history.mcs.st-andrews.ac.uk/HistTopics/Measurement.html.

Ogilvie, K. W., and M. A. Coplan. 1995. Solar wind composition. U. S. National Report to IUGG, 1991–1994. *Rev. Geophys.* 33 Supplement.

Ohlendorf, D. H., D. E. Tronrud, and B. W. Matthews. 1998. Refined structure of Cro repressor protein from bacteriophage Lambda suggests both flexibility and plasticity. *J. Mol. Biol.* 280:129–136.

Olinto, A. V., R. I. Epstein, and P. Blasi. 1999. 26th International Cosmic Ray Conference, August 25–29. OG3.3.03 Acceleration of cosmic rays. Galactic Ultra-High-Energy Cosmic Rays. 4:361. www.icrc1999.utah.edu/~icrc1999/root/og_3_3.html.

Onuchic, J. N. 1997. Contacting the protein folding funnel with NMR. *Proc. Natl. Acad. Sci. USA.* July, 94:7129–7131. www.pnas.org/cgi/content/full/94/14/7129#B20.

Onuchic. J. N., Z. Luthey-Schulten, and P. G. Wolynes. 1997. Theory of protein folding: the energy landscape perspective. *Annu. Rev. Phys.Chem.* 48:545–600.

*Orava, R. 2004. University of Helsinki. Introduction to High Energy Physics. Hadrons, quarks, antimatter and neutrinos. http://www.physics.helsinki.fi/~rorava/johd_3.pdf.

Oro, J., and A. Lazcano-Araujo. The role of HCN and its derivatives in prebiotic evolution. Article excerpted from "Cyanide in Biology," B. Vinnesland, E. E. Conn, C. J. Knowles, J. Westley, F. Wissing. 1981. Academic Press, 517-541, supported in part by NASA Grant NGR 44-005-002.

Overbye, Dennis. "More sci- than fi, physicists create antimatter." *New York Times.* Sept. 19, 2002.

Pace, H., P. Lu, and M. Lewis. 1990. Lac repressor: crystallization of intact tetramer and its complexes with inducer and operator DNA. *Proc. Natl. Acad. Sci. USA.* 87:1870–1873.

Palladino[1], M. J., L. P. Keegan, M. A. O'Connell, and R. A. Reenan. 2000. *Adar,* a Drosophila double-stranded RNA-specific adenosine deaminase is highly developmentally regulated and is itself a target for RNA editing. *RNA* 6:1004–1018.

Palladino[2], M. J., L. P. Keegan, M. A. O'Connell, and R. A. Reenan. 2000. A-to-I pre-mRNA editing in Drosophila is primarily involved in adult nervous system function and integrity. *Cell.* 102:437–49.

Parker, M. H., C. G. Brouillette, and P. E. Prevelige, Jr., 2001. Kinetic and calorimetric evidence for two distinct scaffolding protein binding populations within the bacteriophage P22 procapsid. *Biochem.* July 31, 40(30): 8962–8970.

Parsons, Marie. 1999. "Philae Temple." A feature tour Egypt story. www.touregypt.net/featurestories/philae.htm.

*Pearson, G. Oregon State University. BB 492/592 Spring 2003. *E. coli* gene regulation. http://oregonstate.edu/instruction/bb492/lectures/Regulation.html.

Peck, L. J., and J. C. Wang. 1985. Transcriptional block caused by a negative supercoiling induced structural change in an alternating CG sequence. *Cell.* 40:129–137.

Penrose, Roger. 1989. *The emperor's new mind concerning computers, minds, and the laws of physics.* New York: Penguin Books.

Perry, R. J. 2000. Glue in the light-front pion. *Nucl. Phys. Proc. Suppl.* 90:87–90. http://arxiv.org/PS_cache/hep-ph/pdf/0009/0009070.pdf.

Phan, T. D., M. P. Freeman, L. M. Kistler, B. Klecker, G. Haerendel, G. Paschmann, B. U. O. Sonnerup, W. Baumjohann, M. B. Bavassano-Cattaneo, C. W. Carlson, et al. 2001. Evidence for an extended reconnection line at the dayside magnetopause. *Earth Planets Space.* 53:619–625.

Physicsweb. News for December 1998. "Experiment sees the arrow of time - at last!" http://physicsweb.org/article/world/11/12/3/1.

Physicsweb. News for June 1999. "CERN confirms direct CP violation." http://physicsweb.org/article/news/3/6/13/1.

Prak, E. T. L., and H. H. Kazazian, Jr. 2000. Mobile elements and the human genome. *Nature Reviews.* 1:134–144. http://www.nature.com/nrg.

Pribram, K. H. 1991. *Brain and perception, holonomy and structure in figural processing.* Hillsdale, NJ: Lawrence Erlbaum Associates, Publishers.

Pribram, K. H. 1989. The holographic paradigm and holonomic brain theory. AHP Creativity & Consciousness 27th AHP Conference. Stanford University, California. Conference recording tapes.

Quinn, H. R., and M. S. Witherell. 2003. The asymmetry between matter and anti-matter. *Spec. Ed. Scientific American: The Edge of Physics.* 13(1): 60–67.

*Quinn, H. 2003. Stanford Linear Accelerator Center. Virtual Visitor Center. Parity. http://www2.slac.stanford.edu/vvc/theory/parity.html.

Radman-Livaja, M., C. Shaw, M. Azaro, T. Biswas, T. Ellenberger, and A.Landy. 2003. Arm sequences contribute to the architecture and catalytic function of a Lambda integrase-Holliday junction complex. *Mol. Cell.* March, 11:783–794.

Ramaty, R., R. E. Lingenfelter, and B. Kozlovsky. The source of cosmic rays: 1. Be/Fe evolution and cosmic ray composition. *OG.3.1.03.* http://lheawww.gsfc.nasa.gov/users/ramaty/utah_ramaty.pdf.

Ramaty, R., and R. E. Lingenfelter. The source of cosmic rays: 3. supernova grain composition. *OG.3.1.05.* http://lheawww.gsfc.nasa.gov/users/ramaty/utah_richl.pdf.

*Rasinkangas, R. 2002. Online Space Physics Textbook. Ionosphere. http://www.oulu.fi/~spaceweb/textbook.

Rich, A. 1999. Left-handed Z-DNA; structure and function. *Genetica.* Abstract. 106(1–2): 37–47.

Richard, R. L., R. J. Walker, T. Ogino, and M. Ashour-Abdalla. 1997. Flux ropes in the magnetotail: consequences for ion populations. *Adv. Space Res.* 20(4–5): 1017–1021.

*Rinehart, C. 2004. Western Kentucky University. Biology 220. Bacteriophages. http://bioweb.wku.edu/courses/biol22000/35Bacteriophages/default.html.

*Roberts, G. 2003. Univ. of Wisconsin-Madison. DNA repair. www.bact.wisc.edu/Microtextbook/bactgenetics/dnarepair.htm.

Roessler, E., E. Belloni, K. Gaudenz, P. Jay, P. Berta, S. W. Scherer, L. C. Tsui, and M. Muenke. 1996. Mutations in the human Sonic Hedgehog gene cause holoprosencephaly. *Nat. Genet.* Abstract. Nov., 14(3): 357–60

Roger, A. J. 1999. Reconstructing early events in eukaryotic evolution. *Am. Nat.* Oct, 154(S4): S146–S163.

Rosenberg, S. M. 2001. Evolving responsively: adaptive mutation. *Nature Reviews/Genetics.* July, 2:504–515.

*Rosenstiel, S. L., and J. H. Rosenstiel. 2001. Brandeis Univ. Biology 122. Molecular Genetics. Site-specific recombination. www.bio.brandeis.edu/classes/biol122a/LectureSiteSpRec.htm.

Roth, A. M. 2002. Opening of the Mouth. *Ancient gods speak: a guide to Egyptian religion.* New York: Oxford University Press.

Royal Swedish Academy of Sciences. "The 1999 Nobel Prize in Physics." press release. October 12, 1999. www.nobel.se/physics/laureates/1999/press.html.

Russell, C. T. 2000. Polar eyes the cusp. Proceedings of the Cluster-II workshop: multipoint plasma measurements. *ESA SP-449* edited by R. A. Harris, 47–55. http://www-ssc.igpp.ucla.edu/personnel/russell/papers.

Russell, C. T. 1999. Magnetic stress in solar system plasmas. *Aust. J. Phys.* 52:733–751.

Russell, C. T. 1995. The structure of the magnetopause. *AGU Geophys. Monograph.* 90:81–98.

Russell, C. T., E. R. Priest, and L. C. Lee. 1990. Physics of magnetic flux ropes. *AGU.* 439–453.

Russell, C. T., J. Berchem, and J. G. Luhmann. 1985. On the source region of flux transfer events. *Adv. Space Res.* 5(4): 363–368.

Sandholt, P. E., C. J. Farrugia, S. W. H. Cowley, W. F. Denig, M. Lester, J. Moen, and B. Lybekk. 1999. Capture of magnetosheath plasma by the magnetosphere during northward IMF. *Geophys. Res. Lttrs.* 26(18): 2833.

Sandholt, P. E., C. J. Farrugia, E. Trondsen, B. Lybekk, S. W. H. Cowley, M. Lester, S. Milan, W. F. Denig, and J.-C. Cerisier. 2000. Dynamic cusp aurora and capture of magnetosheath plasma by the magnetosphere during northward IMF. General Assembly, Nice, France.

Sanuki, T., M. Motoki, H. Matsumoto, E. S. Seo, J. Z. Wang, K. Abe, K. Anraka, Y. Asaoka, M. Fujikawa, M. Imori, et al. 1999. 26th International Cosmic Ray Conference, August 25-29, OG.1.1.25 "A precise measurement of cosmic-ray proton spectrum with BESS spectrometer." Vol. 3, p. 93.

Sauvaud, J.-A., R. Lundin, H. Reme, J. P. McFadden, C. Carlson, G. K. Praks, E. Mobius, L. M. Kistler, B. Klecker, E. Amata, et al. 2001. Intermittent thermal plasma acceleration linked to sporadic motions of the magnetopause, first Cluster results. *Annales Geophysicae.* 19:1523–1532.

Schapiro, J. M., S. J. Libby, and F. C. Fang. 2003. Inhibition of bacterial DNA replication by zinc mobilization during nitrosative stress. *Proc. Acad. Sci. USA.* July 8, 100(14): 8496–8501.

*Schombert, J. 2002. University of Oregon. Dept. of Physics. Cosmology. Early Universe.

http://zebu.uoregon.edu/~js/cosmo/lectures/lec20.html.
Schultz, S. C., G. C. Shields, and T. A. Steitz. 1991. Crystal structure of a CAP-DNA complex: the DNA is bent by 90 degrees. *Science.* 253:1001–1007.
*Sefton, I. 1995. University of Sydney, Australia. A glossary of electrical terms. www.physics.usyd.edu.au/teach_res/db/elgloss.htm.
Seki, K., R. C. Elphic, M. F. Thomsen, J. Bonnell, E. J. Lund, M. Hirahara, T. Terasawa, and T. Mukai. 2000. Cold flowing O+ beams in the lobe/mantle at Geotail: Does FAST observe the source? *J. Geophys. Res.* 105(A7): 15931.
Sevilla-Sierra, P., G. Otting, and K. Wuthrich. 1994. Determination of the nuclear magnetic resonance structure of the DNA-binding domain of the P22 c2 repressor (1 to 76) in solution and comparison with the DNA-binding domain of the 434 repressor. Abstract. *J. Mol. Biol.* Jan. 21, 235(3): 1003–20.
Shan, Q., and M. M. Cox. 1997. RecA filament dynamics during DNA strand exchange reactions. *J. Biol. Chem.* April 25, 272(17): 11063–11073. www.jbc.org/cgi/content/full/272/17/11063.
Sharples, G. J. 2001. The X philes: structure-specific endonucleases that resolve Holliday junctions. MicroReview. *Molec. Microbiol.* 39(4):823–834.
Sheldon, R. B. 2004. Quadrupole cusp: a universal accelerator, or from radiation belts to cosmic rays. NSSTC Seminar. March 19. www.batse.msfc.nasa.gov/colloquia/abstracts_spring04/presentations/sheldon.pdf.
Sheldon, R.B. 2000. University of Alabama, Huntsville. The properties of cusp diamagnetic cavities. http://bex.nsstc.uah.edu/RbS/PAPER/istp00.html.
Sheldon, R. B., H. E. Spence, J. Sullivan, T. Fritz, and J. Chen. 1998. The discovery of trapped energetic electrons in the outer cusp. *Geophys.Res. Lttr.* 25:1825.
Sidharth, B. G. 1999. A note on the paper "Quarks or leptons?" *Mod. Phys. Lett.* A14:387–390. http://arxiv.org/PS_cache/quant-ph/pdf/9808/9808053.pdf.
Sidharth[1], B. G. 1998. Toward a unified description of the fundamental interactions. May 6. http://arxiv.org/PS_cache/quant-ph/pdf/9805/9805013.pdf.
Sidharth[2], B. G. 1998. Universe of fluctuations. Center for Applicable Mathematics and Computer Sciences, India. arXiv.quant-ph/9808031 v1. August 19.
Sidharth[3], B. G. 1998. The symmetry underlying spin and the Dirac equation: footprints of quantized space-time. arXiv:quant-ph/9811084V1. November 30.
Sidharth, B. G. 1997. Quantum mechanical black holes: towards a unification of quantum mechanics and general relativity. *Indian J. PureAppl. Phys.* 35:456–471. http://arxiv.org/PS_cache/quant-ph/pdf/9808/9808020.pdf.
Simpson, A. A., Y. Tao, P. G. Leiman, M. O. Badasso, Y. He, P. J. Jardine, N. H. Olson, M. C. Morais, S. Grimes, D. L. Anderson, T. S. Baker, and M. G. Rossmann. 2000. Structure of the bacteriophage phi29 DNA packaging motor. *Nature.* Abstract. Dec. 7, 408(6813): 745–750.
*Sinclair, D. 2003. MBB 222-3 Molecular Biology and Biochemistry. Simon Fraser University, B. C. Lecture 13. www.sfu.ca/mbb/mbb/undergraduate/notes/fall2003/mbb222/mbb222.html.
Skalka, A. 1974. A replicator's view of recombination (and repair). In Grell, R. R. (ed.), *Mechanisms in recombination.* Plenum Press, New York, 421–432.
Slawinski, J. 1987. Electromagnetic radiation and the afterlife. *Journal of Near-Death Studies.*6(2): 79–94.
Slechta, E. S., J. Liu, D. I. Andersson, and J. R. Roth. 2002. Evidence that selected amplification of a bacterial *lac+* reversion (adaptive mutation) with or without general hypermutability. *Genetics.* July, 161:945–956.
Smith, Chris L. "The large hadron collider." *Scientific Amer. Spec. Ed: Edge of Physics.* 2003. 13(1): 53–59.
*Smith, D. W. Fall, 2000. Univ. of California, San Diego. Molecular Biology BIMM 100. Genome fragment isolation: cloning. www.biology.ucsd.edu/classes/bimm100.FA00/03.Cloning.html#B2.
Song, P., R. C. Elphic, C. T. Russell, J. T. Gosling, and C. A. Cattell. 1990. Structure and properties of the subsolar magnetopause for northward IMF: ISEE observations. *J. Geophys. Res.* 95:6375.
Song, P., C. T. Russell, R. J. Fitzenreiter, J. T. Gosling, M. F. Thomsen, D. G. Mitchell, S. A. Fuselier, G. K. Parks, R. R. Anderson, and D. Hubert. 1993. Structure and properties of the subsolar magnetopause for northward interplanetary magnetic field: multiple-instrument particle observation. *J. Geophys. Res.* 98:11319.
*Southwest Research Institute. San Antonio, Texas. Glossary. http://Pluto.space.swri.edu/IMAGE/glossary/pitch.html.
SpaceDaily. "First supernovae quickly seeded universe with stuff of life." news release. September 16, 2003. (accessed October 1, 2004). http://www.spacedaily.com/news/supernova-03i.html.
Stapp, H. P. 1995. Why classical mechanics cannot naturally accommodate consciousness but quantum mechanics can. Theoretical Physics. Univ. of California. http://psyche.cs.monash.edu.au/v2/psyche-2-05-stapp.html.
Stasiewicz, K., C. E. Seyler, F. S. Mozer, G. Gustafsson, J. Pickett, and B. Popielawska. 2001. Magnetic bubbles and kinetic Alfven waves in the high-latitude magnetopause boundary. *J. Geophys. Res.* 106:29503.
Stern, D. P. 1996. A brief history of magnetospheric physics during the Space Age. *Reviews of Geophysics.* 34:1–31. www-spof.gsfc.nasa.gov/Educatcc/Sconct20.htm.
*Stern, D. P., and M. Peredo. Tail of the magnetosphere #23. NASA Polar Wind Geotail. www-spof.gsfc.nasa.gov/Education/wtail.html.

Story, R. M., I. T. Weber, and T. A. Steitz. 1992. The structure of the *E. coli RecA* protein monomer and polymer. *Nature*. January, 355:318–325.

*String Theory Website. Cosmology. Trip through the Big Bang. www.superstringtheory.com/cosmo/cosmo3.html.

Strominger, A. 1993. White holes, black holes and CPT in two dimensions. arXiv:hep-th/9307079 v1 11 Jul 93.

Surette, M. G., M. B. Miller, and B. L. Bassler. 1999. Quorum sensing in *Escherichia coli, Salmonella typhimurium*, and *Vibrio harveyi*: a new family of genes responsible for autoinducer production. *Proc. Natl. Acad. Sci. USA*. February 16, 96(4): 1639–1644.

Susskind, Leonard. "Black holes and the information paradox." *Scientific American Spec. Ed.: the Edge of Physics*. 2003. 13(1): 18–23.

Syvanen, M. 1994. Horizontal gene transfer: evidence and possible consequences. *Annu. Rev. Genet.* 28:237–261.

Teeter, M. M., A. Yamano, B. Stec, and U. Mohanty. 2001. On the nature of a glassy state of matter in a hydrated protein: relation to protein function. Abstract. *PNAS*. Sept. 25, 98(20): 11242–11247.

Tekle, M., D. J. Warren, T. Biswas, T. Ellenberger, A. Landy, and S. E. Nunes-Duby. 2002. Attenuating functions of the C terminus of Lambda integrase. *JMB*. 324:649–665. http://ellenberger.med.harvard.edu/PDF%20files/tekle&landy_jmb02.pdf.

*Terry, T. M. 2000. Univ. of Hamburg. MCB 229: Fundamentals of Microbiology. Viruses, general principles, bacteriophages. www.biologie.uni-hamburg.de/b-online/library/micro229/terry/229sp00/lectures/viruses1.html.

Texas A&M University. "*E. coli* bacteria may be more useful than you think." news release. May 29, 2001. www.sciencedaily.com/releases/2001/05/010529065838.htm.

Thompson, J. F., and A. Landy. 1988. Empirical estimation of protein- induced DNA bending angles: applications to Lambda site-specific recombination complexes. *Nucleic Acids Res.* 16(20): 9687–9705.

Thorne, Kip S. 1994. *Black holes & time warps: Einstein's outrageous legacy*. New York: W. W. Norton & Co.

University of Chicago Medical Center. "Sonic hedgehog shapes the brain." article adapted from news release, March 13, 2001. www.sciencedaily.com/releases/2001/03/010312072303.htm.

University of Missouri-Rolla. "Solar flares: is iron-rich sun the cause?" news release, October 30, 2003. www.umr.edu/index.php?id=1586&backPID=245&begin_at=4&tt_news=220.

*University College London. Department of Biochemistry and Molecular Biology. Biomolecular Structure and Modeling Group. Summary of DNA-binding protein structural families, grouped by DNA recognition motif. http://www.biochem.ucl.ac.uk/bsm/prot_dna/prot_dna_cover.html.

*University of Maryland. Dept. of Astronomy. 2002. Magnetic Reconnection and Thin Current Sheets. www.astro.umd.edu/rareas/spp/spp_research.html.

Van Domelen, D. J. 2000. Ohio State Univ. Dept. of Physics. Getting around the Coriolis force. www.physics.ohio-state.edu/~dvandom/Edu/newcor.html.

Van Gelder, P., F. Dumas, I. Bartoldus, N. Saint, A. Prilipov, M. Winterhalter, Y. Wang, A. Philippsen, J. P. Rosenbusch, and T. Schirmer. 2002. Sugar transport through maltoporin of *Escherichia coli*: role of the greasy slide. *J. Bacteriol.* June, 184(11): 2994–2999.

Velde, H. te. 2002. Seth. *Ancient gods speak: a guide to the Egyptian religion*. New York: Oxford University Press.

Wales, D. J. 2001. A microscopic basis for the global appearance of energy landscapes. *Science*. 293:2067–2070.

Walker, R. J., and T. Ogino. 1996. A global magnetohydrodynamic simulation of the origin and evolution of magnetic flux ropes in the magnetotail. *J. Geomag. Geoelectr.* 48:765.

Weisberg, R., and A. Landy. 1983. Site-specific recombination in phage Lambda. In Hendrix, R. W., J. W. Roberts, F. W. Stahl, and R. A. Weisberg, eds. *Lambda II*. New York: Cold Spring Harbor Laboratory Press, 211–250.

White, John. "Enlightenment and the Body of Light." *What is Enlightenment*. Spring/Summer 2002.

Wieczorek, D. J., L. Didion, and M. Feiss. 2002. Alternations of the portal protein, gpB, of bacteriophage Lambda suppress mutations in *cosQ*, the site required for termination of DNA packaging. *Genetics*. May, 161:21–31. www.genetics.org/cgi/content/full/161/1/21.

Will, Clifford. 1989. "The renaissance of general relativity" in *The New Physics*, edited by Paul Davies. Cambridge University Press.

*Wikipedia Online Encyclopedia. Time Travel. http://en.wikipedia.org/wiki/Time_travel.

Williams, R. J. P. 2000. "Inorganic chemistry of life." *New Chemistry*, ed. by Nina Hall. Cambridge University Press.

Willis, R., ed. 1993. Egypt. *World Mythology*. New York: Henry Holt and Company, 36–55.

Witte, A., G. Wanner, U. Blasi, G. Halfmann, M. Szostak, W. Lubitz. 1990. Endogenous transmembrane tunnel formation mediated by *phi*X174 lysis protein E. *J. Bacteriol.* 172:4109–4114.

Wolf, Fred Alan. 1988. *Parallel universes: the search for other worlds*. New York: Simon and Schuster.

Wu, A. M., G. E. Christie, T. Platt. 1981. Tandem termination sites in the tryptophan operon of *Escherichia coli*. *Proc. Natl. Acad. Sci. USA*. 78:2913–2917.

Xu, D., M. G. Kivelson, R. J. Walker, P. T. Newell, and C.-I. Meng. 1995. Interplanetary magnetic field control of precipitation and associated field-aligned currents. *J. Geophys. Res.* 100:1837–1846.

Yang, Q., N. Breton, M. C. Manning, C. E. Catalano. 1999. Domain structure of gpNu1, a phage Lambda DNA packaging protein. *Biochem.* 38:14238-14247.

Yang, Q. T. De Beer, L. Woods, J. D. Meyers, M. C. Manning, M. Overduin, and C. E. Catalano. 1999. Cloning, expression and characterization of a DNA binding domain of gpNu1, a phage lambda DNA packaging protein. *Biochem.* 38:465–477.

Zirakashvili, V. N. 1999. 26th International Cosmic Ray Conference, August 25–29. OG.3.3.03 Acceleration of Cosmic Rays. "Cosmic ray acceleration by magnetic traps." Vol. 4, p.439. http://www.icrc1999.utah.edu/~icrc1999/root/og_3_3.html.

INDEX

CPSIA information can be obtained
at www.ICGtesting.com
Printed in the USA
LVHW080753091020
668390LV00002B/2